Bottleneck

OUR HUMAN INTERFACE WITH REALITY

To Steve.

Best Wishes
from

Richard Epworth

June. 2014

To my loving wife, Lavinia

"Bottleneck - Our human interface with reality" is also available as an
Amazon Kindle eBook: Reference ASIN: B00H2RE7I0,
first published in December 2013
See **WWW.HUMANBOTTLENECK.COM** for further details

Bottleneck

OUR HUMAN INTERFACE WITH REALITY

THE DISTURBING AND EXCITING IMPLICATIONS OF ITS TRUE NATURE

RICHARD EPWORTH

Goforich Publications

Manuscript edited by Nina Robertson

V2.0, Printed by Imprint Digital

"If the doors of perception were cleansed every thing would appear to man as it is, Infinite. For man has closed himself up, till he sees all things thro' narrow chinks of his cavern."
- William Blake

Contents

List of Figures

Preface

Many years ago, as part of my work in a top UK research laboratory, I calculated the amount of information required to feed an electronic display screen of such high quality that the image would be totally indistinguishable from reality. The resulting numbers were staggeringly huge, so huge that a few days later I awoke realising that human vision must work in a completely different way; that we could not possibly see all that detail simultaneously.

It was the start of a fascination with human perception that has preoccupied me to this day. I began to experiment with a system that tracked eye movements, and went on to develop ideas on the limits of human learning. When I shared them with the notable British psychologist; Richard Gregory, he enthusiastically encouraged me to publish them. Sadly he died in 2010, so never got to read what I have now written. Nevertheless, I dedicate *Bottleneck* to his memory.[1]

This book is about our limited ability to learn from the world around us. Despite myths and wishful thinking, when we rigorously measure the rate that our minds can learn anything new, it appears to be narrow and restricted. I began to realise that this has profound implications for many aspects of our lives, including our technology and psychology.

The result is "Bottleneck", the outcome of two decades of investigations, culminating in two years of intense writing. Throughout I faced two major challenges: I found it hard to believe what I had discovered, so spent time looking for evidence to disprove it. Secondly; the territory I have endeavoured to cover is very broad, describing both the solid scientific evidence for our learning bottleneck, and its softer subjective and philosophical implications.

For this reason the book is divided into four parts: The first describes how our mind learns about the external world, while the second presents more detailed scientific evidence for our learning bottleneck. The third part explores the disturbing implications for us personally, while part four ventures briefly into the future implications of our learning bottleneck. In an attempt to make the book widely accessible, I have included examples from my own personal experience wherever possible.

There are many excellent books on the neurology of the human brain that describe recent discoveries about its internal workings.[2] [3] [4] This is no such book; rather it is about the surprising evidence for our limited learning performance and its challenging implications. If this were a book about sports cars, it would contain no details of the internals; the piston rings, the fuel injection sequence, or the wiring diagram, nor would it describe the optimistic claims of the designer, the manufacturer or the previous owner. It would be an impartial assessment of the cars actual performance, pushed to the limit under realistic conditions, its top speed, acceleration, handling and endurance.

Introduction

There is a paradox: The world we inhabit and experience through our senses, appears incredibly detailed and rich in information. However, there is no scientific evidence that our mind can absorb more than a tiny trickle of fresh information. The inevitable conclusion is that most of the world we are experiencing in each moment is an internal construct or simulation based on our history.

Have you ever looked at a ship in a bottle, and been amazed that such a faithful model of real ship can be squeezed through such a narrow bottleneck? I will show how our world is like that tiny ship, that although our vision of the universe we inhabit is vast, the entire vision itself is created and contained in a space no bigger than our head.

Though we feel we are in direct contact with the world about us, our experience of it is almost entirely an idea of the world constructed from experiences throughout our life. Like the model sailing ship within the bottle, it is out of date, built mostly from old ideas and experiences. But it is the best we have, and every one of us is in a similar position. You may remind me that we have eyes to see the world as it is now, but as I will show you; our eyes mostly see what we already know. Our ability to see or experience anything new is constrained by a shockingly narrow "bottleneck".

The term is metaphorically derived from the neck of a bottle, where the speed of flow of the liquid is limited by the narrowness of its neck. The word is often used by traffic engineers and other scientists to describe a performance limiting region within a larger network.[5] In this book I use it to describe the surprising constraint between the richness of the world we live in, and our ability to learn about it.[6]

We humans possess an incredible imagination. What distinguishes us from other mammals is not our sensory capacity, as that is similar between humans, dogs and owls. However, within our brain we appear to possess a far more complex model of the world around us, somewhat like a computer simulation. When used together with our memory it enables us to predict the future, the past and the present in rich detail. Some computer games are based on simulations of a fictional "reality". These games come with much of the detail of these worlds already defined by the programmer; however, the simulation within our human mind starts from almost nothing at the beginning of our life.

From the moment we are born we steadily absorb a trickle of information through our senses, constructing increasingly complex and detailed simulations within our brain to "explain" the limited amount we sense in each moment. It is not long before we have built an imagined world far in excess of any immediate sensations. Our experience is no longer dominated by what is sensed in that moment, but by an internal model based on our accumulated history, one which is the best match with what we are sensing at that moment. We may not be able to sense more than our dog or our cat, but the far more sophisticated simulations within our human brain allow us to direct our attention differently, and often more appropriately.

I can illustrate how little information from the present is required to create extensive detail within our minds eye, with this brief tale:

As a teenager, my Great Uncle "John" was considered the "black sheep" of the family for reasons I shall not disclose. In 1905 he was conveniently sent away to sea in a four-masted sailing ship, in the hope that it would reform him. A year later his ship was wrecked off Cape Horn, and the entire crew including John were thought lost.[7] Try to picture the scene in your mind for a moment.

Back in England his family received the news and mourned his loss. Then some months later a handful of the crew suddenly arrived back in England, and a bedraggled John appeared on the doorstep to be reunited with his family. He always refused to discuss his ordeal, but I was told that "forever after, he nursed a lifelong and implacable hatred of missionaries".

Can you imagine why that might have been? When we read these few words, we construct a model in our mind that might make sense of them. However, it is likely that our interpretations differ considerably depending on our previous experience of the sea, ships, uncles, missionaries etc. Was the sea rough? The records tell us that it was calm, and that the ship drifted gently onto a "lee shore". The crew could do nothing to stop it, the water being too deep for the anchor to arrest their progress. Has this changed the picture you have in your mind? How were missionaries involved? Tantalisingly, Uncle John never revealed more.

The point of this tale is to show that we are able to construct a remarkably detailed multi-dimensional image in our mind from just a few words. And the image we hold is modified with each new piece of information. For a five year old, the image is likely to be much simpler, having neither the vocabulary nor previous experience around the topic.

Anyone who has enjoyed reading a good novel, or listening to a radio play, will know what a wonderfully rich experience can result from comparatively few words. In the pages that follow I will show how this richness comes more from the richness of our own individual history, than from the words that we are absorbing. These carefully crafted words are simply keys to our own bulging storehouse of memories.

Most of the time we are confidently aware of the differences between what is "out there" now, what is a memory of something out there in the past, and what is merely a product of our own imagination, as in reading this story. Such confidence is considered essential to the functioning of our daily lives, but confusion between them takes place more often than we realise.

When we go somewhere new and gaze at the scene around us, it is easy to marvel at the rich detail that we experience. However, if we examine the evidence we find that much of the detail we perceive comes from other places and from other times. Perhaps you have compared childhood memories with a sibling or someone else with whom you ostensibly shared the same early experiences. If so, you have probably been surprised just how much difference there is between each of your remembered realities.

There is a widely held belief that we can continually absorb enormous quantities of information through our senses, even that we have "photographic" memories. This is a myth, unsupported by any rigorous evidence. Information enters our minds in many different forms including written text, speech and images. By describing all of them using the common language of "bits",[8] I am able to compare the rates at which we can absorb these different kinds of information.[9]

Having done so, I have found no evidence that we can absorb new knowledge faster than a few tens of bits per second. This is remarkably little, as some technologists had previously estimated that our (visual) experience of reality is equivalent to a rate of flow of information a million million times greater than this. Furthermore, it is likely that this narrow limit will be implicit in human biology for the foreseeable future. If this is true, then we need to look again at the difference between data and knowledge, between information and insight, and choose ways forward that take this into account.

Perhaps we are approaching the end of the information age, and are poised on the threshold of an age of insight. "More" is no longer intrinsically good. We are no longer starved of information. Just as "All You Can Eat" restaurants gave way to Nouvelle Cuisine, I believe that we will soon begin to demand delicious, well-prepared portions of knowledge rather than choke on huge quantities of data and information.

This book is about the maximum rate of human learning, and its implications. It is important to stress that I am primarily concerned with the learning of genuinely *novel* information, as distinct from that which has already been learned and is simply being recognised again and added to. I am interested in the speed at which we integrate new sensed information from "out there", into our internal conceptual models; the speed that new stuff reaches our intelligent mind. This approach allows us to speculate upon the limits of human learning.

Our learning bottleneck affects much more than just the world of information, for it touches the very roots of what it is to be a human participating in society. The realization that most of what we experience is a construct from our extended history, gives a new and much needed insight into the science of human prejudice. It reveals that we cannot avoid prejudgement in thought, because it is a fundamental and unconscious human process. However, with vigilance we can become more conscious of its influence in our daily lives.

In the future our species faces a final challenge: If our learning bottleneck is biological, and technology continues to evolve at the current rate, then logic suggests that we should allow intelligent life to evolve beyond the human individual, toward a single intelligent technological being, a global network. Or will we decide that *we* should be the final stage of life's evolution on planet Earth, and attempt to bring further evolution of life to a halt?

Here is a brief summary of what you will find in each of the chapters:

Chapter one explains the crucial difference between the process of learning something completely new, and recognising something that we are already familiar with. It explores the meaning of novelty in images, language and music. The concept of "bits" and "bit rate" are explained using various analogies including the game of twenty questions. This enables the learning rates of widely different kinds of information to be compared.

Chapter two investigates the many limitations in our sensors that we are unaware of. Starting from the legacy of our eyes' evolutionary past, it explains the physical limitations within the human eye itself, such as our blind spot, as well as more psychological limitations such as change-blindness.

Chapter three reveals that everything that we consider is "out there", is actually imagined within our own heads, and describes how mankind's greatest tool is our power of prediction.

In chapter four I show how this predictive tool of ours is based on rules and explanations that we have derived from our previously sensed information. We see how we humans have a compulsion to explain almost everything, however inappropriate or flawed.

I then move on to the objective evidence for our learning bottleneck.

Chapter five reveals the evidence from Shannon's estimates of the information content of language. It presents the evidence from memory athletes who compete in memorising sequences of unpredictable symbols in the fastest time. It reveals the small but finite quantity of information that we can absorb in the briefest glance, and explores how autistic savants fit into the picture.

In chapter six we find that our learning bottleneck also limits the rate at which our mind can communicate back out to the world around us. Although some of our actions in the world can be performed unsupervised by our conscious mind, most require our attention, and this involves taking information in. Measurements of people performing physical skills have revealed remarkably consistent evidence for the learning bottleneck.

Some of the objective implications of the bottleneck are explored in chapter seven, including insights into education, and ideas for how our technology might exploit this understanding.

While previous chapters show that we create the universe we experience, chapter eight brings the realisation that this will be unique to ourselves and our own personal history. We inhabit our own "youniverse". I show how we create personal stories to make sense of our histories, and how we adjust our memories to make our stories cohesive.

In chapter nine I explore the extent to which we are personally responsible for creating the kind of "youniverse" that we experience, how our thoughts do more than modify what our brain remembers, but actually change the nature of the world we inhabit.

Chapter ten tackles the thorny subject of prejudice from the perspective of information, rather than moral judgement. It explains why prejudice is an innate part of our predictive capability, that we are all prejudiced, but blind to the process within ourselves. Harmful negative prejudice is unlikely to be overcome if we naively assume it is something that only bad people do.

Finally in chapter eleven I explore the implications that our learning bottleneck might have for our future. How might we overcome its limitations? Can we use electronic connections into our brains? I reveal the ever growing problem of too much information, and how our ability to create new ideas is limited by our biology. Could we bypass the human learning bottleneck altogether? And if we did, would we be creating a more intelligent form of life than our own?

In the remaining part of this introduction, I reveal what inspired me to look beyond the things that satisfy most of us, to question the widely held assumptions about the world we perceive around us. If you are in a hurry to get to the "meat" of the book, then please feel free to move on to the first chapter. Otherwise, here is where my journey began.

The Facts of Lies

"Tell me something I don't know Mummy?" It was a warm summer afternoon. I was a skinny six year old, thirsting for knowledge while watching my mother who was preoccupied and struggling to make the beds. When I asked that same annoying question for what probably seemed to her the hundredth time, she paused, sighed, drew breath and said: "Would you like to know where babies come from?"

I will never know why she chose that particular moment to reveal the full frank facts of human procreation. Was it her desire to get it over with before I reached an age where she would be too embarrassed to tell me? Or perhaps it was an uncharacteristic moment of frustration with my never-ending requests for new knowledge. As I loved my Mother, I prefer to remember it as the act of a brave young woman of the early 1950's, eager to educate her young son in the fullest sense.

And so she began. I can still feel the warmth of the sun shining into the room, smell the freshly laundered sheets, and see her leaning beside the polished bedroom table as she busily tucked in the bedclothes. But I remember nothing further except the feeling of: "Whooaaoo!, Too much information!", as she described the carnal act of sexual intercourse between my dear Mother and my upright Father, though to be fair, she told it in a clean and clinical way. It was just so unexpected, such a big story and so bizarre compared with all the other clickety-click facts that Mum and Dad had told me in the past. I usually knew just where to pigeon-hole everything my parents told me, alongside all my other safe, sterile objective facts in my mind. And frankly, I really didn't want to have to think about my parents connecting parts of their bodies that I had never been allowed to name, see, or even imagine.

Well, if it was to shut me up, it certainly worked, as I didn't ask another question all day. I was six, I believed everything my parents told me as I trusted them even more than God. So as the evening wore on, I rehearsed in my mind what I had learned, and attempted to marry it up with anything else that I knew around the topic. This was almost entirely unsuccessful, as what little I did know about the birds and the bees, all seemed to be about gardening. But as I began to realize just how strange my new learnings appeared to be, I grew increasingly excited at the thought of sharing my new knowledge at school the following day. Knowledge is power, so at last I would command some major respect from classmates who'd previously treated me as the skinny geek that I was.

Though my mind was buzzing with further questions, I resisted the urge to seek further clarification from Mother over the breakfast table, fearing huge embarrassment for myself if I did, and set off on my walk to school with a spring in my step. I managed to contain myself until the morning break, then gathered a few classmates, and said: "Hey boys, listen to what I know".

I told the tale as best I could remember, but instead of the expected hush of awe and respect for which I had hoped, I got titters, laughter followed by loud guffaws. It appeared that on the topic of human procreation, they were all much more knowledgeable than me, for as if in one voice they united in telling me that I had got it WRONG. The truth, it seemed that all but I knew, was that babies were carried into the world in the beak of a large long-legged bird called a Stork.

I felt humiliated, and even smaller than usual among my boisterous classmates, but worse much much worse, I felt wounded to my very core. For the first time in my life, I knew that my Mother lied to me. Now, from that point on, everything she told me would need to be weighed against others views and thoughts. Was there anyone I could trust to tell me the facts of life, or must I explore the truth of everything for myself?

I never told Mother what had happened at school, but she must have noticed that I was rather withdrawn when I returned that evening. Perhaps she remembered what she had revealed the previous day, and wondered if it had been too soon to teach her little boy about sex? But I had learned something important; that truth is the consensus of the crowd, and trouble comes from listening to strange ideas from lone individuals, especially one who is trusted and loved.

My Mother's strange tale soon faded in my memory, since it made no sense to me at all, until some years later I began to hear similar stories from older children. Slowly, slowly, it began to dawn on me that she had been right all along, and I felt a little ashamed that I had not trusted her. Why am I telling you all this? Well I learned two things that I would never ever forget: The first, that the truth may be both complicated and uncomfortable. The second; that a shared narrative is a powerful thing, even if it has no grounds in reality.

Seeking Illumination

I have always been drawn to the boundaries of knowledge. Even when a small boy, my eyes were forever searching for something, I never knew what, but I somehow held the idea that some amazing thing was waiting to be discovered if only I looked hard enough. I would take a much longer route on my way home from school to walk across a newly ploughed field, my eyes scanning the ground ahead, searching for anything unusual that might emerge from the recently disturbed soil. Consequently I found many things of interest to a small boy: old coins, strange fossils, bits of old clay smoking pipes, and even a very old pair of gold rimmed reading spectacles.

I always felt that there was more to come; the daily chore of collecting coal for the fire from the outside coal-house became an exciting archaeological dig which unearthed bright crystals of Iron pyrites ("fools Gold") and fossilised leaf balls. My weekly pocket money was spent on the bus fare to the city museum, where I eagerly took my latest treasures to show the curators. With hindsight they responded with surprising interest and enthusiasm while attempting to identify some of my more unusual finds. It seemed natural for me to set up my own small museum in my bedroom, carefully printing labels for my treasures using the little rubber letters of my John Bull Printing Outfit.

My father encouraged my interest in science, indeed I might have eventually become a professional chemist as I developed an interest in chemistry at a worryingly early age. When I was five, our family spent a cold rainy summer holiday at Morecambe Bay, on the coast of Lancashire. Being located at the mouth of a river estuary it was more mud-side than seaside. In the absence of beach, we went to the fair and finally arrived at a stall where you had to roll six balls down a slope into an array of slots.

The centre slot scored six, the outer ones zero with the intermediate ones scoring something in between. At the back of the stall there was a very impressive array of prizes, and the sign said that if you could roll all six balls into the centre slot you scored maximum, and could choose absolutely any prize. If you scored a bit less you got a smaller and considerably less desirable prize to take away. The stall holder was not taking any chances, as the surface you rolled the balls down was bowed high in the centre, such that any rolled ball almost immediately fell to the left or right side and hence scored zero, as quickly became evident as soon as my father and sister had a go.

Dad kindly lifted me onto his shoulders so I would be high enough to have a turn myself, and I rolled my six balls, which somehow, unbelievably all went into the centre slot scoring, Maximum! Everyone gasped, including the stunned stall holder (who promptly cancelled his evening class on statistics). Some of those prizes at the back of his stall had been there for years, it was very rare indeed that he had to replace any, as was evident from the dust. He immediately grabbed a very large, but very cheap-looking teddy bear from the back of the stall, and said; "Well done sonny, you 'ave this". Unfortunately I was not into teddy bears. I had already got one at home, one lovingly hand made by my grandmother during a time of post-war austerity, a teddy of carry-able size, with friendly eyes and a firm body based on an empty Tate and Lyle syrup tin.

A small crowd of bystanders had gathered and watched as I rolled ball after ball into that top slot. Now they were reminding the stall holder that I had the right to choose any of the prizes, as that is what he had clearly written on his sign. Being an inquisitive child, I had spotted a large and interesting looking box, high at the back, which had the words "Chemistry Set" on the front together with a picture of "an experiment". Now, that seemed more like it, and so I asked for it. For once my father and the stall holder were united in saying that it was a bad idea, but the crowd were behind me, and sensed a worthy cause (not a lot happened in Morecambe that was more exciting than this). That rather ancient chemistry set would take a bit of replacing and was worth a dozen giant Teddies, so the stall holder put up quite a fight before sullenly admitting defeat, and lifting the box down to my eager waiting arms.

Returning home at the end of the holiday, I was at last allowed to get my hands on my prize. The box itself was a faded green, having been exposed to the elements on that stall for some years, but once opened I was greeted with an array of treasures. It had a strange smell that I could almost taste at the back of my throat, not a nice smell but somehow intriguing. There was a row of corked glass test-tubes full of different coloured chemicals with strange names, a little burner, some Magnesium strip to ignite, and a little book of experiments, some promising to make foul smells, others accompanied by exciting hazard warnings.

My delight was short lived however, as my father had other ideas; the thought of his son being let loose on it was just too much. He insisted that I was far too young for it, and decided that it would be put away for a few years. I performed a fairly impressive tantrum that nevertheless failed to change his mind, but was at least rewarded within a few days with a very small substitute chemistry set, one that Health and Safety would have been proud of. Frankly, it was useless; the most exciting experiment merely turned water from pink to blue. I bided my time, and a year or so later finally got my hands on the big box, and so began my exciting chemistry years. It was tough growing up in the early nineteen-fifties, before the days of drugs and stuff. My only access to childhood hazards was through chemical incendiaries and lethal voltages.

I quickly learned how to make bombs and rockets, but ran into resistance from the local chemists shop, when buying the three ingredients of gunpowder in the precisely correct proportions for the best bang, a problem I resolved by using three different chemists shops. Then one day my uncle gave me a very old book on chemistry. Uncle Nick was a Falstaff-like character, an amateur thespian with a deep booming voice that passed through walls unattenuated. He later presented me with his entire collection of dangerous swords and daggers for my little museum, so he was definitely not health-and-safety man!

The thick black leather-bound book had a distorted spine and dark black pages inside the front and back covers that gave it a sinister air, like the black-edged business card of an undertaker. Even without its precious pages of spells and potions, it reeked of alchemy. This was no Harry Potter fiction, but the real deal from the past, from a time more than a century ago, when chemistry books were never required to be safe for the children. It told the terrible truth of just what excitement could be had from chemicals. This book of power was never meant to be read by precocious little boys like me, and I knew it.

I eagerly explored its pages seeking out exciting looking experiments. One promised that "anyone attempting to mix together substance (A) with (B) or (C), "is almost certainly risking the loss of their sight in the resulting explosion", (I have omitted the actual chemical names, just in case a young boy of similar disposition should chance to read this). Having acquired the necessary ingredients, I planned to perform the experiment in my secret narrow space between our garage and that of the house next door. Not being entirely foolish, I decided that this dangerous mixing should be done at a "safe" distance, and so I improvised an extended stirring mechanism using the clothes prop that my mother would otherwise use to support the clothes line. I braced myself for something exciting, stirred away, but absolutely nothing happened. Finally in desperation I just set fire to the whole experiment which generated some sparks and flame but nothing like what the book had promised.

So now I knew that I should aim high. There were two other experiments in that book that carried particularly dire warnings, one which was claimed to produce a brown oily liquid that "exploded on exposure to bright light". That seemed the kind of thing that I was after, but I couldn't work out how I would set up the experiment in the dark. As I hadn't been blinded in the earlier experiment, my sight was still a key faculty, so reluctantly I decided to go for the other experiment, the one that produced a gas that "when bubbled through water will explode on contact with air generating remarkable smoke rings". I won't list the chemicals required, except for one; sticks of Yellow Phosphorus. Now I am sure many of you will appreciate that Phosphorus does not have an entirely benign reputation, achieving most attention during wartime, but the Yellow sort was particularly interesting as it has a natural disposition to burst into flame on exposure to air.

Now how to get hold of the stuff? I heard that in my city there was a supplier of chemicals to schools, who would sell "poisonous" chemicals to children if they came with an ID card "signed by parent or guardian" (it was a while ago!). I duly got the requisite card from the supplier, and persuaded my Dad to sign it, by telling him that I needed to renew my supplies of slightly poisonous Copper Sulphate that I used for electroplating things (an essentially worry-free experiment). So with my precious pocket money I took the bus into town, duly purchased my chemicals and returned clutching a large glass jar full of my nice Yellow Phosphorus sticks, which incidentally were immersed in water to stop them catching fire spontaneously. Sitting on the front seat on the top of that double decker bus, I could feel the excitement, knowing that should the jar be dropped and broken, a dangerous fire would ensue.

I never did carry out the originally intended experiment. I was nervous about the part where the whole of the glass experimental apparatus needed to be purged with (explosive) town gas, to prevent the whole experiment exploding before we reached the goal of the exploding smoke rings. However, I nursed those precious poisonous sticks of Phosphorus as if they were my dangerous pets, and once in a while I would carefully lift a piece out of the protective water with a pair of metal tongs, and "play with it". Sometimes that meant simply placing it onto a surface, waiting for it to dry and watching in wonder as it spontaneously caught fire and burned with a bright yellow flame and unpleasant smell.

But I found that I could achieve much greater excitement by crushing a Phosphorus stick into the footpath just outside my house, causing the pavement to burst into flames just as the local schoolgirls came past on their way home. For a shy boy such as myself, this seemed a promising substitute for an otherwise absent chat up line. The girls were certainly impressed, as evidenced by their startled expressions, but sadly not at all in the way I had hoped. My enthusiasm for fire led to some fairly scary moments: I once set fire to my entire chemistry set by accidentally dripping molten burning phosphorus into it. On another occasion I accidentally set fire to a room in the house, with a mixture of Ether and petrol. I eventually managed to extinguish the flames, but the evidence lingered; the burned curtains, my sister's melted guitar, and my footprints permanently recorded in the melted plastic floor tiles. Father was not amused.

I began to realize that a career in chemistry might be dangerous for both myself and for the world. My father had helped me to build a simple crystal set, probably as a diversion. Soon I discovered the exciting world of electronics and developed a passion for it that grew throughout my youth. I built radios, HiFi's, Geiger counters and all manner of gadgets, encouraged by an enthusiastic teacher at school, and it all led me to study for a degree in Electrical/Electronic Engineering at Manchester University.

In my last year, in addition to our other studies and experiments, we were required to undertake a final year project with a partner. The University had various topics in mind, but we were also allowed to choose one ourselves. I teamed up with my friend Paul Sinclair and we discussed what would be a suitable task. Infrared light emitting diodes (LEDs) had recently been invented and a local electronics company was making prototypes.[10] We proposed that we should design and build an optical transmission system. It was an ambitious plan, but the Professor accepted the idea, and we went ahead.

Most students saw these projects as a nuisance, to be done as simply and quickly as possible, allowing them to focus on their studies towards their exams. I however, found the project much more interesting than sitting through some of the boring lectures and spent rather too much of my time on it during my final year. I scrounged fast transistors from the local computer company where I had worked for the summer.[11] Glass optical communication fibres had not yet been invented and so it was just a free-space transmission system transmitting light through the air at 1 Megabit per second. The range was somewhat limited by the optics we had available; Paul had "borrowed" a lens from his mother's cine camera, but with hindsight the rest of what we did was impressive for its time, and especially for undergraduates with negligible resources.[12]

That experience became key to my future career. I saw an article announcing some research work at a British research laboratory: Standard Telecommunications Laboratories (STL), where a team were pursuing the dream of communicating over long distances using light.[13] Charles Kao and

George Hockham had just published a now historic paper, proposing transmitting information as pulses of light through thin strands of glass fibre.[14] [15]

I applied for a job, and my knowledge of optical communication sufficiently impressed them at my interview, that they offered me a position, despite the fact I was competing with many bright and better qualified scientists and engineers. I was lucky to join when I did, for STL was an exciting place to work, full of all kinds of creative scientists, many who had previously contributed greatly to the war effort.

And so I began a 40 year relationship with optical fibre communications. In 1966 optical fibre communications was just a dream within a small group of scientists at the laboratory. I was fortunate and privileged to be a part of the team that turned that dream into today's reality, and in 2009 Charles Kao was awarded the Nobel Prize in Physics in recognition of the significance of this pioneering technology.[16] He later received a British knighthood.[17]

I have spent most of my working life, researching ways to squeeze ever increasing quantities of information through tiny hair-thin fibres made of glass. These optical fibres now form the basis of the majority of the world's electronic communication networks, including the Internet. Today our globe is criss-crossed by vast numbers of optical fibre cables, buried under our streets and across the floors of our oceans.

Although the first optical fibre communication systems could only carry a few tens of simultaneous telephone conversations on one fibre, over the years we developed ways of transmitting ever-greater information rates. Today it is possible to transmit data 240 kilometres at 100,000 Gigabits per second through a single glass fibre no thicker than a human hair, enough data for more than a billion simultaneous phone conversations.[18] [19]

Coming to my senses

You may think that this is seems more than good enough, with little need to improve the capacity of optical fibre any further, and you may be right. However, back in the 1980's, just one Gigabit per second was as much as we could communicate through a fibre, so as a senior member of the research team I was under pressure to come up with a justification for continuing to fund the research. I needed to dream up a "killer application"; an application that would demand vastly more information to be transmitted through the fibre, and which would be sufficiently exciting to the paying customers that our research funding (and hence our jobs) would be secure for the following years.

I thought that visual information would be the most demanding application and would offer the best justification for our research programme. Today's technology makes it possible to record and recreate audio (music and speech) with such realism that in the right circumstances one is unable to tell the difference between the recording and the original. We seem to be able to capture and then subsequently recreate all the information that our ears can hear, providing us with what can reasonably claimed to be "total acoustic fidelity!"

Our sense of vision however, is a much tougher challenge, for despite the hype, even the best of today's High Definition TVs only provide us with a moderately sharp picture. No-one looking at an image of Mount Everest would be fooled into believing that they were actually seeing Mount Everest itself, even with the latest 3D technology however, the ultimate high definition television would provide an image so accurate, that we would be unable to visually detect the difference between the image and a real view of the object.

So I calculated the information rate that would be required to feed an image display of such High Fidelity, that it would be completely indistinguishable from reality: HiFi Vision. A potential application for this would be remote high quality "Telepresence", where a family spread across the globe might have the (visual) experience of being in the same room. Another would be to make "Virtual Reality" actually look real. Either way it would certainly be the ultimate Home Cinema kit.

I based my calculation on the following properties of the human eye: The ability to resolve fine spatial detail, the extent of our field of view, the speed of response to changes in the scene, the accuracy with which we can resolve colour, and depth/distance resolution (see Appendix 1 for more details). Using quite conservative values gave me a bit rate of around 100,000,000,000 bits per second! or 100 Gigabit/s. Furthermore, I discovered that I was not the only one thinking along these lines, for in 1987 Eric Nussbaum of Bell Labs made a similar calculation and published a ten times larger figure of one Terabit per second (which is 1,000,000,000,000 bits per second).[20]

More recently, Jim Crowe, the Chief Technical Officer of the Telecommunications Network Provider: Level3, made a similar calculation and came up with the even larger value of 15 Terabits per second (15,000,000,000,000 bit/s). His context was for a High Fidelity "Telepresence" communication system, in which two people at different places on the planet could experience sharing the same space. In Wired Magazine he stated: "When I couldn't find anyone working in neurophysiology or artificial intelligence who had an inkling about the bandwidth of the optic nerve, I approached the problem myself from a different angle. I calculated that to produce an encompassing stereoscopic, hemispherical image a foot away from the face, with 24-bit colour, 2,400-pixel(/inch) resolution, and 30 frames-per-second refresh, would take 15 Terabits per second one way, or 30 Terabits full duplex".[21]

These vast numbers of bits may mean little to you at this stage, but in the next chapter I explain why these things called bits are a unique and valuable way of quantifying information. Meanwhile the number of bits per second is a way of quantifying how rapidly we can communicate information. We can compare these figures with some things you might be familiar with: A conventional land-line phone conversation corresponds to about 64,000 bits per second (which we write as 64kbit/s), and when we watch Internet TV we rely on a broadband connection of a few Million bits per second. So this display device, this High Fidelity TV set would need to be fed with more than a million times more information per second than required by a typical TV or video image today. It can be very difficult to appreciate differences over this scale, but if we use the flow of water as an analogy, it is like comparing the flow produced by emptying a one litre bottle in a second, with that of emptying the entire contents of an Olympic swimming pool in the same short time.[22]

When I first estimated these big numbers I was delighted. I thought that I had found the perfect justification for continued funding of our research team, and that my colleagues and I would have secure employment in our pet research topic for many years to come. But when I thought about it more, a little alarm bell rang in my head though I managed to ignore it for a while. Jim Crowe had related the 15 Terabits per second to "the bandwidth of the optic nerve" feeding information from the visual scene, via the retina in the eye to the brain. Initially, I too thought that this huge bit rate represented the information rate of the visual reality that we experience. My argument went as follows: If we can see imperfections in the image when we reduce the bit rate below this value, it implies that the human visual experience corresponds to a higher bit rate. Conversely, once the bit rate equalled the bit rate of the human visual experience, then the image would be indistinguishable from reality, and any further increase would provide no benefit.

So I thought: The human experience of the world can be ascribed an information rate of around ten Terabits per second (I was assuming that the visual experience contained vastly more information than all the other senses combined, which seemed a reasonable assumption bearing in mind that a few hundred kilobits per second seemed sufficient for high fidelity audio.) Ten Terabits per second did not seem unreasonable. My own experience of life seemed so rich, so detailed, and so full of interesting "bits" and pieces!

But the more I thought about these big numbers, the more I began to realize that I was missing something, and as it turned out, I was missing a lot. I started to learn about the physiology and psychology of perception, and became increasingly suspicious of the supposed need for such high information rates. What bothered me was this: Even if such a high resolution display could be built, merely to generate and feed the electronic signals to such a display would be far beyond the speed and complexity capabilities of current electronics. Yet the visual perception process in our brain manages with remarkably slow neurons (although admittedly quite a lot of them!). I started to wonder how my eyes and brain could possibly give me such a high quality view of the world.

I began to suspect that my subjective experience of a scene was rather different from that which my physical eyes had seen. Such musings were taking me into dangerous territory. The majority of people who worked at the lab were physicists, engineers and chemists, who had little time for psychological ideas. They held a healthy respect for physical reality and mistrusted subjective ideas that were difficult to test with any rigour. I suspected that venturing into psychological territory might lose me the respect of some of my colleagues, but I had always been drawn towards ideas that lurked on the edge of safety.

Learning about seeing

And so I began to study the science behind visual perception, initially just with the idea of developing ultra-realistic display technology, but soon I began to appreciate the remarkable processes involved. I talked to experts, and went to conferences on the science of eye movements and on the emerging field of Virtual Reality. I was fortunate that the laboratory where I worked had until recently been part of a multinational company[23] with a very broad remit. I had a sufficiently good track record for them to trust me to "follow my nose" for a while, away from my main field of optical communication.

I soon acquired an eye tracking system,[24] which measured where my eyes were pointing, i.e. it tracked the point of my gaze, and I linked this to a computer and monitor. This system required me to wear a pair of special spectacles with infra-red sensors that generated signals according to where my eyes pointed, and I wore this system for much of the time for the next couple of years, to the bemusement of my colleagues who continued to develop optical fibre communications.

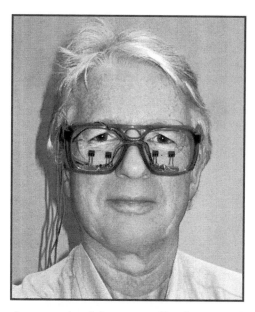

Figure 1: The author wearing his personalised eye tracking spectacles.

The team who developed graphics interfaces for new software were supportive; as a point-of-gaze monitor could reveal which region of the display caused difficulties, and enabled them to modify their designs appropriately.

During this period, I developed an extensive suite of computer programs that could exploit point of gaze information.[25] One of these programs demonstrated just how little information we absorb from an image at any moment, by blurring the image everywhere except the very centre of gaze. Despite eliminating most of the content of the image, the subject wearing the eye-tracking spectacles could read a page of text quite easily. It proved that high resolution only provides value around the very central part of our vision.

Another program recorded precisely which words have been read within text, and the duration spent reading that word, and this enabled the computer to recognise comprehension difficulties within the text. I also explored the use of point of gaze as a means of deliberately selecting and then initiating actions. This led me to create a set of on-screen buttons and I explored how I could "press" them just by looking at them. This revealed just how little control we really have over our eyes. Though we might imagine such a system could provide a very fast way of controlling systems, the reality is that it is necessary to incorporate an additional cumbersome delay to ensure that one's mind really knows what one's eyes are about to do with a careless glance!

In 1991 the parent company changed ownership, and the laboratory became focused almost completely on telecommunications, so there was no longer any justification for continued work on eye movement controlled technology. Furthermore everything that I was now learning highlighted the possibility that there might be much more efficient ways of communicating. This was not a popular message within a business that benefited from the inefficient communication of raw data through increasingly higher capacity optical fibre communications systems.

And so in my daily life I returned to focus on telecoms research, but in my spare time I began to relentlessly pursue the implications of what I had learned. I had found that "seeing" is not at-all what it seems to be, and began a journey to explore whether the capabilities of the eye and our other sensors, were a bottleneck, restricting the flow of information from the outside world to our internal consciousness. It was only later that I discovered that our minds present an even narrower learning bottleneck.

The more I learned about the learning bottleneck, the more amazed I was at its narrowness, and began to feel that I should write something to make people more aware. I discussed the ideas with various experts in the field, especially with the notable British psychologist; Richard Gregory (who sadly died in 2010),[26] and he enthusiastically encouraged me to publish something on it. I still found the implications sufficiently incredible, so for some time I searched for evidence that disproved it. If I had found such evidence, I would have been quite relieved that I did not have to spend my time writing about it. I never did, and so found myself writing this book. Now, in part one I will describe the amazing way that our mind learns about the external world.

Bottleneck

OUR HUMAN INTERFACE WITH REALITY

Part 1

How the outside gets in

Chapter One

Our Learning Bottleneck

A goldfish knows nothing of the true nature of water,
until it falls outside of its bowl.

In this chapter I introduce the idea of the limited rate that we can learn new information and investigate what novelty might mean within different kinds of experience. I explore the idea of the mind as a container for information to be filled through our senses, and show how we can describe different kinds of information using the language of digital bits.

The Speed of Learning something New

Sometimes in order to understand something close to us, we have to stand well back, to step right outside the problem to see it in its entirety. I have chosen to do this for human learning, to probe what are the true capabilities of the human learning "machine" by exploring the evidence. What might another superior intelligence make of our own learning capabilities? And how might we meaningfully measure them?

Just for a moment, imagine that intelligent aliens from another world have landed on our planet. The fact that they got here suggests that they are way ahead of us. They can see that we are a primitive but intelligent species as evidenced by the technology we have spread across our planet, and they want to characterise our intellect, to record our specification, as they do in all such encounters. They need to decide how they will interact with us: Do we humans have sufficient learning capability to justify sharing their greater knowledge with us, or are we just potential exhibits in their Zoos (or maybe a potential high protein food resource!)? They need to know how rapidly we can learn new things, how quickly we can integrate new experiences into our existing internal ideas.

Having established limited communication with us, they find that we humans hold strong beliefs about our capabilities, much of which is accurate, but some of which seems completely unsupported by evidence. One such belief is that we humans are close to understanding how the human brain works. Another is that we are able to take in a huge amount of novel information continually; indeed some believe that every tiny detail of our life's experience is stored away in our brain somewhere, and that its retrieval is the only difficulty we face.

The aliens have heard this story on many occasions before, especially when primitive creatures are arguing for an upgrade in their status, and have found that the simplest of intellects often have the greatest delusions about their own powers. We humans apparently believe that we are handicapped if we can receive no more than a few Megabits per second of information via our broadband networks, yet surprisingly we have yet to produce evidence that we are capable of learning at more than a tiny fraction of this. The future status of mankind (and even our survival) now rests on our ability to come up with some experimental evidence that we possess a rapid learning ability. So fellow humans, just where is the evidence?

There is however, a serious point to this little tale, as I use it to highlight the lack of evidence to support the belief that humans can learn fast. As I will later show, the maximum sustained information flow from reality to our consciousness is surprisingly low, no more than a few tens of bits per second. You might argue that the human mind has vast numbers of brain cells operating in parallel; doesn't that mean that we take in so much more? No, it is the internal processes that exploit the incredible complexity of our brain. I am interested in the surprisingly limited connectivity between this incredibly complex organ and the external world.

It would appear that we are like a supercomputer which only has a simple low data-rate dial-up connection with which to input data. I am not seeking answers to "What is inside our skull?" or "How clever are the contents?", but only: "How fast can this intelligence learn?"

Human Learning Performance

A human being has many skills and we often make the mistake of underestimating just how incredible these are. For example, the failed attempts to implement the 1950's vision of a robotic house worker have shown that many human tasks that we find deceptively simple are still beyond our ability to replicate through technology, even now. Some of our capabilities are accurately assessed and well documented; human physical performance is measured with great accuracy through various athletic sports.

Events such as the hundred metre sprint or the high jump are assessed against absolute measurements and do not intrinsically require an adjacent competitor for comparison.

Our mental skills however, are more difficult to quantify and measure. In education, what has been learned over an extended period of time is often measured by some kind of exam. A year of absorbing information on a particular topic is typically assessed by the ability to recall the remembered information over an hour or so. When we watch our sporting champions demonstrate their physical performance at televised events such as the Olympics, we are interested in both the comparative performance (who won) and the absolute record.

However, memory is almost always measured differentially, in competition with other people. Our champions perform in contests such as Master-Mind[27] or in Spelling Bees.[28] The problem with memory performance is that we don't have any quantitative measures. So for example we do not know if human memory performance has increased through recent history, in the same way that physical performance has. Note also that the spectators of most contests have little interest in how long it took the performer to *acquire* their skills, whether it is a test of their physical skills or their mental ones. Indeed the performer may be proud to have sacrificed years of their life in order to achieve and demonstrate their mastery during their brief performance.

Traditionally the success of education has been measured by exams that are in effect little more than tests of the students' memory.[29] This may be increasingly inappropriate as the function of memory is now readily provided by electronic digital memory.[30] Mental skills such as problem solving and creativity, which are therefore probably of increasing importance, are much more difficult to measure. However, good students learn that conceptualising a subject allows them to deduce answers instead of simply learning all the answers, and good teachers appreciate that there is much more to education than the mere acquisition and regurgitation of facts.

What do we know about the *speed* of learning, the rate at which humans can absorb "new" information? Not much it seems. Historically we have had little interest in it. A test or exam to assess this skill might involve exposing the candidate to some completely novel information over a period of an hour, then examining their ability to recall this information at some time in the future convenient to the candidate. The key difference is that our exams usually measure the quantity of relevant information a human can store, but here we are interested in the *rate* at which a human can accumulate novel information. The word "novel" is crucial here. I am only concerned with that portion of the incoming information that is completely new to the individual. Though it certainly doesn't feel like it, there is increasing evidence that a large part of what we think we are experiencing "now" is a recollection of things we already know from similar past experiences.[31] We are unaware of the distinction between what is new and what is known. I will return to this in greater detail later.

The importance of learning speed becomes apparent if we consider the idea of a new born human brain as an information processor linked to largely empty memory. We know that it takes time to acquire skills such as walking, talking, reading, and we have no reason to believe that the rate of learning has increased significantly over the last few centuries. Improvements in the speed that students learn higher level concepts such as Physics are probably due to greater clarity of the ideas and improved teaching methods. Few would dare to suggest that Aristotle, Archimedes or Newton would have been any slower at learning than smart people today. It is even possible that modern man has lost some of his edge as a result of the increased effectiveness of today's teaching methods, and hence has a lower learning speed. Another possibility is that the more complex environment we find ourselves in results in a slower rate of integrating new knowledge. After all, many simpler creatures have faster responses than we humans. This raises the question; is the rate that we can learn limited by our biology? Could we transcend that limit?

We are living on a world of exponentially increasing quantities of information. In the past it was feasible for a polymath such as Newton to learn much of what was knowable in his day, especially scientific knowledge. That is no longer possible. Hard Drive storage capacity has increased one hundredfold in each of the last three decades.[32] We are becoming buried in information, the detritus of the information age. More is not necessarily good, since it can make it more difficult to find what is meaningful. We used to think that to have information meant having power, but it is like having possessions or food, you can have too much. When we learn in daily life, we do much more than simply take in data and store it.

Sensed Incoming Information

All sentient creatures process information, something that is happening outside, registers inside. In the simplest case a single sense might directly trigger a single response in a process we call a reflex. The simplicity of this process enables the fastest possible response, and speed may be crucial to the creature's survival. For example, when I pull my hand away from something hot or sharp, I only become aware of my reflex reactions after the event. At the other end of the scale are considered responses, those involving our consciousness, such as when noticing a flashing blue light in the rear view mirror; is it the police? Was I speeding? What is the speed limit here? Does the police car need me to get out of the way?

With more complex processing two or more sensations might be required to trigger an action. A shark might simultaneously sense both the movement visually, and the electric field associated with a live prey, leading it to bite. When optical fibre cables were first laid on the ocean bed, some that were installed near the Canary Islands failed unexpectedly. When the damaged cables were brought to the surface, large teeth were found embedded in it that were subsequently identified by experts to be those of a "crocodile shark" (we can only speculate what happened to the rest of the shark as the cables carry a very high voltage). Initially no one could understand why the sharks should choose to attack the new optical fibre cables, as this type of failure had never happened with the previous generation of coaxial copper undersea cables, and why should it only occur in this particular geographical location?

Eventually it was realized that the sharks were sensing the combination of movement due to the unusually strong sea current that flowed around the islands which caused the cable to vibrate, plus the presence of a strong electrical field. Live fish give off a small electric field, and when sensed together with movement it usually suggests food. It seems that the sharks had perhaps mistaken the cable for a very big juicy worm. All modern transoceanic undersea transmission system cables carry a very high voltage to supply power to the undersea regenerators which boost the signal at several points along the way. However, the earlier coaxial cables by necessity had a metallic screen which had the effect of hiding this high voltage from the sharks' sensitive senses. These new optical fibre cables did not need such a screen, as the information was carried as pulses of light guided along hair thin glass fibres within the centre of the cable. The absence of a screen meant that the high voltage electric field could be sensed by the sharks, encouraging them to bite into the cable, with potentially fatal consequences!

When this process was understood, the cable design was modified to include a thin metallic foil screen, whose only function was to hide the electric field from the sharks and it proved to be one hundred percent effective. This story is an example of how a living creature processes multiple sensations to make a prediction. In this case the prediction was flawed; they were neither prepared by their own experience, nor through that of their ancestors inherited via their DNA. More intelligent creatures have more complex processes involved in decision making. Their lives depend on high level internal conceptual models of the external world.

Simple reflexes do not involve the conscious mind in the decision process. However, many such reflexes pass information to our conscious mind retrospectively, to let it know what had happened, so for example we learn not to touch hot things in the future. Other reflexes such as balancing while standing or breathing are completely unconscious, until we consciously choose to give them some attention, so it is not just emergencies that are handled as reflexes. For example, whilst running up a flight of stairs, occasionally I have suddenly become conscious of what my feet are doing, and have tripped up as a result. The delay in passing information through my conscious mind is just too long, so any response is out of synchronism with my feet. Similarly with playing a drum, it is just not possible to drum while being conscious of each individual drum stroke, one can only be conscious of the patterns. As you will see later, the majority of rapid physical skills are best achieved through extensive practice beforehand, with the minimum of conscious intervention during the task.

This book is about the limits to communication between reality and our human consciousness. One of the things that distinguish humans from other creatures is the incredible complexity of our world model, built through learning, and shared through communication. For this reason I have chosen not to explore the limits for simple reflexes. A creature such as a shark has a vast array of sensors on the surface of its body: smell/taste, electric field, touch, sight, sound. It is conceivable that the total information capacity of this interface may be large. But as I am interested in what the senses can contribute to our insights of our greater world, I have ignored this low level information, because the information content is significantly reduced before being presented to our consciousness. For example "Ouch!" does not usually tell us hot/cold/sharp or which finger until a few moments later when our brain has posed that question to our sensors. So the information rate that I am addressing is the speed of integrating new sensed information from "out there", into our internal conceptual models; the speed that new stuff reaches our intelligent mind.

Our Mind as a Black Box

Scientists and engineers frequently use the concept of "The Black Box".[33] This is a device, system or object which can be viewed solely in terms of how its output relates to its input without any knowledge of its internal workings, that is, its implementation is "opaque", or "black". Almost anything might be described in terms of its black box characteristics: a transistor, an algorithm, or the human mind. The opposite of a black box is a system where the inner components or logic are available for inspection.[34]

The idea is that when dealing with complex systems, it can often be extremely useful to temporarily ignore the complexities that lie within a system, and describe the system only in terms of what is observed at the surface of the "box", in other words simply how the internal system interfaces with the rest of the world through its inputs and outputs.

In our everyday life we interact with many "black box" systems, of which cars, computers and TV sets are good examples. Although there are many different technological implementations of these functional systems (petrol/diesel/hybrid cars, terrestrial or satellite TV), we know how to interact with them through familiar interfaces.

When dealing with a black box there are a couple of rules: The interface should be straightforward, well defined and easy to understand. (Even children can master iPads and work the new TV). You should not need to know anything about what is inside, all you need to know is the interface. (Few of us know just what is under the bonnet/hood of our car, or how our TV works).

Consider the analogy of a Hi-Fi audio system, and its response at high frequencies. The magazine review may promise incredible performance because the internal electronics uses some super "cool" technology, possibly involving the use of words such as "nano" or "quantum". However, the serious customer might want to know the results of measuring how high a frequency could pass into the amplifier, and how high a frequency could emerge from the loudspeaker. If the amplifier and loudspeaker are integrated into a single sealed unit, then the customer would probably be happy to know how high a frequency can pass through the whole system. The discriminating customer generally does not care precisely where within the system the limit occurs, only the actual performance of his whole system.

Of course we are not always discriminating. Sometimes our sense of our self depends on the belief that we have some better "stuff" than our neighbours, stuff like cars, cameras, HiFi system, or even the superficial attractiveness of our partner. In this situation we may simply collude with the "spin", so that we can feel special. We may have invested a great deal in our illusions, we may have spent vast sums on special "low-Oxygen Copper" cables for our loudspeakers, believing that they "vividly enhance the experience by providing an essential purity to the music" (or some other dubious claim by an unscrupulous supplier).

If you want to stay with the comforting illusion of being immediately in touch with reality, then this book may not be for you. It has been said that "philosophy tells us what is possible, and science tells what is true"[35]. I want to use science to peer past the emperor's new clothes at "the truth" behind human learning.

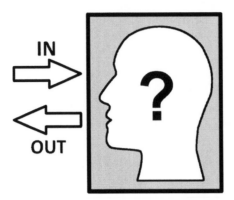

Figure 2: We can consider the human mind as a "Black Box" and simply measure the overall performance: "information in" and "information out".

Treating the human mind as a "black box" in the context of learning, allows us to ignore all the largely unknown details of the hardware (& software) within the brain,[36] so we then only have to consider how we might test the performance at the human interfaces: The black box approach allows us to get a useful performance estimate by measuring the overall throughput performance: "data in" to "data out", a form of simple benchmarking.

Although I often use the language of computing and communication engineering in this book, I only do so as a tool to gain new insights. I have no reason to believe that the human brain actually works like a piece of man-made engineering. Some parts of the brain might do so, but it would be arrogant of me to assume so. However, sometimes when science grinds to a halt in the details of a problem, it makes progress by standing back and exploring metaphors and analogies for those things that are not yet understood. Though the black box approach may at first seem a gross simplification, it can be a powerful tool when dealing with systems with hidden or unknown complexity such as the human brain.

Alan Turing, a key member of the team that famously cracked the German wartime military coding of the Enigma machine, used the "black box" approach to great effect when he proposed the "Turing Test" of a machine's ability to demonstrate intelligent behaviour.[37] In his test, a human judge engages in a natural language conversation (for example via a keyboard) with a machine designed to generate performance indistinguishable from that of a human being, and also with a human. All the participants are separated from one another. If the judge cannot reliably tell the machine from the human, the machine is said to have passed the test. The comparison is made purely in terms of what goes in and out, with no consideration of what lies within. So Turing considered a machine to be intelligent if we cannot tell if it is a human or not when considering it as a black box, in other words if we cannot determine from the outside whether a human operator is concealed within the machine.

What do we consider to be our "box"?

If we want to explore human learning using this approach, we must decide what exactly constitutes our "box"?. I can choose to define the boundary of my metaphorical "box" wherever I want, but my choice is driven by the need to eliminate ambiguity. I want to define the interface such that it does not intersect any part of the processor: the human brain and associated nervous system. I don't know enough about the workings within the brain to know how to apply partitions within, and furthermore not all processing occurs within the brain itself, so I choose to consider my box to be the surface of the body.

If I were to choose an interface further within the body such as the retina or the optic nerve, I would have to make some very dubious assumptions since we are unsure what processing occurs within them. For example the retina is in effect part of the surface of the brain, and we do know that much information is discarded before being passed on via the optic nerve. As you will later see, the raw information capacity of human eye is far greater than the information capacity of learning.

Information might flow in or out at any point on this surface. Some regions on this surface can communicate at a much higher information rate than others, for example: our eyes, ears, nose and the tips of our fingers. Similarly, the main organs we use to output information are our mouth and our fingers. The real information "bottleneck" however, is almost certainly not the surface nor is it likely to be localised, but is a distributed constraint resulting from the complexity of the process of integrating new sensations and experiences into our internal model. (A useful analogy would be automated systems for recognising car registration plates; these are generally not limited by the performance of the camera itself, but by the speed at which the computer program can interpret the signals from the camera). It would be hugely difficult to measure these limits within the human brain itself, but the measurement problem becomes tractable when we stand back and look at the performance of our "black box".

What lies within our box?

Introspective Learning

This should become clearer if I describe the learning process that does not cross the boundary of our "box"; learning by introspection. This often occurs together with learning by sensing, but there are some situations in which this is the only learning process taking place, for example during daydreaming, contemplation, meditation, or even during sleep. We can still "learn" while sensing nothing whatsoever, in that we can convert large amounts of previously ingested information, into succinct forms of knowledge and predictive rules. Between meals our body digests what we have recently eaten, extracting valuable nutrients, and so it is with our mind; it converts loosely connected low level information into useful high level concepts, when not distracted by sensory experiences.

Introspection is the process of understanding what we have already learned, and this understanding helps us focus our senses on whatever we predict will be most valuable to sense next. For example it helps direct our gaze. The learning bottleneck may or may not apply to this internal process, for I have no way of measuring it. Even if we insert electrodes into the brain, we don't understand the language it uses to communicate with itself. However, for the purposes of this book this does not matter, for I am specifically interested in what flows in from outside. But before moving on I want to clarify the difference between learning through our senses, and learning through introspection.

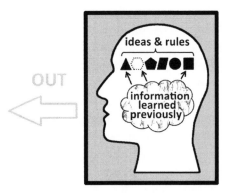

Figure 3: Introspection: When our senses provide no information, nothing enters from outside our self, but we can continue to learn through introspection, and act through skill.

In our mind we recognise patterns in the information that we had previously received through our senses, to create new mental models and rules, and to refine old ones. Later when we are open to experience the world, they enable us to recognise what is familiar, to focus our attention and gaze on what is different.

The process of introspection operates for much of the time, and appears to compete for mental resources with the process of sensing. Reflecting on something familiar out there, reduces our ability to sense what is out there in that very moment, so when we are encountering a novel experience, too much introspection can be a distraction. Even while totally absorbed in introspecting or daydreaming, we can direct information outwards provided that we do not require confirmation that we are achieving what we intend, for example while exercising a familiar skill such as touching our nose.

However, skilled mental tasks are often dominated by introspection. Consider the mental processes for two people when playing the game of chess, one an expert, a Grand Master; the other an equally intelligent individual but completely new to the game of chess. When the newcomer is first introduced to the game, his attention will be focused on the board, the number of squares, the pieces, how they differ from each other. He will want to learn from his partner, how each piece is allowed to move, the rules of capture, whether all the squares can be used, and in what situation is the game won. So much to learn; so little time for introspection.

The expert is already familiar with the layout of the board, the number of squares, the variety of pieces and the allowed moves. Furthermore he will have rehearsed a myriad of sequences of game moves, both in reality and within his mind. When he sees his opponent make a move, he immediately considers a range of future scenarios, calculating a whole sequence of possible future moves by his partner and himself. Introspection dominates his process. For each move, the only thing that he senses is the specific piece being moved by his opponent, for he already has an accurate image in his mind of the locations of every piece on the board. If the lights should suddenly fail, he could continue to plan his game unhindered, whereas the beginner would be lost.

How much information are we born with?

Our information "black box" is a container for our knowledge of the external world and is almost empty of information at birth. We are born with some inherited information encoded within our DNA, which is passed on to us by our parents. The totality of the information encoded in human DNA has been calculated to be around 6 Gigabits, though only a tiny fraction of this is information specific to Homo sapiens. Some of this information is shared across most lifeforms, and much of the remainder is information crucial to the survival of our species.

Studies of mature identical twins separated at birth suggest that adult personality is defined roughly equally by both Nature, our genetic programming and by Nurture, our early life experience. It is true that our inherited nature has a big effect on how we experience our lives.[38] However, the sheer quantity of information that we subsequently learn through our lifetime completely dwarfs that which we are born with.[39] So though the twins may have somewhat similar personalities, one might become a historian while the other a surgeon, so have subsequently absorbed widely differing sets of knowledge.

There is also a key difference between these two kinds of information: That which we are born with is in the form of rules and information crucial to our initial survival. This information has been refined through evolution over many thousands of years and optimised for the physical survival of our species. It is a set of rules, "ready to go", tried and tested over many generations. We can therefore expect inherited information to be very efficient (in terms of its value per bit of information). We get a glimpse of this efficiency when we see the incredible intricate beauty of ferns, and appreciate that similar shapes can be created mathematically from a tiny amount of information input to a Fractal computer program.

We might compare the inherited information with which we are born, with the very basic operating system (or BIOS) installed within a PC during its manufacture.[40] When a PC is first switched on, this provides it with sufficient intelligence to be able to subsequently load a complex operating system such as Windows, and various additional programs for dealing with email or word processing. Like a new-born baby, the raw PC is fairly dumb but has huge potential. A PC can only go on to perform highly complex tasks when it has acquired such programs and additional data.

Inherited information probably provides us with the very basis of our mechanism for perceiving things; however, it is not the source of most of what we perceive. The comparatively small amount of information that we inherit, has the sole purpose of maintaining our species, and provides very little assistance at exam time, or in our daily office jobs. It pre-programs our ability to learn, to absorb information, and probably also to develop language.[41] However, it provides us with a negligible amount of information when compared with that which we later absorb through our education. There is no trace of Shakespeare within the DNA of families of actors. The "almost empty mind" of a new-born child may be ignorant of the world it has entered, but it is an uncluttered system with learning capabilities beyond any technology that man has yet created.

In contrast, the information that we subsequently learn often has a low value per bit (train timetables, integrated circuit identification codes) and only gains significance when related to previously learned information and conceptual models. We slowly integrate learned information into a set of new rules, which gradually increase in complexity as we absorb more information over the years. So our black box is nearly empty at birth but comes with a few incredibly valuable jewels at the bottom, (which may become somewhat buried in useless information later!). Most of the information to which we are subsequently exposed gains significance only when related to previously acquired information and conceptual models, when we are able to match it with something we expect and recognise its significance.

If we observe a truly random image, the only information we might learn from it might be about its general structure (for example is it coarse or fine?). But if we have seen something similar before, we may recognise what is familiar about it. Through our lives we slowly integrate the information we sense into sets of new rules, and these rules gradually increase in number and complexity as we absorb more information. So although we are born with some pre-programmed information crucial to our biological survival, the amount is small in relation to that contained in an adult educated mind. Over the years this "container" is filled with knowledge at a rate which varies depending on our exposure to new experiences and information.

I want to reiterate the distinction between *new* information entering the mind, and the active processing of previously memorised information within the mind. The former involves the senses, the latter does not. Of course in most circumstances both processes occur together, and there is plenty of evidence to suggest that they compete for resources: Thinking about a difficult problem causes our senses to be dulled, an effect I use deliberately whenever I visit the dentist! Equally, observing a candle flame intently can still the busy mind. For most of the time we are able to both sense and reflect simultaneously to varying degrees. We consider something while observing it, comparing what we experience with what we are familiar with, comparing what we expect with what we are sensing, and modifying our future expectations.

In the following figures and discussion, where I have referred to "the world", I mean something or everything that lies outside our mind. The descriptions would equally apply if we substitute something else for the "the world", for example a dog, these typed words, or global warming. For everything "out there" that we have experienced, we hold an idea in our "mind's eye". It will be incomplete, contain inaccuracies and be out of date, just as an old school globe is only a limited representation of the Earth.

Figure 4: Our idea of the world is inevitably incomplete, inaccurate and out of date, like an old school globe.

Our incomprehensible brain

"If the human brain were so simple that we could understand it, we would be so simple that we couldn't"
- George Edgin Pugh[42]

The human brain is an incredibly complex organ with fine structural detail right down to the level of neurons. It is likely that the precise mechanisms that lie behind human perception and intelligence are equally complex. It is intrinsically impossible to fully describe a complex system, using a less complex system, so it seems unlikely that a single human mind can ever fully understand itself. (Similarly, if we consider a computer as an electronic brain, we would not expect a single computer (alone) to be able to fully "understand" itself, i.e. to be able run a simulation of itself that was fully detailed and not an approximation). So any valid "understanding" we might claim to have of our brain's architecture, must by necessity be a very limited approximation of the structure.

It has been possible to ascribe functions to the various "lobes" of the brain by observing the effect of localised brain injuries on human perception and behaviour.[43] [44] [45] Recent developments in brain imaging provide us with much higher spatial resolution than was previously possible without using invasive techniques, such as surgery or implanted electrodes.[46] Functional Magnetic Resonance Imaging (fMRI) measures brain activity by detecting associated changes in blood flow. These methods rely on the assumption that brain activity involves use of energy, so the brain maps are maps of energy consumption during a specific mental task. This is a bit like measuring the change in temperature distribution throughout a computer while running different computing tasks.

Every improvement in brain imaging resolution has brought greater awareness of the complexity of the architecture and functioning of our brain, even for what we might consider quite simple mental activities. The latest brain scanners can now localise activities to within a few millimetres. However, these brain imaging techniques cannot tell us what is actually happening within individual neurons, as even the highest resolution systems only measure the average effects over a brain volume containing millions of neurons. There is no way we can deduce the precise "wiring diagram" of the brain, and we have little insight into the specific detail of the interconnections between neurons.

So despite learning much more about which specific regions of the brain are active when carrying out particular tasks, we remain ignorant of finer details of our brain's architecture. Equally we cannot measure changes faster than one per second, so cannot measure the nerve signals individually.[47] Yes, we can insert electrical probes to monitor a few individual neurons, but without a wiring diagram, we are faced with an insurmountable task to work out precisely what is going on. So despite the great progress in brain scanning technology, we still remain largely ignorant of how the brain actually works.

In complete contrast, modern electronic equipment is usually designed with precisely defined interfaces and connectors, such as the ubiquitous USB connector that enables us to interconnect between our computers and so many of our electronic gadgets without a moment's thought. However, the internal structure of our human brain is a puzzle of such complexity, that we have no idea how to electronically connect to it, despite what you may have seen in the film "The Matrix".[48] Where real progress has been made, it has been in connecting to our sensors, to interface with the human sensory nervous system rather than the brain itself. These developments have been vital in improving the lives of those with sensory impairments, and one of the best examples is the use of cochlear implants for the profoundly deaf.[49]

An array of electrodes is implanted within the cochlear, part of the inner ear, and these are stimulated by electrical signals derived from a microphone. The ability to "hear" again has to be learned, for we do not know precisely how to interface with the cochlear. Fortunately, the human brain is very flexible and over a few months, soon learns how to interpret the electrical stimuli as sounds. Similarly, a limited form of "vision" has been provided to the blind, via an array of tiny electrically stimulated solenoids on the subject's body[50] or electrically stimulated electrodes on the tongue,[51] fed with signals from a camera. But it is absurdly optimistic to believe that we will soon be able to intelligently access the detailed internal workings of the human brain via an electrical connection, in the way so often portrayed in Science Fiction.

So it seems that we humans may have exaggerated ideas of our observing and learning abilities. Indeed, we are easily impressed by the totality of what has been learned, without caring much about the speed of the prior learning process. If we are going to understand or measure these abilities, we need to avoid being distracted by the complexities and unknown details of the brain's structure.

The way forward is to use the idea of the mind as a container for information, and then to simply explore the limits of what goes "in" and "out". However, when we do this we must take care to distinguish between sensing things that we already know, and sensing truly novel information, whether that be within images, text, speech or music. And if we are to make meaningful comparisons between our human capabilities and those of the technology we now surround ourselves with, we must find a way to describe this flow of novel information using a common language, and that language uses digital bits.

A bit about bits - how we encode information

I have used the word "information" quite a lot so far, and must make clear that I use it in the information theory sense; to describe what we *could* know about something, rather than what we *do* know, or even what we believe to be of value of what we know. This is a rigorous use of the word as it does not require us to ask a receiver of information whether it has meaning or is pure nonsense (a completely subjective opinion!). We can consider knowledge to be information that has meaning.

In order to progress further, we need a way of quantifying information, and to do that we need a more precise language, one that is unambiguous and will allow us to compare very different kinds of information.[52] Binary digits or "bits" are the simplest most convenient form, as bits are now the basic language of computers and the digital world. The word bit was invented by John W. Tukey, an eminent statistician, while working at Bell Labs. He coined it as a contraction of the term "binary digit" and as a handier alternative to "bigit" or "binit". It was first used and credited to J.W.Tukey in Claude Shannon's famous paper on information theory.[53] John Tukey also coined the word "software". Incidentally we will read more about Claude Shannon later.

Unlike decimal numbers which cover ten different values, a bit is either a One or a Zero, a Yes or a No. If I toss a coin, one bit is sufficient to describe the result: Heads or Tails. Twenty bits in a row can be used to precisely describe the results of twenty coin tosses: 11010001etc., meaning: Heads, Heads, Tails, Heads, Tails, Tails, Tails, Heads, etc. Note that our digital format (11010001) is much more compact than the equivalent text with the same meaning.

Binary digits are all or nothing, so in comparison with conventional analogue signals; they are much more immune to being confused by imperfections in the signal, such as distortion, background interference or noise. Digital bits are now the dominant format for communicating almost all information around the globe, providing perfect transmission at any distance. They are equally successful as a means of distributing recorded music and video today.

The old analogue recordings made on magnetic tape were degraded each time they were copied; the valuable recording was increasingly buried in the accumulated noise. Binary digits or bits, can be copied any number of times with effectively zero deterioration, so any number of successive digital copies can be as perfect as the original. This presents new challenges for copyright legislation, because copies are completely indistinguishable from the original.

How digits encode an analogue value

So an individual bit is a perfect way of communicating a simple Yes/No, but what if the information is something more complex, a value such as a large number, or a more precise measure such as a distance? How can we use these binary digits (bits) to accurately describe something of which we have no prior knowledge other than the range of possible values?

Imagine the following completely hypothetical situation: I am an anxious parent who wants my adolescent son to tell me how he got on in the recent maths exam; I want to know precisely where he came in the class as a percentage. I have no idea what to expect but anticipate the worst as I never saw him studying. Now my son knows that his result was just above average (53%), but refuses to answer my questions with anything other than a yes or a no, in other words he will only respond using binary, offering no other possibility.

I could simply ask a succession of questions about where he came as a percentage: Was it 1%? No. Was it 2%? No, etc., until I reached the correct answer and got a Yes, but that would take somewhere between one and a hundred questions to reach the answer. I might be lucky and guess correctly with my very first question; however, it would take 50 questions on average before I got the right answer by this method,[54] i.e. half the number of possibilities.

There is, however, a much quicker and more efficient way that involves asking a succession of questions that home in on the number, each answer providing me with an increasingly accurate approximation to where he came in the class.

1/. "Are you in the top half?"

Answer: "Yes". So we know it's more than 1/2, but that is a very broad approximation. We have pinned the answer down to the top half of the range, but I want to be more precise, so I ask a second question:

2/. "Are you in the top half of the remaining top half of the range?" (In other words is he in the top 3/4?)

Answer: "No". So now we know that the answer lies somewhere between 1/2 and 1/2 plus 1/4 (so between 50% and 75%).

I can continue this process of asking successive yes/no questions each time to determine whether he is in the upper or lower half of the previously determined range. Every additional question successively halves the possibilities, so doubles the accuracy of my estimate.

So if I ask him five successive questions as described, and get the sequence of answers: Yes No No No Yes, (which I can express as 1 0 0 0 1), and I can work out the approximate percentage as follows:

1 x 1/2 plus 0 x 1/4 plus 0 x 1/8 plus 0 x 1/16 plus 1 x 1/32, which approximates to 53%.

This has taken me just 5 questions, instead of the average of 50 required if I go through each possible answer in turn, so is far more efficient. Note that 5 questions gives me an accuracy of 1 part in 32, because 2x2x2x2x2 = 32.

The following figure illustrates how the number of bits we use to characterise something, determines the accuracy; the fewer the bits, the coarser the information.

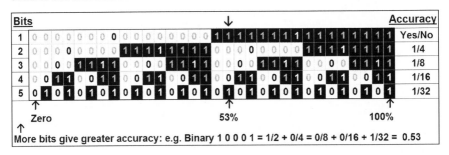

Figure 5: A diagram showing the accuracy achieved using increasing numbers of bits, from one to five. For any given percentage, the digital "word" can be read off from top to bottom, with the most significant bit at the top. A single bit only tells us Yes or No, whereas 5 bits enables us to characterise something to an accuracy of one part in 32

(3%) because 2x2x2x2x2 = 32. Note that every additional bit doubles the accuracy.

Most parents would not need to know their child's position in class to this accuracy (unless they were in the top three!), but there are many things that we need to be more precise about, the number on a lottery ticket for example. Because every additional question doubles the accuracy, asking twice the number of questions dramatically increases the accuracy. A total of 10 questions would provide an accuracy of 0.1% (1 part in 2^{10} = 1 part in 1024). Similarly, asking a total of 20 simple yes/no questions would give an accuracy of better than one part per million.

This reveals the incredible power of binary digits, for a mere 20 questions can determine any number between one and two multiplied by itself 20 times (2^{20}), which is 1,048,576. Each question immediately discards half the possible answers, whereas the simple sequential questioning only discards a single value out of the entire range of possibilities. If instead I had sequentially asked: Is it 1? No. Is it 2? No etc., then on average it would have taken me half a million questions to reach the answer. I might get lucky and get the answer earlier, but the binary successive approximation method homes-in on the correct value in the least number of steps, and always takes the same number of questions to reach an answer of given accuracy.

Do you remember the game of Twenty Questions? This is an oral game in which one player selects a word or object, then the other players attempt to guess its identity by asking a sequence of no more than twenty questions, answerable only with a yes or a no. Typically the word might be absolutely anything, but if it were a random number, then twenty questions would be sufficient to correctly guess any number up to just over a million.

This successive approximation encoding process is the same as we use in the world of electronics wherever we convert an analogue signal to digital information, whether it be a sound pressure, light level, temperature, or displacement (we call this process "digitising"). For measures or numbers that can fall anywhere within a known range, this is the most efficient coding we can possibly achieve, by which I mean that it requires the fewest number of bits to store or communicate the information.

Redundant but valuable

Achieving the ultimate in coding efficiency is not always a good thing; sometimes a less efficient code is beneficial. If the coding is perfect, a single bit that is incorrect can change the meaning dramatically. Getting the first bit wrong in the earlier example would change the 53% into 5%! In situations where not all the bits can be read or received correctly we benefit by using an inefficient form of coding, one with redundancy. The word "redundant" has come to mean "of no value", particularly when applied to employment, but in the world of communication, redundant information describes the situation with multiple copies of the same information. Now if we know the first copy is perfect, then yes, additional copies add no value, but if the first copy may be imperfect for any reason, additional nearly identical copies will allow us to get a better estimate of the correct information.

An example of a crude error correcting code would be one in which each bit is sent three times and the decision based on two out of three when they are not all identical. Much cleverer error correcting coding is used on CDs so the music can be faithfully reproduced despite the loss of large numbers of information bits due to defects in manufacture and subsequent scratches caused by wear and tear. The tracks of data on a brand new CD look quite a mess when viewed under a high powered microscope, with many areas that are clearly seriously flawed. However, the sophisticated error corrective coding that is employed to make the CD tolerant of scratch damage during normal wear and tear, also allows the manufacturers to have a very relaxed manufacturing process during pressing, without in any way impairing the quality of the reproduced music. In principle, CD players could provide users with a monitor of the basic error rate for each disk, but this would just make HiFi users completely paranoid and lead to many complaints in circumstances where the reproduction was absolutely perfect thanks to the error corrective coding.

The digital age has made error free communication possible and this is a completely new phenomenon for Homo sapiens. Most forms of human communication are potentially vulnerable to errors. When listening to someone speaking, their message is often in competition with other sounds: other voices, the sound of the sea, background music, or the hairdryer, and also with our own distracting thoughts; "sorry, what was that you were saying?" So our language has evolved to contain sufficient redundancy that we get the message under these difficult circumstances.

So in the absence of errors there is an optimum way of encoding random information, but completely random information is quite unusual in our daily lives. It is more typical for us to have some prior knowledge of the relative likelihood of different answers. If I ask the question: "How many fingers do you have?", then at first sight there are ten possibilities, but immediately I have made an assumption of what is likely, based on my prior knowledge. I assume that the answer will almost always be 10, with rare alternatives of 5 (amputee), 0 (double amputee), with a very slight chance of 11 or 12 (genetic anomaly). So armed with this prior knowledge I might assume 10 and be correct 99% of the time. If I were a glove manufacturer I would consider this good enough. My informed prejudgement or "prejudice" makes life much simpler for me. Similarly, faced with "How many legs does this unspecified creature have?" I might assume symmetry and so expect the answer to be an even number, possibly 4, or 2 (bird, human), 6 (insect), 8 (spider), 100 (centipede? Wrong!), 1000 (millipede? Wrong!). So to describe all possible numbers up to 1000, would require 10 bits (2^{10} =1024) but the first four possibilities (2, 4, 6, 8) would cover almost all likelihoods, and only requires 2 bits (2^2).[55]

I could ask: Is the answer either 2 or 4?

If the answer is "No", then I ask "Is it 6?"

If the answer is "No", then based on just these two questions I have probably got the right answer, "8".

What about the other possibilities? I might choose to ignore them as it makes my life much simpler. Alternatively I could ask a third question: "Is it Eight then?"

If the answer is "No", then in my mind the number of possibilities suddenly explodes:

Any of the most likely four values, but minus a leg? My next question might be "Odd or Even?"

So you see that questions we ask about things in the real world generally come with expectations of likely answers. Our previous experience predisposes us towards some answers.

Earlier I showed how twenty questions could be asked to determine a number, but in the real game of twenty questions the answer can usually be anything, that is absolutely anything, and for a mature human that covers a lot of territory. A child playing the game for the first time might just take twenty guesses "in the dark" and their chances of success would be very low. However, an experienced player will intelligently choose each successive question in a way that homes-in on the answer. "Is it a living thing?" Yes, "Is it human?" Yes, "Is it a real person?" No... Knowing the interests of the other person can help enormously. Knowing they are obsessed by the film Star Wars might prompt one to ask: "Is it a character from a movie?" Yes, "Is it Darth Vader?"

So to summarise, with completely novel information there is an unambiguous way of describing the information content in bits, but in the everyday situation it is hard to resolve what part of the information is reliant on that which is already known. Information can be of much greater value when gathered successively and intelligently, which ideally is the method used by a questioning police detective, scientist, investigating journalist, or a mechanic carrying out a repair on an engine or a washing machine..

How fast do bits flow?

So we can measure the *quantity* of information in bits, but the bottleneck we are concerned with is a constraint on the *rate of flow* of information, and this is usually measured in bits per second, the "bit rate"[56] and the shorthand for bits per second is bit/s.

Here are two examples of 1 bit per second of human information flow:

One meaningful Yes/No every second

One value or number estimated to 10 bit accuracy every 10 seconds

(Using 10 bits we can define a value with an accuracy of 1 part in 2^{10}, which is 1 part in 1024, i.e. to about 0.1% accuracy)

When writing about huge numbers of bits per second we use a form of shorthand as follows:

1000 bits per second is 1 kilobit/second (1 kbit/s)

1,000,000 bits per second is 1 Megabit/second (1 Mbit/s)

1,000,000,000 bits per second is 1 Gigabit/second (1 Gbit/s)

1,000,000,000,000 bits per second is 1 Terabit/second (1 Tbit/s)

We often hear the word "speed" used when dealing with bit rates (e.g. "a high speed Internet connection"), but the measurement unit is information per second, certainly not velocity (which is a measure of how fast something travels). So "speed" is really a misnomer. However, to be consistent with the commonplace meaning I will use "speed" when I am talking about information capacity in bits per second. Appendix 5 provides more details about bits and Bytes, and the abbreviations commonly used for large numbers of bits.

We will return to the topic of the velocity of communicating information later, but let's briefly compare the velocity of various communication mechanisms:

Electronic communication relies on three main technologies:

1/. Electromagnetic waves propagating through the atmosphere or through free space. This would include wireless radio wave communication e.g. to and from satellites, and also using beams of light. These signals travel essentially at the speed of light. They travel in straight lines (though may be scattered by buildings or the troposphere), and this severely limits the distances reached across the Earth's curved surface. For communications between mobile phones and base stations this is the only option.

2/. Electric current carried in metallic cables, such as the telephone cables carrying telephone and broadband signals to our homes.

3/. Light (which is a very high frequency electromagnetic wave) guided along the centre of thin transparent fibres of glass.

The signals carried through copper cables and optical fibre cables travel at roughly two thirds of the maximum speed of light, as they are slowed a little by the presence of a "dielectric": the insulation material in the copper cable, and the refractive index of the glass in the optical fibre cable. However, as cables can be bent round corners and follow the curvature of the Earth, they have become the dominant means of communication between fixed locations.

You may be surprised to learn that the signals travel through a "fast" connection at the same velocity as a slow one. Individual bits travel from end to end in the same amount of time, however they carry much more information (typically by squeezing many bits close together in time). So a "fast" connection is really a "fat pipe" instead. Never mind the speed, it's the width. A higher information capacity connection is "faster" in the sense that it can deliver a file or message of given size in a quicker time. Using the analogy of water, a fatter pipe with greater capacity, can fill a water tank quicker.

Light travels at almost 300 Million metres per second (through empty space), so the speed of light probably seems instantaneous to us within our everyday experience, especially when compared with the speed that sound travels through the air or the speed that nerve impulses travel through our body. Sound travels at 343 metres per second (1,236 kilometres per hour). Nerve impulses travel at different speeds depending on the source of the signal: from our muscles they travel at 119 metres per second and touch sensations at 76 metres per second. Some pain signals travel at a much slower speed of only 0.6 metres per second - a mere crawl, which explains why we learn that we have stubbed our toe a moment or two before we experience the resulting pain.[57]

In this section we have learned how we can quantify information using the language of bits, and how duplicated information can protect us against the partial loss of information. We have also seen how to describe the rate at which information can flow in bits per second, and this will be a vital measure when we come to consider the rate at which we can learn.

What's New?

In order to distinguish between what is being learned and what is already known, we must clarify what we mean by "New information". From the moment we are born we absorb information about our surroundings through our senses. But we also interpret everything we sense in relation to what we have sensed before and remembered. The innocence of birth is soon lost as we learn to interpret our latest sensations in relation to an internal model built from what we have already experienced. Although it may seem that we are fresh observers, the more learned and experienced we become, the more we experience the meaning of what we sense, rather than the pure sensations themselves. This process is to "make sense" of our experiences, to integrate them into some logical construct that can be useful to us from this time forward.

When we see a bird flying nearby, or hear a piece of music, most of our experience is just what we expect to see or hear. Without paying attention we experience only what we expect to experience, however, if we do, our attention lies in the difference between what we expect and what we are able to observe. This difference is the only truly *new* information, so if we are to understand the limits to learning new information, we must explore the meaning of novelty in what is sensed. We must be careful to distinguish between the raw information rate attributed to a sensation, and the new information learned about what is sensed.

Novelty in Images

The eye is a highly complex sensor. Our retina provides us with a vast array of light sensitive cells; the rods which are sensitive only to brightness, and three types of cones which are especially sensitive to red, green and blue coloured light, respectively. Apart from when we are a new-born baby, almost everything that we see contains much that we are already largely familiar with. I can illustrate this by showing you a very unusual image:

Figure 6: An image consisting of a thousand (40 x 25) random black and white blocks.

It would be incredibly difficult to accurately remember every part of this image of random blocks because it is so unusual. In a more typical scene, the observer might expect areas of similar texture, separated by extended boundaries. Note how our mind tries to find familiar patterns within the random image above. When we were children we may have seen "faces" in the patterns on the curtain. Our mind tries to make sense of what we see by trying to relate it to some previously experienced image. It is very difficult to estimate the novel information content of everyday images without knowing the previous experience of the observer.

Photographic memory

Many believe that we store images of whatever we see within our brain. There are a few individuals who are especially good at recalling image details. We call this skill eidetic memory and describe these people as eidetikers[58], but the idea that memory works like a camera appears to be a myth. Alan Searleman writes: "Is there such a thing as a photographic memory?"[59] "You might expect that an individual who claims to still see a picture after it has been removed would be able to have a perfect memory of the original picture. After all, a perfect memory is what is usually implied by the commonly used phrase "photographic memory". As it turns out however, the accuracy of many eidetic images is far from perfect. In fact, besides often being sketchy on some details, it is not unusual for eidetikers to alter visual details and even to invent some that were never in the original. This suggests that eidetic images are certainly not photographic in nature but instead are reconstructed from memory and can be influenced like other memories (both visual and non-visual) by cognitive biases and expectations."

So there is no evidence for "photographic memory" except as an internal illusion which makes us overconfident in what we can recall when we witness unusual events. However, there is evidence that some people are better at remembering detail, but worse at integrating what has been seen into their conceptual model of similar experiences. Prodigious Savants[60] demonstrate remarkable feats of memory but all exhibit some other mental impairment. Half have autistic spectrum disorder, while the others suffer from forms of developmental disability or other brain injury. Almost all savants have a prodigious memory of a special type, which is described as "very deep, but exceedingly narrow".[61] It is deep in the sense that they can recall many pieces of information, but they have a hard time putting it to use.

Novelty in Language

Spoken and written language contains a large proportion of redundant information (meaning duplicated, not useless). Language has evolved to retain its meaning despite being immersed in high levels of background noise, and conflicting crosstalk from other people's voices. It is this redundancy that makes predictive text possible, and why "Texting" requires much less data than the equivalent speech. When the Texting feature was first introduced on mobile phones, the network operators were very surprised at how popular it soon became. They had assumed that people would always prefer voice communication, but texting was quick, convenient and allowed the sender to avoid an immediate conversation. The electronic digital text communication channel is completely free of errors , so a single "u" can mean "You" without risk of an error changing the meaning.

Handwriting is potentially flawed; differences in how individual letters are written, can make them ambiguous (is it an "a" or a "d"?). Redundancy in language ensures that the meaning is not lost or changed due to single character errors, indeed several individual letters can be omitted, "wit?out los?ng ??? mes??ge". Recognising this redundancy has been invaluable in the past when cracking coded text messages, so a good code must conceal this redundancy.[62]

Prior to the digital age, almost every form of communication was prone to errors, whether by badly transcribed letters or faded ink on a manuscript, or actual speech interfered with by a background of noise, so human language has evolved to be optimised for that situation. However, thanks to modern electronic technology, digitised signals can be communicated with essentially zero errors. As pure electronic communication becomes a greater proportion of all our messages, we may evolve a more succinct, more economical form of language, derived from texting perhaps.[63]

However, here is a word of warning for those hoping to achieve clear interpersonal communication; the more succinct the message, the greater the opportunity for misinterpreting any emotional content in the message - as I have found to my cost. We do not have unambiguous ways of communicating feelings, so tend to do so by being verbose, using several words that together convey our message. The message sender may believe that their succinct message is unambiguous and inoffensive, but the recipient has far greater opportunity to misinterpret it based on their own emotional state, if there is little redundant content. Redundancy in emotional language is a pleasant form of error correction, and the very basis of romantic poetry.

To get an idea of how much redundancy there is in written language, try to quickly scan-read the following sentence:

"Aoccdrnig to rscheearch at Cmabrigde Uinervtisy, it deosn't mttaer inwaht oredr the ltteers in a wrod are, the olny iprmoatnt tihng is taht the frist and lsat ltteer be in the rghit pclae".

So we can successfully interpret text with many errors in any positions. We use our intelligence and our existing knowledge to predict successive words in a sentence so the loss of whole words can often be tolerated. This shows that the information content of language is far smaller than that of the sequence of characters.

It is very difficult to estimate the true information content of conventional language as the degree of redundancy depends on the prior knowledge of the recipient. Someone with zero knowledge of language would be unable to predict what letter or what word was coming next, and would require a much slower rate of communicating words or symbols to stand any chance of remembering what was communicated (they would not know that a "q" is always followed by a "u"). Knowledge of the world also has an effect on redundancy; for example the phrase "the sky is blue" is more likely than "the sky is red", and much more likely than "the sky is green". I will return to this subject in chapter 5, where we look in more detail how we might determine the information content of language more precisely.

Novelty in Music

A typical HiFi can reproduce signals over a frequency range from 20 Hz to 20 kHz. We need to sample that signal at twice the highest frequency in order to faithfully capture the highest frequencies.[64] With sufficient number of bits to achieve a good signal to noise ratio we might end up with a bit rate approaching 1Megabit per second. It would be easy to imagine that an acute listener might be taking in information at this rate. However, modern iPods and MP3 players can provide us with high quality stereo audio with significantly lower data rates (~20 kbit/sec). This is achieved by exploiting insights into how our mind perceives sounds (Psychoacoustics).

It has been discovered that we have a very limited capability to simultaneously hear all that is present in complex sound experiences; one sound can completely mask another. This phenomenon has been exploited extensively in Dolby processing.[65] The process significantly improves the perceived quality in situations of noise and limited dynamic range and is applicable to not just music, but any audio signal that is subsequently heard through human ears.[66] Dolby processing has been used extensively to improve the performance of magnetic tape recording systems, most notably with cassette tapes, where you may have seen the Dolby symbol.

All popular music, whether classical or contemporary, contains high levels of redundancy by its very nature. The pattern of sound has a repetitive structure, both in the rhythm and the notes. A note is a pressure wave that repeatedly oscillates back and forth at a given frequency, and the rhythm is a repeating sound pattern. Furthermore, for any sequence of notes, some subsequent notes are more likely than others.

The Pianola (also called the Autopiano) and music boxes may be viewed as early extreme forms of compression technology, in that they created music of high quality with very little input information. These used holes in a roll of paper or foil, or in a disc, or pegs on a drum to activate and control the notes. The modern equivalent of these is the electronic MIDI interface, whereby the "music" is a set of instructions representing the manual playing of an instrument, e.g. the movement of the keys on a musical instrument's keyboard.[67] These instructions are then used to "play" multiple notes on a virtual instrument, whose musical characteristics need to be defined just once. This method is a very efficient method of encoding for long pieces of music (compared for example with the MP3 format), or where the instrument characteristics are already known or assumed: e.g. standard synthesised instruments.

It's playing in my head

When we listen to a much loved piece of music, we may think that we are hearing it all, with all its subtle nuances, but the reality is that we are playing the copy of the piece within our mind from memory. If it is not exactly the same as the one we are familiar with, we may notice the differences. Perhaps there is now a scratch fifty two seconds into the second movement, or is the flute a bit flat?

The implication is that any enjoyment of complex music must be learned over time. So when we listen to a performance, we are actually listening to an internal memory of similar performances. This internal performance runs synchronously with the external live performance. If we give it our attention we are able to perceive differences, but not so many differences that the novel information content is more than a few bits per second. It is a kind of Vernier,[68] a comparison of two things that are nearly identical; the external sensation with the internal expectation, giving a heightened sensitivity to the differences.

Pause for a moment, and remember a favourite piece of music. Listen to it playing in your mind. There are no sound waves, yet you faithfully hear it playing in your mind, the memory of a sequence of auditory sensations, remembered sequentially. You may occasionally discover a piece of music "stuck in your head", and may even wake up to it still playing. Memories of iconic pieces can be triggered by no more than the first second or two of the piece, as is demonstrated in competitions to "name that song". The sound of the very first chord alone may be sufficient for you to identify a few popular recorded songs.[69]

So listening to music is a process of comparing what is expected; the sequence of notes, the rhythm etc., with what we already know from our previous experience of music within our culture, and of the piece of music itself. Peter Vuust[70] writes that "music, by creating an anticipatory framework in which the significance of each event is played out against a larger temporal structure of expectations, anticipations and tensions, taps into fundamental, survival related brain mechanisms associated with predicting future events. The predictive coding theory postulates that local brain structures at different hierarchical levels in the brain are responding to discrepancies between incoming signals and their prediction or model of these events with an error message that is fed forward in the system calling for an updated model that fits the input better".

To summarise, the music we hear is mostly a copy playing in our head, modified by the difference between what we hear in our head and what we hear with our ears. With this in mind, the maximum rate that new information enters our head is determined by the maximum rate that we are able to notice differences between the two. So if we wanted to measure the true learning rate under these conditions, we might introduce a few changes into a familiar piece and measure the maximum rate that changes can be noticed. If you think about it, you will see that it is unlikely to result in an information rate of more than a few bits per second at most: a shift in pitch here, an early cymbal there, etc.

Learning and Liking

Most of us find pleasure in music, admittedly in very different kinds of music. When we are first exposed to music from other cultures, we can find it difficult to appreciate the beauty and hear only the strangeness, the novelty, and it can take a considerable time to learn to appreciate it. For example, if we are unfamiliar with the Arabic world, most Arabic music tends to sound very similar to us. We may pride ourselves in having eclectic musical tastes, being open to new music, but for us to enjoy a piece of music that we hear for the very first time, it must be hugely similar to music we have heard before. Both likeability and memorability are intimately tied to our previous musical experience, so will be dominated by our culture and the shared musical tastes of our friends.

When new compositions by the great composers were first performed in public, they often had a very poor reception. Only later were they recognised for their greatness. Popular music faces the challenge of being enjoyable on the first or second listening, and still enjoyable in the longer term. It seems that we can only take so much novelty and still enjoy it, and this is probably also true of most other forms of art. When the music is very unstructured and has few recognisable patterns, few would claim to enjoy it, while at the other extreme we can soon tire of too much repetition within the pattern of notes. Alva Noë writes that:

> "We are attracted to music in the Goldilocks Zone", and "Music is a lot like clothing. We like our jeans pre-worn. When it comes to music, we like the familiar unfamiliar. That is, we like things we've never heard before that sound like things we have heard before. If the music is too familiar, it's dull. But if it is genuinely new, if it really is novel, then it is obnoxious".[71]

Likeability is not the same as memorability: Karl Szpunar investigated people's responses to new musical experiences at the University of Toronto.[72] He measured the development of both the likeability and the memorability of samples of music when subjects listened to the same samples many times. He did this for two specific ways of hearing the music: 1/. The subject's attention was focused on the notes of the musical piece, and 2/. The subject's attention was focused on a challenging non-musical task, so they only heard the music in the background subconsciously.[73]

He found that music's likeability and memorability developed differently, depending on whether the notes were focused on or not. When attention was focused on the notes, the pieces became progressively more memorable with each hearing as one might expect, but surprisingly their likeability changed very little. Conversely, when the music was played but not given attention, its likeability evolved with each successive hearing, typically increasing with number of hearings, reaching a peak then falling off with more and more hearings. This is typical of the popularity of "Pop" music versus time. However, the falloff in likeability was sooner when the listener's attention was focused on the musical notes, which suggests that likeability depends on novelty. When greater attention is given, all that is within the music to be learned may be learned much sooner. A less surprising result was that the memorability of music hardly increased when heard without attention. Karl's work showed that we develop a liking for music more by hearing it in the background than by listening to the individual notes.

So it seems that we will experience most listening pleasure when the new musical experience is broadly similar to our previous musical experience, yet where there is still more to be learned. We can become bored when we have learned all there is to learn from listening to a piece of music. Longer and more complex music such as classical orchestral pieces offer more learning potential, and indeed generally take longer to develop likeability, but consequently are less popular among the population as a whole than simpler more "catchy" pieces.

In this chapter, I have revealed that most of what we experience is what we have learned previously and already know. Our senses are focused on the small amount that is new, what we cannot expect, and this is then integrated with our complex internal ideas of what is out there. Although the rate at which we can learn is almost certainly of strategic value to us, competitive events that demonstrate that ability are extremely rare; tests of mental skills, such as exams and quizzes, are based entirely on our ability to quickly recall what has previously been learned quite slowly.

If we are to compare rates of learning in different contexts, we must quantify our experiences in the ubiquitous language of bits per second. The process of converting a value into binary digits, or bits, is similar to a game in which an answer must be found using the minimum number of yes or no questions. Lastly, I have explored the meaning of novelty across a wide range of our experiences, of images, language and music.

New information about the world around us can only enter through our senses, so in the next chapter I examine the capabilities of our senses, especially our eyes, and reveal that they sense far less than we imagine.

Chapter Two

Sense and Sense Ability

"Of all the senses, sight must be the most delightful."

- Helen Keller

We have many senses: sight, sound, smell, taste, touch (temperature, pressure, pain), motion and balance, yet sight is the one whose loss we fear most, for it gives us the power to resolve the world around us in multidimensional detail. Most of us take it for granted, at least until it starts to fail us. We believe that we have a clear view of what lies before us, yet you will soon learn that we have little insight into what we can and cannot actually see, for our mind deceives us. In this chapter, I explore what makes a seer, how our seeing compares with that of other creatures and with our other senses.

Evolution of the Seeing Eye

The majority of sentient creatures are sensitive to light to some extent, but the simpler ones lack the mental processing power to interpret a large number of light sensitive nerve cells as a representation of some *thing* out there. The simple sea urchin has no eyes as such, yet senses light through light sensitive cells at the end of their spines which cover their whole body.[74] They cannot see, but can respond slowly to the direction of illumination and to shadows. Their spines provide their protection so they do not require fast responses. Similarly, starfish have light sensitive cells at the tip of each arm.

A simple creature such as an insect might simply have the ability to jump in a direction opposite to the direction from which a shadow passes over it. This is possible with a minimal number of cells plus some rudimentary signal processing between adjacent cells. Even though the human eye is much more complex, we see similar processing occurring within human peripheral vision, leading us to flinch away from the image of large objects entering our field of view.

In general, the light sensitive cells in living creatures have surprisingly poor sensitivity to the absolute intensity of the light - this enables them to function over a wide range of brightness conditions. They are, however, very sensitive to *changes* in light level (the same is true of most of our senses), and for a simple creature this is a benefit in responding to threats and prey. The frog exploits this feature and adds some rudimentary image processing. By sitting perfectly still by a pond, the image of the view ahead focused onto its retina is completely stationary and so gradually fades to grey, that is until the moment when a fly passes through its field of view. At that moment all those cells that experience a change in light level are triggered. Some basic processing confirms that the object traversing the field of view is of "Fly-like" shape and the sticky tongue is shot out. Sometimes it catches a fly and the frog is replenished.

It is of course more complicated than this; the frog is also programmed to jump when it experiences bigger changes in the visual scene which might be caused by the shadow of a predator falling across its field of view. None of this requires much brain activity which is fortunate as frogs are not generally known for their intellect. Experiments have shown that they are unable to use vision to locate themselves in their habitat, or learn from their visual experience.[75] However, their responses are remarkably fast, much faster than our own as the simplicity of their neural processing buys them valuable speed. Just try catching flies with your own hand and you will appreciate that frogs are innately superior to humans in that particular skill.

Birds are smarter than frogs. They need to be in order to fly through three dimensional space without crashing. They also need to interpret what they see over a wide range of distances, whereas a frog has no interest in a fly if it is further than the reach of its tongue. Many birds of prey exploit the fact that the cells in their eyes are most sensitive to changes in brightness, in order to recognise live prey. They capitalise on the inability of the eye to resolve an image that is completely static on their retina for more than a few seconds. Watch a small bird that feeds on worms. It keeps its head and eyes stationary for several moments and when it moves, it moves its head in sudden jerks. During the stationary period the image of the static scene falling on the bird's retina fades to grey. However, the slightest movement of a tiny worm within the field of view is immediately highlighted, (similar in effect to those motion sensing security cameras). So a bird with a small head and brain can quickly locate a moving worm.

A larger bird like a chicken can even use this technique while walking with a continuous forward movement of its body. It achieves this by simultaneously manipulating its long neck to keep its head and eyes stationary in space until it reaches the limit of stretch. Then it abruptly jerks its head forward to a new stationary position, thus allowing it to keep the visual scene static upon its retinas during the time between these jerky head movements. This repeated jerking of the head may seem odd behaviour to us, but it enables the chicken to manage with a small brain and small head. This enhanced sensitivity to changes in a static image does not involve the creature's consciousness, but is instead a simple signal processing occurring within the retina itself. It is therefore much faster than a conscious recognition that change is occurring. Compare this with the far more complex computational task of sensing movement of a target within a static scene, but from the perspective of a moving point of reference. This would require a bigger and more energy hungry brain and lead to a much slower response (and it is worth remembering that "it's the early bird that catches the worm").

This static staring behaviour is quite common in creatures with small brains. I once watched a Kestrel, a small bird of prey, hovering in a strong turbulent wind at the edge of a cliff. I was quite close to it and watching it through binoculars could see the tiniest details of the bird. Its two big eyes seemed rigidly fixed in three dimensional space while its body and wings twisted wildly this way and that. It was engaged in a continual struggle to keep the image of the scene stationary upon its retina while the wind buffeted it (somewhat like the automatic image stabilisation in professional photographic lenses). By staring fixedly at the scene below, it allowed the entire complex static scene below to fade, revealing only the things that moved, some of which might be potential prey. When it detected the movement of some small creature, it briefly dived to a new closer hovering position, until finally diving to catch its prey.

Small creatures generally react quicker than large ones. We are far better predictors than we are predators, more suited to the relentless pursuit of bigger beasts over complex terrain. (I can plan a suitable place to ambush the buffalo tomorrow.) However, our eyes have evolved from similar origins to frogs and birds and we have inherited this same fading property when we are exposed to static images for more than a few seconds,[76] or even less.[77]

So why do we not notice this fading phenomenon when we gaze intently at a static scene? In our normal life our eyes make unconscious movements, flicking around the scene to overcome this limitation. Our eyes are never truly stationary for very long, but move in successive abrupt rotations or "saccades".[78] Not only do our eyes rotate abruptly when we move our point of gaze around the scene, but even when we think that our gaze is stilled our eyes continue to make many much smaller jerk-like, involuntary eye movements (micro-saccades).

We can observe this fading effect ourselves if we can suppress these movements. One way is by relaxing deeply (or meditating) while gazing fixedly at a scene. (For most of us this is not easy without a bit of practice.) If the image contains no sharp features or is blurred then small residual eye movements will produce little change in the image falling on the retina, and this can be achieved by defocussing the eyes.

Try fixing your gaze on a single point on an image of a human face. It takes some concerted effort to keep your point of gaze fixed, and is a lot easier doing this with a picture than with a living person. Maybe focus on the pupil of the left eye. First the colour starts to drain from the image, and then the contrast gradually decreases over the whole image. Residual eye movements cause any edges in the scene to be highlighted (this is spatial differentiation or edge sharpening). With patience and training one can reach the point where the image has almost faded to very low contrast grey, but then any eye movement instantly gives us a grotesque edge enhanced version of the face with high contrast.

There are many optical illusions that exploit this fading effect. Usually they involve staring at an image which has a clearly identified point on which to fix our gaze but little other sharp detail, enabling one to see the effects of fading.

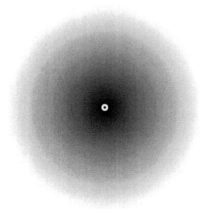

Figure 7: Fading Disc. If you stare fixedly at the central dot for ten seconds or more, the broad grey disc will start to shrink. As it fades you may notice small eye movements revealed by the sudden appearance of bright and dark patches.

Our human eye

The key components of a human eye are the retina which is an array of light sensitive cells, plus a focusing mechanism that projects an inverted image of the scene onto it. There is also a variable diameter iris that adjusts the size of its aperture (the pupil), to reduce the dynamic range of the light levels that reach the retina. All of this so far is similar to a camera. The dominant focusing element of the human eye is actually the curved outer surface of the eye, not the lens within the eye. The lens itself is weaker at focusing as it is immersed in a liquid gel (the vitreous humour) whose refractive index is not very different from that of the lens itself, thus reducing its focusing power. However, this internal lens is elastic and we are able to modify its shape by contracting the ciliary muscles around its periphery. This enables us to change the overall focal length of the eye, enabling us to bring elements of the external scene into sharp focus upon our retina over a wide range of viewing distances.

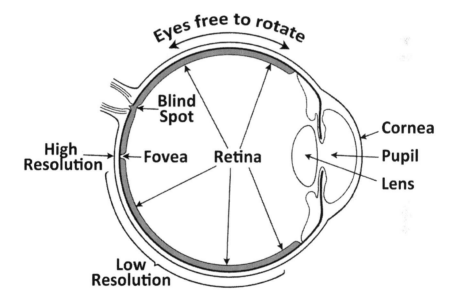

Figure 8: Horizontal section of a human right eye, showing the key components. Only the small portion of the image which falls on the Fovea can be seen in high resolution. The rest is blurred.

Earlier I described our impressive ability to resolve image detail, brightness and colour, which led to vast estimates of the information capacity of human vision. But these estimates are seriously flawed because the eye's impressive performance characteristics only apply over a limited range of conditions: We cannot simultaneously resolve fine detail and fast changes in brightness. We can only see the fastest intensity fluctuations away from our centre of gaze. Most significantly though, despite the fact that our eyes provide a wide field of view (130 degrees horizontally), we can only resolve fine detail in the central 1 to 2 degrees of our vision, the tiny part of the image that falls on the central Fovea of our eye.

Away from this central region, the power of the eye to resolve fine detail in the scene is dramatically reduced.[79] It is reduced by almost 40 percent for a mere degree offset from the centre of our gaze. Everything that we see outside this tiny central region of our eye's field of view is increasingly blurred with increased angular offset from the centre of our vision, so if we need to resolve detail we must focus the centre of our gaze directly at it.[80]

Within this central region we can resolve around 10,000 pixels or points. Although in general we can resolve a wide range of light intensities, at this fine level of detail we only have one bit of intensity resolution, in other words we can only say if it is black or white. The rest of the retina accounts for 10 times more pixels, so overall a human eye is no better at resolving spatial information than a 0.1 Megapixel digital camera. However, the sensing elements in our eye are distributed in a very non-uniform manner, providing excellent resolution immediately around the centre of gaze, and much poorer resolution elsewhere.

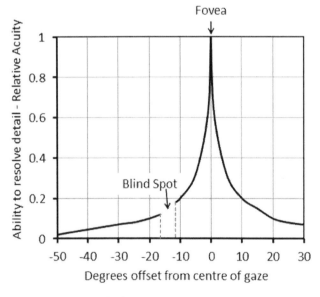

Figure 9: Eye resolution versus angle.
Fine detail can only be resolved at the very centre of our view.

The visible detail falls off dramatically with increased viewing angles, so the power of the human eye to resolve detail is very different from that of a camera. The digital sensors within today's cameras (and photographic film similarly) are designed to have uniform sensitivity and fast response across the whole area. In contrast the retina is more complex, only the very small central region can resolve fine detail. At the extremes of our field of view our peripheral vision is highly sensitive to broad changes in brightness and movement, but provides us with negligible conscious information about the scene.

You can demonstrate this by getting someone to wiggle the fingers of one hand in your peripheral vision and asking you to say how many fingers. Note that at the widest angles, you can detect the movement yet you cannot count how many fingers you are moving. These outer regions appear to be optimised to detect things that are moving into our field of view. Their primary function is to initiate our reflexes. For example to attract our point of gaze to something moving in the corner of our view, or to enable us to pull away from a falling branch as a quick reflex action, rather than as a slow well-considered decision.

Our peripheral vision has a faster speed of response than our central vision. When wide-angle TV and computer CRT (Cathode Ray Tube) screens were first introduced, many people complained of an annoying flicker and some even complained of migraines. The only thing that had changed was the wider range of angles over which the viewer's eyes viewed the screen. A moving TV image is created from a sequence of successively displayed static images, like a movie film. When the standards for TV transmission were originally set up, the "frame rate", the rate at which successive images are flashed on the screen, had been optimised for viewing a low resolution TV image on a small screen, one seen by our central vision which has a slower response than our faster peripheral vision. Wider screens placed the edges of the picture in our peripheral vision so we became aware of the flicker due to the frame rate. Fortunately modern flat panel screens have resolved this problem (both through a more constant image and higher frame rate). When we notice flickering fluorescent lights it is usually in our peripheral vision.

If we calculate the effective pixel resolution of the human eye in order to compare it with that of a digital camera, we find that it provides only one tenth of a Megapixel resolution (contrast this with digital cameras of ten or more Megapixels which are commonplace today). However, we do not experience our vision as a uniformly blurred low resolution image because the equivalent pixels are distributed in a very non-uniform arrangement. The eye has a wide field of view but with a concentration of effective pixels around the centre of our gaze which we unconsciously direct through our eye movements, towards the parts of the scene that our subconscious mind considers to be of greater interest.

The eye is not a camera, though there are indeed some similarities. Both have a lens to image the scene onto a surface, and both have an adjustable iris to control the brightness of the image falling on that surface, but that is where the similarity ends. A photographic camera produces a replica image of a scene, which can then be looked at using our eyes. Our eyes do not in any sense generate a high resolution *image* for our brain to *see*, even though we can perceive objects in high resolution. The surface of the retina is the last place that the two dimensional image appears, from that point onward it is just signal processing. The vertebrate retina and optic nerve have probably evolved from similar tissue to that of the brain[81], and some basic signal processing occurs between neighbouring photoreceptors even before the signals pass via the optic nerve to our brain. This crude processing decodes the presence of edges within the imaged scene. This explains in part why there are about 150 million photoreceptors and yet only one million optic nerve fibres connecting the eye to the brain.

The Flicks

If we are to build a sharp and clear impression in our mind of the visual scene that lies before us, we must scan our narrow field of view around the scene to pick up the key details. Our eyes do this for us by flicking the direction that they are pointing, rather like a partially sighted man might explore details of the scene immediately around him using the tip of his white stick. When we move our gaze around the room we may think we are smoothly exploring the scene, but in reality our eyes are moving in discrete abrupt jumps between stopping points. Similarly when our attention is drawn to something in our peripheral vision, our eyeballs quickly rotate to align it with the centre of our vision. These abrupt eye rotations can be as fast as 600 degrees a second and are called saccades.[82]

Between these jumps, our eyes maintain a stationary image on our retina in fixations lasting for at least a tenth of a second. Typically these jumps undershoot by about ten percent, followed by a second or even third corrective step. My eye-brain makes an educated guess of how large the first jump needs to be, and then when my point of gaze has fallen sufficiently close to be able to resolve the precise position of the target, it makes one or more additional more accurate jumps to land on (or sufficiently close to) the target.

Each of these jumps takes time and delays the moment when any high resolution detail from the scene can be resolved. In addition we take in very little visual information during these jumps, while the direction that our eyes are pointing is changing. This is partly due to blurring resulting from the fast motion of the image across our retina, but also because our brain suppresses information sensed immediately prior to and during a saccade, in a fascinating effect known as "saccadic masking".[83]

You can easily observe saccadic masking by looking at your face in a mirror and glancing back and forth from one eye to the other. You will not observe any movement of your eyes nor experience any evidence that the optic nerve has momentarily ceased transmitting. Your eye-brain system not only hides your eye movements from you, but also hides the evidence that anything has been hidden. Of course, someone else who is watching you will see your eyes moving back and forth. So the reality is that we experience repeated periods of actual visual blindness, yet another constraint of which our conscious mind is completely unaware.

Using my eye movement tracking system that I described earlier[84], I measured how my eye rotated in response to a small target light appearing to my left and attracting my attention. The resulting graph is shown below.

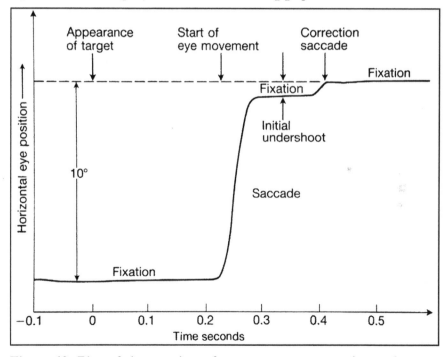

Figure 10: Plot of the rotation of my own eye versus time, when my attention is drawn to a small light ten degrees off to the left.

Note that absolutely nothing happened for 0.2 seconds, and then my eye suddenly rotated by almost the full amount required to land precisely on the target. My eye would only be able to "see" that I had undershot the target after it had made this initial large jump because from my starting position, the small target light could only have been resolved as a big blur. My eye then made a second smaller corrective jump in rotation, enabling my point of gaze to land sufficiently close to the target for me to resolve fine detail. As far as my conscious mind was concerned I had "immediately" looked at the target light, yet the graph shows that there was a total delay of 0.4 of a second before I could clearly discern it. In this example, two successive jumps were sufficient, sometimes one is sufficient, other times three are required. The results of these experiments exploring how my eyes actually moved were a revelation to me. I was amazed that I had never previously noticed just how blurred my vision is outside the very central region.

Graphs are all very well, but there are things you can try yourself which will give you an idea of how the things I have described relate to your own vision. Hold out your thumb at arm's length and focus on it. The width of the thumb's image that falls on the back of your eye will completely cover the high resolution part of your retina. If you fix your gaze one side of your thumb, the other side will be somewhat blurred. Now switch your gaze back and forth from one side of your thumb to the other. You might just be able to sense that your eye muscles are jerking the pointing direction of your eyeball through a small angle.

Here is a way to experience these jerky eye movements more readily. Just close one eye and gently place the tips of your three middle fingers on the closed eyelid. Now keeping your head still, look around the room with your other open eye. You should be able to feel the sensation in your fingertips of your closed eye jerking from one pointing direction to the next.[85]

Now gaze at the palm of your outstretched hand. Visually explore the lines on your palm and on your fingertips. Notice how your point of gaze has to move to each fingertip to be able to resolve the detail there. The overall impression you have of a crisp image of your entire hand, is only achieved by your eye flicking back and forth to build that picture in your mind.

If you are reading this book in a public place and don't want to appear a bit odd trying the things I just suggested, here is something you can try while still gazing at this book. Pause for a moment, and try staring fixedly at any one word within this paragraph of text. See how difficult it is to read the words on either side without allowing your point of gaze to move from word to word.

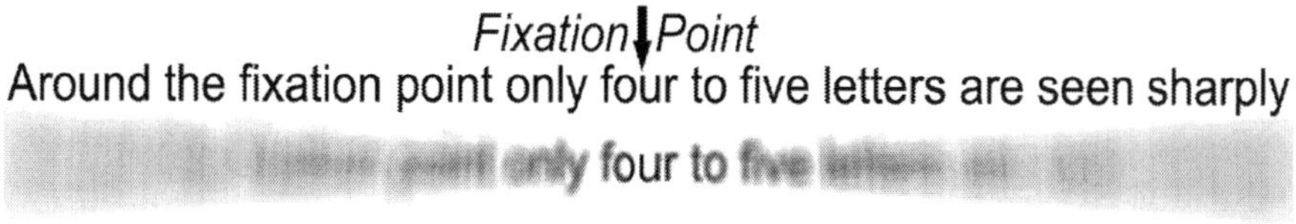

Fixation↓Point
Around the fixation point only four to five letters are seen sharply

                  only **four to five**

Figure 11: When we focus our eyes on text, we can only resolve a few letters at any one moment, those away from the centre of our point of gaze are increasingly blurred.

This image simulates what we would see if our eye's gaze did not jump from word to word, but stayed fixed upon the word "four".

Our eyes have a mind of their own

It takes significant effort to suppress the tendency of our eye to move towards whatever attracts our attention. So although we have conscious control of our limbs, our eyes are less obedient. This means that although we can monitor what our eyes are doing, the use of our eye movements to initiate conscious commands is fraught with difficulty. We do not consciously know that we are looking at something until a significant fraction of a second after our eyes have fixated upon it, so it would be highly dangerous for us to use our immediate point of gaze to initiate an action such as switching on the cooker or firing a missile at a target.

When I was working on eye movement controlled technology, I developed an on-screen keyboard in which the act of looking at a button "pressed" the button. It was necessary to incorporate a delay and to monitor that my point of gaze had dwelt upon the "button" for a sufficiently long time that my conscious mind knew what I was about to initiate, and that I was not just glancing across. This means that selection and initiation using our point of gaze is inherently slow if it needs to be accurate, and so is a less valuable human-machine interface for able-bodied individuals. However, it can be a valuable means of communication for those who are almost totally paralysed.[86]

However, we can acquire useful information by monitoring our point of gaze. Some intelligent compact cameras use it to force the auto-focus mechanism to focus on whatever attracts the attention of the photographer looking through the viewfinder. Many more applications are possible; a computer that knows what we are interested in, can subsequently give it more attention on our behalf. For example, it might know to retrieve relevant web pages for us. In the future we might envisage a system that monitors potential hazards for a driver or a pilot: when our eye momentarily fixates on something in the visual field, it may suggest that "we need to keep an eye on that". The camera equipped computer could then keep many "eyes" on potential hazards; the car in the adjacent lane that is driving erratically, the football bouncing into the road, or the third enemy aircraft in the dogfight, and draw our attention to the most important by flashing a light in our head-up-display.

Before reading any further, count how many "f"s there are in the following piece of text:

Finished files
are the result
of years of
scientific study
combined with
the experience
of years

How many "f"s did you see? You may be surprised to learn that there are 6 "f"s!

Having linked my eye movement tracker to my computer to monitor the precise point where my gaze fell on a computer screen, I then used it to record what happened when I read text on the screen. It revealed that I could only read a word by looking directly at it, the word that my eyes were actually "focusing on". Normal reading involves a sequence of flicks of the eye (saccades), from word to word, skipping nonessential words such as "the" and "of"! Suddenly I understood why effective proof-reading is so difficult to do, since it requires us to consciously suppress our natural tendency to skip words that are not key to our understanding. By the way, if you missed some "f"s, can you see which ones and understand why?

When I read text quickly, the eye tracker revealed that at any given moment my actual point of gaze was typically several words in advance of the word which I thought I was reading. So I was not physically reading the actual word that my mind thought it was reading. Furthermore if I really had been looking where I thought I was looking, it would have been impossible for me to have clearly read the highlighted word because the eye only has a narrow field of view with high resolution, and the word I thought I was looking at would have been blurred beyond comprehension. The explanation is that my brain only allows me the experience of "reading" a word, at the moment when I finally comprehend it, and this occurs a significant fraction of a second after the image is sensed by my retina and fed to my optic nerve, so several words later.

So these experiments with my eye-tracker revealed that I lived with the illusion of a scene filled with sharp detail. It also showed that I am generally unaware of where my eyes are actually looking, and am often deceived about the timing of events.

In addition to these abrupt saccades, our eye is also able to move in a smooth way, though not under our conscious control. If we try to make our point of gaze move in a smooth circular path, for example either by looking at an image of a circle or by imagining one in our mind's eye, our point of gaze simply makes a sequence of direct jumps from one static point on the circle to the next, drawing out a crude multi-sided pattern rather than a smooth circle as illustrated in the next figure:

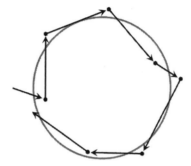

Figure 12: Our point of gaze moves in abrupt jumps when we look around a circle

Despite our inability to make our eyes move smoothly by *conscious* effort, we do have an impressive ability to smoothly and *unconsciously* track a specific visual feature within an image. Our eyes can track quite complex movements even when the feature of interest is obscured for a second or two. This accurate predictive tracking relies on a complex mental model of what is being watched or followed, and presumably was of great benefit to early man when tracking prey which was frequently obscured, for example when moving through a forest. If we look at a part of the image that is moving with respect to the background scene, our eye locks onto it and will smoothly move to track the movement, such that the feature stays imaged onto the small central part of the eye, the fovea. This is referred to as "smooth pursuit" eye movement (See Appendix 1).

It is interesting to note that attempts to replicate the performance of our eyes through the technology of cameras and computers have been comparatively unsuccessful except within artificially tidy scenes. The computer vision system is easily fooled into thinking that the tiger behind the tree is two half tigers, or just groups of stripes.

Measurements of how eyes track moving targets have revealed that there is a 150 millisecond delay before our eyes are able to initially acquire a target and start tracking it, and an equal delay in stopping following the track of a target that suddenly stops or disappears.[87] Remarkably, once tracking, there is zero delay in this process even when tracking complex motion, in other words our point of gaze does not in any way lag behind the target. This shows that we use a complex predictive model to completely compensate for the delays inherent in our senses, nerves and eye muscles. Furthermore, head movements and eye movements perfectly compensate each other to provide accurate tracking while our body is in motion.

For example, when our attention is drawn to something off to the right hand side of where we are facing, it is our eyes that perform all the initial rotation required, but then our head begins to rotate to the right to face the object of our attention, thus allowing both of our eyes an unobstructed view. Once our head starts to rotate our eyes then begin to rotate to the left, in an exactly equal and opposite direction, the one perfectly compensating the other until our eyes are facing forward in our head again. Remarkably, we are unaware of any of this, provided we are healthy, though it is easy now to understand why sometimes it feels like our "head spins" when we are not.

Our eye movements are mostly beyond our conscious control. However, because our eyes have a natural ability to smoothly track something moving within our field of view, there is a trick we can use to make our point of gaze move wherever we wish. Simply fix your gaze upon the tip of your finger, and move your finger along the desired path. The eyes no longer move in abrupt jumps but will smoothly follow the motion.

When we learn to read as children, we often use this technique to force our point of gaze to move to the right (or to the left for Arabic readers). This helps train our reading eyes to make successive jumps from word to word, repeatedly in the same direction along the line of text. As reading is a comparatively new human skill, evolution itself has had insufficient time to provide us with this innate ability.

Are you looking at me?

Although we are not conscious of the majority of our own eye movements, we are quite good at observing the eye movements of others, and we have a remarkable ability to tell whether someone is looking directly at us, or at someone just to our side. Indeed, a woman wearing a low cut dress may be much more aware of where her male friend is gazing, than he is himself.

The ability to determine another's point of gaze has had benefits to our survival ("Are you looking at *me*!"), and is vital in face-to-face social interaction within groups. We achieve this feat by observing the amount of the whites of the eye visible on each side of the iris.[88] This gives us a good indication of the azimuth of the gaze. We also get a somewhat less accurate estimate of the elevation of the gaze by observing the position of the upper eyelid (which incidentally moves up and down racking the pupil of the eye).

The electronic eye-tracking spectacles that I used in my work exploit exactly the same principle. It is known as a "Limbus" eye tracker, (the limbus being the border between the white of the eye and our darker iris). The system generates a crude but useful measure of where the eye is pointing relative to the head, by shining infrared light onto the eye and simply measuring the amount reflected, side to side, and top to bottom.[89] Much more accurate and easier to use eye-tracking systems have since been developed using simple cameras and infra-red illumination to monitor the eye pointing direction.[90]

Humans are unique among the great apes in having highly visible exposed white sclera (the whites of the eyes) surrounding the darker coloured iris. In other apes these parts of the eye are well camouflaged. It seems that our eyes have evolved to make it easy for others to discern the direction of our gaze, so in our interactions we can benefit from knowing where others attentions lie. But we are not alone in possessing this skill, a surprising range of vertebrates[91] including goats[92], crested macaques, dolphins, jackdaws[93], and rooks[94] are able to recognise gaze direction and use it socially. Recent investigations of red-footed tortoises have revealed that they too exhibit gaze following and are surprisingly intelligent.[95] I guess if you are very slow, it pays to be smart; think "The Hare and the Tortoise". It is interesting to note that most of these creatures can also read human gaze in addition to that of their own species.

Blindness of the sighted

"The senses deceive from time to time, and it is prudent never to trust wholly those who have deceived us even once."

- Rene Descartes

Each of our eyes has a Blind Spot, a "hole" in our field of view. It is where the optic nerve penetrates the retina, where there are no light sensitive cells. If we really saw what each eye is capable of seeing, we would notice a blank hole in the scene. This missing information is filled in subconsciously by our imagination.[96]

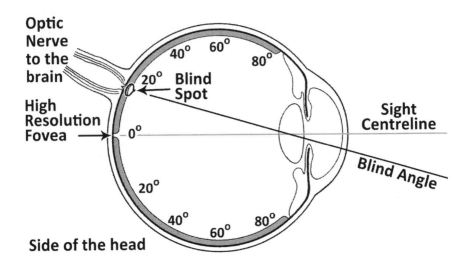

Figure 13: Horizontal section of the eye.

The eye is sensitive to light over a wide range of angles, but for light entering between 11 degrees and 16.5 degrees to one side of our centre of gaze, there is a completely blind region where the optic nerve exits the eye.[97]

You can explore the existence of your blind spots by holding a pen or pencil roughly at arm's length. Hold it horizontally. Close your right eye. Now focus your open left eye on the right-hand end of the pen. If you are lucky, the other end of the pen will now fall within your blind spot. While maintaining your focus on the right-hand end of the pen, carefully manipulate the orientation of your pen and you can "probe" the size and shape of this blindness in your field of view. You need to overcome your instinct to switch your point of gaze to the other end, as this will spoil the effect I want to illustrate.

Here is another way to reveal the existence and power of your blind spot. In the image that follows you can make the rabbit completely disappear into the background:

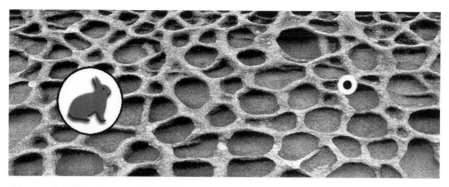

Figure 14: Find your Blind Spot:

Close your right eye. Then with your left eye, gaze intently at the spot on the right. If you adjust your viewing distance to be about twice the width of the image, you can make the rabbit on the left completely disappear, the background will replace it.

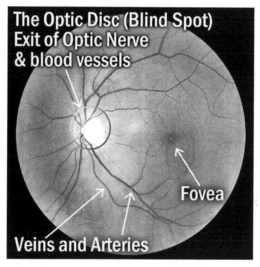

Figure 15: The retina of my left eye, showing the small dark central Fovea (the only part that can resolve detail in the scene), the array of blood vessels and the Blind Spot circled on the left where optic nerve exits the eye.

The eye in humans and other invertebrates is not constructed in the "obvious" way, in that the retina appears to be constructed back to front: The light sensitive cells are on the back side of the retina, not the front where they might receive the incident light directly. Light has to pass through layers of neurons and the network of veins and arteries before it reaches the sensitive rods and cones. The blood vessels which are clearly visible in the above figure significantly obstruct our view (though we don't notice it). The further disadvantage with this arrangement is that all these connections: the nerves and the blood vessels have to exit the eye through a hole in the retina, and that is what creates our blind spot. In contrast the retinas of Cephalopod's eyes are configured in the apparently more logical way round.[98] These include such creatures as the squids which have acute vision and have no blind spot, so I guess evolution got it right that time! The fascinating thing is that we are completely blind to our "Blind Spot". As Sir David Brewster wrote in 1832:

> "We should expect, whether we use one or both eyes, to see a black or dark spot upon every landscape within 15 degrees of the point which most particularly attracts our notice. The Divine Artificer, however, has not left his work thus imperfect ... the spot, in place of being black, has always the same colour as the ground".[99] [100]

We may think of ourselves as quite aware, yet we don't notice this "hole" in our view. Why not? There are several reasons: For each eye the blind spot is offset to the outer side of our field of view. So with both eyes open, one eye can see where the other eye is blind. OK, but why don't we notice when we close one eye? Did you notice some difficulty keeping your focus on one end of the pen while putting your attention on the other? We naturally shift our point of focus to the point of attention as our vision is so much sharper, so are less likely to notice missing visual information off to the side.

If you are unfortunate enough to suffer from visual migraines, you may already be familiar with the sensation of a blind area within your field of view (which is often bounded by an annoying flashing zigzag pattern). Because migraines are the result of events in the visual cortex of our brain, and not within the eye, the effects appear identical in both eyes, so the blind region noticed in one eye cannot be compensated for by the other eye. On the occasions when it has happened to me, I have initially been surprisingly unaware that I am missing a major fraction of the field of view of both my eyes, and only noticed some vague difficulty in seeing things. Sometimes it only became apparent when I was speaking to someone, and noticed that I couldn't make out one side of their face.

Healthy individuals only have the one naturally occurring blind spot within each eye. However, blind spots are a common after-effect of strokes, and can also be caused by accidental exposure to high intensity lasers. Detecting these lesions is not easy. The subject is often completely unaware of their existence. When you have had your eyes tested, you may have been subjected to a test where you were asked to focus on a central point while lights were flashed in various places your field of view. You may have been asked to report whether you saw one, two, three, or none. This test is designed to locate any unnatural blind spots on the retina, which the optician can subsequently investigate using an opticians microscope.

In the laboratory sophisticated eye movement tracking systems have been used to completely stabilise an image upon the retina, totally compensating all eye movements. This has enabled blind spots (scotoma) on the retina to be simulated, and provided insight into how our brain fills in missing detail.[101] It is as if our brain does not want to bother us with the fact that we are missing a significant part of the picture, so it does its best to patch the missing area with content and texture to match the surrounding area.

This effect is very similar to that created using the "content aware fill" tool, in recent versions of Adobe's Photoshop image processing software, which does exactly the same to a selected portion of an image. It predicts how the region should be filled, based on the surrounding images and texture.[102] When Adobe first revealed this feature, many commented that it had finally destroyed the myth that "the camera never lies", (which was hardly news to most of us). Equally, the evidence of our unconscious filling-in of our blind spot is a key piece of evidence that we do not see "the whole truth and nothing but the truth".

Change Blindness

Another unconscious blindness is Change Blindness, the term used to describe situations where an observer is remarkably insensitive to significant changes in the scene observed.[103] Some of the most impressive demonstrations of change blindness use an animation that alternates back and forth between a pair of images that are largely identical.

In normal circumstances when we switch back and forth between two such images, we can easily spot tiny differences. This was exploited in the electronics industry to check electronic circuit board assemblies for missing or incorrectly placed components: An optical viewing system is set up in which the view is switched back and forth between the circuit board being inspected, and a perfect circuit board. If the two boards are accurately aligned, the human observer sees an overall static image except where there is a missing or different component; and there the observed image flashes conspicuously. Our ability to memorise details in an image are poor, so this was a far more effective way of detecting mistakes visually, than simply comparing what was seen, with what was remembered should be there.

Just as with the bird of prey described earlier, our attention is easily drawn to changing parts of the image. However, if we briefly introduce a third intermediate image that is a uniform neutral grey while switching between the other two images, we find that we have completely suppressed this sensitivity of our retina to small changes in an otherwise identical image. A simple explanation is that now nearly every part or pixel of the image falling on the retina experiences a change. Even the parts that are identical in the two main images experience a change to grey and back, so our hitherto focused attention is now distracted by the changes in the whole image.

Some of the most impressive demonstrations of change blindness are of this type, animations that flashed back and forth between two mostly identical images, but with a grey frame between. When I first watched one of these on the Web I was completely unable to spot any difference. After ten minutes of scrutinising I began to convince myself that the animation had been wrongly labelled or was not functioning properly. I finally saw it, but only after systematically breaking down the image into sections and carefully staring at each bit of the image, section by section. What was even more remarkable, and indeed shocking to me, was that once seen, it stood right out, I could not miss it. I just could not comprehend how I had not seen it earlier. A search for "Change Blindness" on the Web will reveal many examples of this fascinating phenomenon, which is one of the clearest pieces of evidence that most of what we experience is a simulation in our heads.[104] [105] [106]

Gorillas easily missed

A similar phenomenon is "inattentional blindness", defined as "the failure to notice a fully-visible, but unexpected object because attention is engaged on another task, event, or object".[107] Probably the best known example is a short video of two teams of players passing a basketball around. Students were shown this video and asked to carefully count how many times the players wearing white passed the ball. A casual viewer will be surprised at one point to see someone dressed in a gorilla suit enter the scene, mingle with the group wave its arms, then exit. However, when the students were questioned after watching the video a significant proportion had failed to notice the gorilla at all, and they were shocked when the video was subsequently replayed to them. It seems that their intense concentration on the difficult task made them blind to a major and unusual aspect of the scene.[108]

In a slightly bizarre derivation of this original study, skilled radiographers were subjected to tests of their ability to spot tiny tumours in a number of lung X-Rays, a few of which included a superimposed image of a small gorilla. When the radiographers were later questioned, 83% were found to have missed the gorilla image, even though measurements with an eye tracker clearly indicated that many of them had gazed directly at it at some point. "They look right at it, but because they're not looking for a gorilla, they don't see that it's a gorilla".[109] Their acquired skill in spotting tumours probably makes them more blind to spotting the gorilla images than the average person. These phenomena are attracting an increasing amount of attention from experimental psychologists and from philosophers, because they suggest that humans' internal representation of the visual world is much sparser than usually thought.

Inattentional Blindness is not only visual despite the name, it applies to hearing too. Polly Dalton and Nick Fraenkel set up an experiment that combined the "cocktail party effect" with a passing gorilla! They asked subjects to listen to a stereo "dummy-head" recording of two men and two women each having independent conversations, but asked the subjects to focus on either the men's conversation or that of the women. Half way through the recording a man enters from the back of the room and for 19 seconds walks through the scene uttering "I am a gorilla".[110]

At the end of the experiment, about half the subjects had completely failed to "hear" the gorilla voice. In one experiment only 30% of those who focused on the female conversation noticed the "gorilla", which might suggest that the women's conversation was more interesting than that of the men, but in that experiment the gorilla voice occupied a stereo position closer to that of the men. I also suspect that if it had been a higher pitched woman's voice repeating "I am a gorilla", these biases might well be reversed.

We have seen that although our eyes and other senses may be acute, our mind's eye is surprisingly blind to many things that should be conspicuously "staring us in the face". Later I will return to the subject of what our conscious or unconscious mind can "see", but for now, it is time to leave our elusive gorillas behind and return to some more basic facts about our human senses.

Putting figures on the facts

Later in this book I explore the limits to learning something new, when expressed using the precise language of information: i.e. in bits per second. So let us briefly look at what is known about the information capacity limits of the human eye itself: It is estimated to be somewhere around 6 Megabits per second, taking into consideration the actual measured resolution and speed of response of the eye. In The Oxford Companion to the Mind"[111], Robert Ditchburn describes the reasoning as follows:

> "Accurate data is available only for the central region of the retina (a circle whose diameter is 2 degrees in the visual field) and the total information capacity of the visual system is about ten times that of this central circle, the fovea. The number of points that can be resolved within this central circle is

about 10^4 (i.e. 10,000 pixels). When the eye is working near the limit of resolution, contrast discrimination is poor and at the limit of resolution, a person can distinguish black from white but not discriminate any intermediate shades of grey, therefore he associated just one bit of information with each of the resolved points. For the central region the highest rate that flicker can be observed is about 50 cycles per second, so that the information capacity is $50 \times 10^4 = 500$ kilobits per second".

Measurements of contrast sensitivity with coarser sinusoidal patterns with various shades of grey gave almost identical results.[112] [113] Neither of these estimates includes colour information, but it is estimated that the additional information due to colour is no more than about 20 per cent, making 600 kilobits per second in all for the central region. Given the estimate that the total information capacity of the visual system is about ten times that of this central circle, the fovea, this gives a total figure (per eye of around) 6 Mbits per second. This is a million times smaller than the 15 Terabits per second that Jim Crowe had speculated was "the bandwidth of the optic nerve".[114]

Ditchburn also commented that:

"Jacobson estimated the capacity for the ear at about 10,000 bits per second.[115] Thus the central region of the retina has about 50 times the capacity of the ear and the whole visual system has about 500 or 600 times the aural capacity....... In the situation involved in the evolution of the higher animals, decisions vital to survival had to be made mainly or solely on visual information. A wide variety of situations was encountered, so a vast information capacity was needed. Yet the amount used in making a decision had to be limited to the minimum required for a correct decision. This limited amount had to be processed to yield an action as rapidly as possible. If too little information was processed so that there was a considerable chance of a wrong decision, or if too much was processed so that the decision came too late, the animal did not survive. Those species which did survive usually had a large visual information capacity but were able to select a small number of bits for processing towards an action decision".- Robert William Ditchburn.

Are two eyes better than one? Probably so, at least it feels better to observe through a pair of binoculars than a monocular scope, but the pair of images we see are usually strongly correlated, i.e. very similar, so it is unlikely that two eyes will give us twice the useful information capacity of one eye. If the image contrast is very low, for example when we are peering through mist or in very poor light, we might expect a useful gain in performance, in our ability to recognise features. However, if depth information from the scene is an important part of the task then binocular vision may be especially valuable.

Another way to consider the importance or otherwise of binocular vision, is to ask ourselves; in what situations are those who have sight in only one eye at a disadvantage? Close distance sporting skills, operating machinery, driving a Formula One car; yes, there are definitely situations where people with monocular sight are penalised, and these are ones where depth perception is of great importance. However, throughout most of life's activities the absence of sight in one eye does not hinder significantly.

I am often surprised to discover that some of my friends and several public figures have limited sight in one eye. Monocular vision would appear to have negligible impact on the process of education, and we have no hesitation in temporarily obscuring the vision in one eye of a young child with a "lazy eye" (to encourage the lazy eye to develop healthy movement and co-ordination with the other eye). Closing one eye when we are in class has no effect on our ability to learn, and there is absolutely no evidence that people with monocular vision can only learn half as fast.

If we cover one eye the image you see does not become half as bright, despite the fact that we have halved the amount of light available to us. We have two eyes but "see" from one single point of view. We all tend to have one dominant eye, you can find which is yours simply by pointing at a distant object and checking which of your two eyes is lined up with your finger. However, despite this eye dominance, we do not have the experience of our sight being offset to the dominant side, (as we do when we drive a car for example). No, our mind somehow constructs a view as if we had a single central eye, but with depth perception. But also note that when we cover one eye, the image we see does not immediately become flat two-dimensional or shift sideways to align with the remaining open eye. We have to pay attention to become aware that we have lost most of our ability to resolve depth, though our sense of depth is quickly restored just by moving our head. People with only a single functioning eye do indeed experience the same three dimensional world that the rest of us do.

What about colour? You will note that in the previous discussion, including colour information only increased the figure by only 20%, and you might expect that our ability to independently resolve three primary colours would mean that the above figures should be multiplied by three. Despite the emotional significance of colour (bringing "a bit of colour into our lives"), it carries very little detailed information. It may surprise you to know that we are unable to sense colour with the centre of our gaze as the fovea at the centre of our retina is insensitive to colour. It has no colour sensitive cells (the cones), only the colour independent cells (the rods). The rest of the retina which is dominated by cones is unable resolve detail, so although colour feels like it adds significantly to our overall visual experience, in reality it feeds very little information to our brains.

Printers of cheap posters and comic magazines exploit this fact; we can tolerate quite poor alignment accuracy between a black and white outline, and the "splodge" of colour that is intended to fill in the space between. Somehow our brain brings the colour and black & white components of the image back into alignment in what we perceive, enabling crude printing methods to be used.

When TV technology was extended from Black & White to Colour, we might have expected to need to transmit three times the information bandwidth for each of the three primary colours. However, an understanding of the psychology of colour perception meant that sufficient additional colour information could be provided with just an additional 5% of bandwidth. It is worth noting that in the European (PAL) TV system, the grey scale (luminance) information occupies 6MHz of bandwidth, but the colour (chrominance) information only requires an additional 300 kHz. Incidentally, have you ever noticed that it can take a few seconds to notice that the TV image has changed from black and white, to colour?

For most situations the grey scale information is the most valuable; however, colour is more important when it carries key information that is not readily accessible in a monochrome image, such as with food. The black & white illustrations in my mother's old recipe books rarely get my juices going. Some things can be "off colour" without being "out of shape".

What about our other senses?

I have chosen to focus on our sense of vision as this is generally considered to be the most powerful of all our senses. Our hearing is generally considered to be our second most valuable sense, and the raw information rate achieved by the eye is about 600 times larger than Jacobson's estimate of that achieved by the ear, at 10 kilobits per second. Now this may seem unsurprising as we are often told that "a picture is worth a thousand words". Being blind is obviously a huge disadvantage in tasks such as navigating through public spaces, but as you will see we do not necessarily learn 600 times faster by seeing than by listening.

Our sight may provide incredible sensitivity to spatial detail, but is quite insensitive to absolute colour information, for this varies greatly with illumination conditions (which typically vary through the day). Our hearing however, provides weak spatial resolution but high sensitivity to spectral characteristics such as pitch and tone, and also to timing. The trained ear can detect patterns that would otherwise not be noticed when presented visually.

One of my scientist colleagues when faced with an incomprehensible electrical signal, would convert it to an audible signal so he could listen to it on headphones, as he felt he could detect patterns and structure more readily this way.

None of our other senses such as taste, smell, temperature, touch, or the position of our bodies in space, seem to carry comparable amounts of raw information. Consider taste: The average person can distinguish quite a few different tastes, but not rapid changes in taste. So gourmet meals have a somewhat limited repertoire of different tastes.

Our sense of smell is similarly slow. It is suggested that a few people can detect around 1000 different smells, corresponding to 10 bits/smell.[116] If they were exposed to a new olfactory stimulus every second, this would correspond to 10 bits/sec. In practice we would not expect nearly as fast performance. Dogs "snort" to displace the previous scent and maximise their sensitivity to a new scent.

Back in 1966 I visited Disneyland in California where there was a small cinema display provided by the famous Bell Research Laboratories, in which aromas were blown into the room in synchronism with key scenes within a movie. Unfortunately the sensation took time to reach our noses, and lagged behind the release time. All I can remember was the confusion between the smells and images of a rose and farm manure!

Attempts to produce a full cinema movie with smells were also unsuccessful: In the 1960 film "Scent of Mystery"[117] several different smells were synchronised with action in the film. The Smell-O-Vision system (Yes really, that was its name!) piped the smells to individual seats via a mile of plastic tubing in total. Thirty different smells were released during the two hour film, including those of flowers, the perfume of the mystery girl in the film, a smoking tobacco pipe, an orange, shoe polish, port wine (when a man is crushed to death by falling casks!), baked bread, coffee, lavender, and peppermint. It was not a success. I feel sure that at least one critic will have commented that "the film stinks!"

Those of us who are fortunate enough to be fully sighted tend to fear blindness more than the loss of any other sense. So let us examine the reasons why it is our most prized sense:

1/. It offers by far the greatest range (billions of miles).

2/. It provides us with very high spatial (angular) resolution, enabling us to resolve tiny details at a distance.

3/. It is fast, not just that the information sensed travels at the speed of light, but also that we can move the focus of our attention from one object to another with a brief flick of the eye.

Compare this with touch (short range), hearing (poor stereo spatial resolution) and smell (very slow, poor spatial resolution). We are able to quickly direct our visual attention where our mind tells us will be most useful, and this hugely increases the value to us of the limited information we subsequently take in. When we swing our gaze to focus on something of visual interest, it is like the blind man exploring the shape of a physical object or feature with the tip of his white stick. Our vision enables us to reach from the tip of our finger, right out to distant stars with the briefest glance.

The other key factor as we have seen is the greater information capacity of the eye itself. When we compare what we imagine we perceive with what we actually perceive, the greater raw capacity of our vision enables our perceiving mind to ask more detailed questions, and recognise finer differences. All our other senses are spatially blurred when compared with our sight, but before we assume that sight is our most valuable sense we should remember that it only tells us about appearance, and this is the downside. Appearance now dominates so much of our lives, while content and reality receive less attention. Appearance is superficial, in the sense that it is only the very surface. It provides a quick judgement that is often at odds with what is within if we take the time to learn.

Sensing a change

While some of our senses can sense the absolute value of a sensation, others are merely sensitive to the differential, the change in what is sensed.[118] While we possess a remarkably accurate measure of the position of our limbs, for most phenomena we can only sense changes. For example we are unable to sense the absolute air pressure, so cannot act as a barometer or altimeter, yet are very sensitive to rapid fluctuations in pressure, i.e. sound waves. As any engineer will tell you, it is far easier to measure a change in a parameter, than to measure its absolute value with precision. But even with fluctuating sensations such as sound waves, they are less noticeable when they are continuous. We may even forget that they are present when we have been exposed to them for a while, such as the noise of the engine in a car or plane, the washing machine, our heartbeat.

There are many things that we are unaware of until they are brought to our attention, and then we cannot understand how we could have ever missed them as they now seem so obvious. We fail to notice gradual degradations in our senses. Have you ever noticed that you have got things floating in your eye, little worms, or that there is an incessant whining in your ear(s)? "Floaters" and Tinnitus are fairly common experiences, more so as we get older.

Most of the time we are unaware of many things that impede our vision and this is the reason why we are encouraged to go for regular eye tests. However, if we find ourselves in bright grey featureless conditions such as under a hazy sky, or in a grey mist, then suddenly some visual defects may become evident. If we have never seen them before and particularly if we see something that looks like a worm (that is what strands of protein in the eye often look like), we may panic. When people spot these for the first time they will often rush to hospital to have their eyes tested, convinced that they have suddenly developed this problem, whereas in fact this condition had been developing slowly over many years.

I have plenty of floaters.[119] The first time I ever noticed them, I was a teenage choirboy participating in a religious service at my school, kneeling as if to pray while the school Chaplin droned on and on and on. My eyes were defocused and gazed into the dark shadow beneath the pew in front of where I sat, while my stomach growled for breakfast. Suddenly I had an amazing vision; no, not the road to Damascus kind favoured by the Chaplin, but illumination of a more physical sort. A beam of sunlight streaming through the chapel window had caught the edge of my eye. Now I was suddenly wide awake and exploring what happened when I changed my position slightly and altered my angle of view. I was able to see several slowly drifting worm-like things in my eye, and was very relieved to see that they weren't wriggling. I noticed that flicking my eye left and right sent the entire menagerie charging-off out of sight, only to re-emerge drifting, floating back into my field of view (hence the term "floaters"). Changing my position again, I was then able see the spider-like shadow of the array of blood vessels on my retina. What a truly amazing morning. Hunger forgotten, I had to revise my cynical opinion of the power of prayer.

Half a century of degradation later (I'm referring to my eyes), I now have a veritable zoo of floaters of all shapes and sizes. Sometimes one of them chooses[120] to sit right in the centre of my vision, causing the sight in that eye to be somewhat blurred. However, the floater that causes me the most problems is one that appears as a small black dot in my right eye, near my centre of gaze but offset to the right of my field of view. For most of the time I just don't notice it at all. However, when I am walking in nature looking for wildlife, as my gaze flicks back and forth my attention is repeatedly drawn to this moving black dot, which for just a brief instant my mind interprets as something moving into my field of view, a bird, a plane, superman?

An ophthalmologist who was examining my daughter's eyes commented that she had "the floaters of a sixty year old" (she is only young), to which she replied "but Dad always told me that it's quite normal to have lots of floaters". He laughed and explained: "well that's because you both share a genetic condition that leads to increased floaters. In other words I had thought that my own experience was typical of everyone else, a mistake I have repeated many times in much broader contexts.

A similar situation exists for a phenomenon known as Tinnitus, a noise that is "heard" in either one or both ears, not created by sound waves, but by nerve impulses generated within the ear itself. There is really no sound at all, nothing that could be heard by another listener, or picked up using a microphone. Tinnitus is another age related complaint, but can also result from exposure to loud sounds so is more common with people who have worked in noisy environments, or those exposed to very loud music such as rock musicians.

My tinnitus is a loud high-pitched whining in my left ear. Remarkably I am completely unaware of it 99% of the time, despite the fact that it obscures other sounds (particularly in the same frequency range) and contributes to my slight deafness. If I listen for it, it sounds loud and obvious, and I can't imagine that it's been there all along. Occasionally it confuses me; a few days ago I was about to set up a microphone for my speech recognition software, when I suddenly noticed that my computer was making a lot of noise, whining more than usual. It took me a few minutes to realize that this was not my computer but tinnitus within my left ear. My relatively quiet computer is located on the left side of my desk.

Tinnitus and floaters become incredibly evident when we focus our attention on them, yet are unnoticeable for much of our time. At least with a floater we can make it disappear simply by closing our eyes, it is after all just the shadow of something within the liquid aqueous humour of our eye, cast onto the retina by the light that is entering the eye. So when we close our eyes it disappears and we forget about it.

However, tinnitus is always there. We cannot close our ears in any physical sense; furthermore putting our hands over our ears doesn't change the volume at all. Many people when they first discover they have tinnitus, immediately direct their attention towards it and notice that it seems deafening. If you were subjected to such a noise by a neighbour day and night without respite it might drive you crazy, so many people go to their doctor and tell them that this noise has suddenly started and that it is interfering with their lives, even though it has been present for a long time. Though some doctors prescribe sedatives for them, the most effective remedy is to direct one's attention elsewhere, to not get obsessed with the sound as if it were caused by a noisy neighbour, but to think of it more as the sound of the sea, or an audible signal to let us know that we are still alive!

The Denture Sensor

I have revealed some of the intrinsic strengths and weaknesses of our senses, and next I will explore the part played by our imagination. Before moving on, I want to share a bit of fun with you. To be creative, it helps to be able to connect with the child part of oneself, the part that knows how to play, indeed companies like Google now recognise this, and provide their staff with suitable play areas. I was fortunate to work in a research environment that tolerated a few wacky diversions during breaks in the work.

Although optical fibre was pioneered for use as a communications medium, we were always looking for other novel applications of the technology. We experimented with a variety of incredibly sensitive sensors for sound, vibration, temperature, rotation and other physical phenomena, all based on fibre optics, and colleagues and researchers from other departments soon came to expect to be shown all kinds of sensing devices with very high sensitivity.

In most laboratories you would find oscilloscopes, though this is less true today as computer screens have now largely replaced them. An oscilloscope is a piece of electronic equipment that displays a waveform of some sort, typically a voltage which might be derived from something that is being measured or monitored. Among users it is simply referred to as a "scope". You may be familiar with the device used in hospitals that displays a patient's pulse as a waveform on a screen; this is an example of an oscilloscope display. In our laboratory almost everyone used a scope; people were very familiar with seeing a little bright spot scanning rapidly across a screen, tracing out some important waveform or other.

One day while looking at an oscilloscope screen in the distance, I noticed that when I clicked my teeth, I simultaneously saw a brief oscillatory waveform on the oscilloscope. How could my jaw actions cause a waveform on the oscilloscope? This fascinated me and after a bit of experimentation I worked out that the effect was caused by my eyeballs bouncing! To be more precise, as I clicked my teeth, the vibration was transmitted through my skull to my eyeballs and caused them to rotate slightly, oscillating about the vertical axis. As the spot scanned smoothly across the screen of the oscilloscope (set to scan at 20 milliseconds per division), the point of gaze of my eyes moved up and down slightly. In the absence of any teeth clicking, the image of the horizontally scanning point of light on the oscilloscope screen would normally be imaged onto the retina of my eye, as a horizontal line of illumination. But because the direction that my eyes were pointing was bouncing up and down, it drew out an oscillatory waveform on my retina instead. So although there really was no signal going into the oscilloscope and it was in reality "flat-lining", I personally saw a waveform that appeared to be on the screen, but which in truth was only on my retina.

I asked one of my colleagues to click his teeth while watching the screen, and he was immediately fooled into thinking that I had built a very sensitive microphone. He found it difficult to believe that this was just an illusion, even after I showed him that the oscilloscope was not connected to anything. I suddenly saw the potential for having a bit of fun (and also as a tool for exploring how we respond to new perceptions). I flippantly called it "the denture sensor", not realizing at the time how appropriate that might be.

Now, having been fooled himself, my coleague was eager to see how someone else would react. So I began a sequence of "behavioural experiments", in which naive colleagues drifting into our department would be shown our "denture sensor". Previously gullible subjects eagerly gathered round and pretended that they too could see the waveform on the 'scope when the new victim clicked his teeth, whereas in reality only the "clicker", (i.e. the person clicking their teeth together), would see a waveform. A plausible story was concocted to explain why the subject did not see any waveform when others in the room clicked their teeth. We told them that we used a microprocessor to recognise and filter out the signals from all those people who had previously been tested (At that time, there was so much publicity for the recently invented microprocessor, that people were prepared to believe that it was capable of almost anything). I set up a dummy "sensor" next to the 'scope, using a coil of optical fibre wound onto a cardboard tube and this all added credibility to the idea.

Those who had previously been taken in by the illusion were absolutely delighted to see each new victim fooled (I think it made them feel so much better about their own earlier gullibility). New subjects reacted in different ways: Almost everyone was fooled initially, and only the occasional one worked it out without being given several major clues. Once people had it fixed in their mind that they were seeing a signal on the scope - rather than in their eyes and mind - it was surprisingly hard to convince them otherwise.

Because the effect is the result of an angular change in the pointing direction of the eye, the waveform appeared to get bigger as the viewing distance from the screen increased. In reality the observed eye bounce waveform stayed constant size as it had nothing to do with the 'scope, but the size of the scope screen diminished with distance, so in comparison the signal seemed to increase in size with distance. Now almost everything else in Physics *decreases* the further away we are from it, (typically inversely to the square of distance), so this was a very disturbing observation for our subjects, yet they still could not recognise that the waveform was only in their heads.

Only one single person got it first time, and he had previously observed something similar. The rest needed to have it explained to them. One, seeing it as a challenge to his intelligence insisted: "Don't tell me, I will work this out if it kills me", and of course we had to intervene for health and safety reasons after he had failed to work it out for a worryingly long time! Another stormed out and avoided visiting us for some weeks. You may think we were cruel, but play is a vital tool in creating an inventive environment (at least that is what I had planned to argue in my defence if the management discovered what we were up to). Those who didn't bolt learned something important too. They learned just how easy it is to misinterpret an observation.

One day I demonstrated it to the labs Chief Scientist and he too was initially fooled and then very intrigued. A few weeks later, to my horror he swept in through the doors accompanied by a large group of dignified and respectful Japanese visitors, saying: "Richard, I have brought the head of Sony Electronics for you to show him your clever sensor". Now the British sense of humour has always been difficult to translate into Japanese, especially using words like "denture". I felt pretty sure that someone's blood might have to be ritually shed if I were to humiliate the big boss in front of his entire entourage of more junior staff, (who incidentally seemed unable to stop repeatedly bowing respectfully). All I could think to do at that moment was just to quickly explain the whole thing before demonstrating it, which completely eliminated the impact (and the fun!). Frankly, I could tell from the look on the big man's face that he thought we were a load of idiots, and as he and his disciples swept out through the door, I realized that it was time to cut back on this particular avenue of research and focus on what we were supposed to be doing.

Many years later, on the last working day before the Christmas break, my colleagues persuaded me against my better judgement, to set up the "denture sensor" again so we could entertain ourselves with the reactions of those whose only reason to visit was to eat our mince pies. We had fun catching out quite a few of our visitors, but then who should enter but the managing director himself, who had just dropped by to wish us a Happy Christmas. Sensing the atmosphere of fun, he asked what we were doing, and I felt obligated to give him the full treatment (it was almost a festive holiday after all).

Well, he saw no waveform, it just did not work for him, and he was clearly almost as confused as the Japanese visitor. After he left, I speculated that what we had been playing with all this time, *really was* capable of detecting the presence or absence of dentures. I certainly didn't have the nerve to ask the director if he wore dentures, or whether they were attached with vibration damping adhesive. That was the last time we played the game. If you want to experiment with the phenomenon yourself, see the www.humanbottleneck.com website where I provide details of how to make your own denture sensor.

You may be wondering why I have related this tale, and how it might be relevant to the topic of this book. Well it taught me two very important things: First; that an incorrect explanation can be very difficult to displace despite new evidence to the contrary. Secondly, it was a clear example of how things that are going on in our head (bouncing eyeballs in this example), are all too easily interpreted as things happening in the outside world, and revealed just how difficult it is to appreciate the difference (in the absence of an additional honest independent observer).

In this chapter I have described how our eyes evolved and have left us with a legacy of limitations to which we are in essence, blind. I have shown that even healthy eyes have serious limitations that make them physically incapable of "seeing" what we actually experience as "seeing". For example if we were to see what our eyes physically sensed, we would experience a kind of tunnel vision where only the very central part of our field of view revealed any detail, and that part would have no colour. We are almost completely unaware that our eyes flick their gaze around the scene to pick out details that are only visible with the very narrowest field of view, and fail to notice our blind spot.

These limitations are the result of the physical and biological structure of our eyes. However, our ability to take in the visual scene is even more limited than this, since our sensors are not the ultimate bottleneck. I have described how our mind is blind to otherwise conspicuous experiences when our attention is diverted, but next I will show just how little of what we experience is sensed in the present moment. We make up the difference, based on what we expect from our history. It is not just the blind-spot in our eye that we fill in, but the blindness to most of what surrounds us in our daily life. Why we are blind to these limitations? It is likely that we have evolved to stay ignorant, since it has been of no value to be aware of perceptual limitations that we cannot do anything about, at least not until now.

In the next chapter I reveal that it is our imagination that provides us with the clear vision that we experience.

Chapter Three

Seeing requires Imagination

"The eye sees only what the mind is prepared to comprehend."
- Henri Bergson[121]

I began by believing that our senses absorb vast quantities of information, estimated at more than ten thousand Gigabits per second, but as we have now seen, our eyes and other sense organs are quite limited in their capability and can only resolve a millionth of that figure. Furthermore, phenomena such as change-blindness and our inability to notice our blind spots suggest an even narrower constraint to our ability to learn. So having begun my quest for the ultimate demanding requirement for high bit rate communication, I encountered a much deeper question: What limits the flow of information from external reality to our mind within?

Don't worry, this is only a simulation

I started to realize what many already knew; that our moment to moment experience of all that is "out there" in the world, is in truth the result of an internal simulation in our mind, internal reflections on a model of our world which we have constructed over time. When we experience something, the "end customer" for that experience is our conscious mind. Our eyes do not project an image onto an internal screen; it is our mind that holds the idea of what that external scene represents. Our knowledge and insight only increases if we can incorporate what we are sensing into our internal ideas, our internal models, our simulation of reality.

"Is this the real life? Is this just fantasy?"
- Freddy Mercury[122]

The idea that all we experience is only an illusion of reality, is an uncomfortable one, and therefore unacceptable to most people, especially to those of us with a background in the hard sciences. We do so dearly want to believe that we have moment by moment access to the reality that surrounds us. It makes life so much simpler, safer and more predictable. While most people struggle with these ideas, they are certainly not new to philosophers; Immanuel Kant, in his 1781 "Critique of pure reason", reasoned that we cannot experience the world as it is, but only as an internal perceptual replica of the world. Today psychologists and experts in the field of perception have to deal with subjective realities all the time.[123]

Perhaps more surprising is the extent to which these ideas have been accepted by some of the brightest minds in the more physical sciences.[124] John Wheeler, Physicist and Professor Emeritus of Princeton University, and also the man who popularised the terms "Black Hole" and "Wormhole", said: "Useful as it is under everyday circumstances to say that the world exists "out there", independent of us, that view can no longer be upheld. There is a strange sense in which this is a participatory universe" and: "There is no out there *out there*", he said in his attempt to explain the prediction of quantum physics, that simply by observing something, we change it.[125] Scientist Erwin Schrödinger (famous for his hypothetical "Schrödinger's cat"), said:

> "We do not belong to this material world that science constructs for us. We are not in it; we are outside. We are only spectators. The reason why we believe we are in it, that we belong to the picture, is that our bodies are in the picture".[126]

So I am reassured that some of the smartest minds in science are comfortable with the idea that we do not have direct access to "out there", though it is understandable why many who fear the implications, think the idea is completely crazy.

The idea that the life we experience is just a simulation has been widely explored in fiction, philosophy and of course in computer games. When I discuss these ideas with people for the first time, some say "Oh you mean like in the film The Matrix?"[127] This film portrays our lives as being lived within a single simulation running on a huge malign computing machine, into which we are all connected via a plug. The rather dubious premise of the film is that the machine needs humans as a source of energy (its power supply!), and provides us humans with the simulation as a means of keeping us all content.

It doesn't sound quite so plausible when I spell it out like this, but the film and its sequels are thought provoking. If you haven't seen the film yet, I hope I haven't spoilt it for you.

So the answer is No. The key difference is that in The Matrix, someone or something knows what is going on. It assumes that while the people are fed a limited distorted reality, that there is a knowable objective world out there, the truth of which is gradually revealed to us the audience, as the film progresses. In my explanation of the way things are, no-one has access to the big picture, we all simply construct our own model of the big picture based on our personal journey of experience. Our models will differ hugely from individual to individual.

A more extreme yet plausible idea is that we do not physically exist at all, but are simply "living" within a computer simulation run by a post-human species that is simulating part of its ancestry.[128] This idea is based on the assumption that many intelligent civilisations are likely to exist somewhere else in the vast universe, and that the power of computers is developing sufficiently rapidly, that a civilisation some way ahead of our own will have sufficient computing power to simulate absolutely everything we experience, and is very likely to have done so. It has even been suggested that the simulation may have to be stopped if those of us being simulated spot what is going on, so brace yourselves!

What about computer games? There are some similarities between the process of human perception, and the virtual worlds of a computer game such as The Sims.[129] But instead of being pre-created by some game designer, our internal model of reality is created and grown from almost nothing. It is then gradually built upon throughout our lives, fed by information received as nerve impulses from our senses. It is continually updated and modified by our sensory inputs: by everything we see, hear, touch, taste, and smell. We can turn away or switch off the Sims game, but we cannot switch off the game of life, as long as we live and learn. Despite the experience we have of being closely in touch with the reality of the present moment, the shocking truth is that we are more closely in touch with our history, which is only slowly modified by our moment by moment experiences.

Homo Sapiens: The Great Predictor

"Man is the only animal that laughs and weeps; for he is the only animal that is struck with the difference between what things are, and what they ought to be."

- William Hazlitt[130]

When we are born we come equipped with little more than is necessary for our initial survival, so we arrive with some inbuilt behaviours in response to our senses, our reflexes. Here are a couple of examples: a light flashed to one side of our field of view will draw our gaze, and we naturally pull away from sharp objects. We share these reflexes with many other sentient creatures, for they are what enable us to function as soon as we are born into this world, enabling us to breathe, feed and survive initial threats. But humans have the mental power to understand so much more about what we sense, things especially relevant to our particular situation.

Immediately after we are born, almost all we experience is new to us. Paradoxically, this is the time in our life when we are most in touch with reality. Before long, most of our experiences, though containing novelty, are related to our previous experiences. For example, when babies just two days old were exposed to a short sound which was then immediately followed by a change in brightness in the room, the babies learned to expect the latter after only eight similar experiences.[131] Their minds had learned a simple rule that predicted an expected outcome, one of the first of many predictive rules they would learn.

As we have more and more experiences, our internal model becomes an increasingly accurate predictive tool, growing in power as it is continually refined and updated with each fresh sensation and experience. The room around us no longer ceases to exist when we close our eyes, for despite the lack of instantaneous evidence for its continued existence, our internal model tells us it is still there. Learning becomes the process of comparing what is sensed, with what our increasingly complex internal model predicts we should sense, and then adding to, or modifying our model to minimise the difference between our experience and our prediction. This is how information flows in from the external world.

The first psychologist to make a systematic study of cognitive development in children was Piaget.[132] From birth to age two (what he called the sensorimotor stage), infants develop their ability to coordinate their physical actions with their sensory activity. At the start of this stage, children's behaviour is dominated by reflexes, such as crying when hungry and suckling, but by the end of it they can use mental images. For example, they acquire the concept of object permanence, realizing that objects still exist even when the objects are not present or are out of sight. This means that the child's mental image persists, when the optical image disappears.

Simple sighted creatures use their eyes as basic sensors of movement. We on the other hand have a huge information processor (our brain) that is largely dedicated to interpreting sight and our other senses as inputs to a highly detailed internal representation of our external world. This is what makes Homo sapiens so special, we are the great predictors. Our key feature is not our sight, but rather our in-sight. Using a set of sensors whose performance is not particularly outstanding within the animal kingdom, we are able to predict things in three dimensional space around us, and both forward and backward in time. For example we might predict that tomorrow we will find the buffalo at the waterhole over the hill, or that Venice will be submerged by rising sea levels in the next century. While a smart predatory animal might perform the former, only Homo sapiens can predict (and even cause!) the latter.

Figure 16: Even dangerous predators were no match for early man's predictive skills. - Cartoon by John Cox

When Pavlov rang his bell a few seconds after his dogs received food, no connection was made, but if it was rung a few seconds before they were fed, they learned to salivate in expectation of food, with just the bell ring alone. An arbitrary stimulus that repeatedly appears to predict something important, such as pain or pleasure, gets incorporated into the dogs' predictive model, and so it is with us humans. However, a dog has a very simple sense of time so probably can only develop predictions over short time scales. In information terms it might only ascribe one bit to describing whether something is now, or in the future. It would be difficult to train a dog to perform a similar response at some specific time in the future; for example a day after the bell was rung.

We humans however, have an intrinsically more detailed measure of time, even without the support of clocks. We endeavour to make associations, linking cause and effect over wide ranging time scales, many years in the case of industrialisation and climate change. We are superb learning machines that develop internal models or simulations of all that we repeatedly experience. By comparing the output of our simulation with what lies before us, i.e. with what we are experiencing, we are able to focus our very limited sensing capability on the difference. This enables us to take in mainly what is new to us, so that we can develop and refine our internal simulation to greatest effect.

Seeing only what we can imagine

"..the senses do not give us a picture of the world directly; rather they provide evidence for checking hypotheses about what lies before us. Indeed we may say that a perceived object is a hypothesis, suggested and tested by sensory data."

\- Richard L. Gregory[133]

Contrary to what we appear to experience, we do not have a clear view of the immediate world that we inhabit, but instead we have a deceptively clear view of the world that we imagine (Note that the very word "imagine" implies a visual experience). This idea can feel both confusing and unsettling, but may be easier to understand if you imagine yourself being blind from birth, and building a picture in your mind of the world around yourself mainly by touch. Think especially of the way a blind person uses their "white stick" to trace the edges of objects, the kerb, or the leg of the table. For those of us fortunate to possess sight, this is surprisingly similar to the way we unconsciously move the narrow focus of our attention to check out the details of the world around us. The blind person relies extensively on their memory of what to expect; the layout of the room, the street, the form and orientation of the table. So too do we who are sighted, for seeing is imagining based largely on past experience

This is all too apparent when we awake in the dark of night, and begin the journey to the bathroom. City dwellers rarely experience the real darkness of night, but many of you may have had the following experience: You awake to "the call of nature" and not yet fully alert begin to negotiate the familiar journey from bedside to bathroom. Although you cannot actually see, you successfully negotiate the three-dimensional space of your bedroom from memory. That is until "Bang!" you walk into a wall and are shocked fully awake, to the confusion of realizing that you are not in your familiar bedroom, but staying with friends.

Until that moment you were walking through the wrong memory space, your familiar bedroom at home, not the guest room at your friend's house that you were only briefly acquainted with earlier that evening. Suddenly the spatial world of just a moment ago collapses into nothing, to be replaced by a new construct. You fumble for a light switch; do you remember where it was last night? Where might you expect a light switch to be, based on previous experiences of bedrooms and switches? Close to a doorway? And at what height?

When you finally restore some illumination, your eyes dart around, as you quickly realign yourself and update your memory of the room that you left when you went to sleep. Now, all too suddenly the shocking experience of walking into a solid wall has made sense. Perhaps you had previously been dreaming that you were in some strange place and were struggling to find a bathroom, as sometimes happens to me.

Trusting our simulation

We need to trust our simulation of reality, if we need to check out all the details of what lies before us in this moment, in real time, we will be almost paralysed. If we are to function in the world we must learn to trust our idea of what is out there. The following examples might give you some idea of what I mean.

Among some of the more bizarre things that I have experienced is the act of running blindfold. I did this as an exercise in trusting another person. I was blindfolded and placed at one side of a sports field, and my (sighted) partner for the exercise stood at the far side facing me. The instruction was that when they shouted "Go!" I had to run as fast as I could towards my partner, who would shout "Left", "Right" or "Stop" as necessary, to safely direct me towards them.

The first time you try this, it feels impossible to break into a run, you hesitantly move forward waving your hands in front of you in an attempt to discover whether it is really safe to move forward. However, if you can come to really trust your partner to guide you and keep you safe, you can run flat out. Then the fear changes into a wonderfully exhilarating experience (For me it felt like the exciting first stages of free-fall while skydiving!).

Recently I heard a blind person on BBC radio describing how he organised a similar experience for himself. He found a large empty beach and carefully paced out the path where he intended to run to make sure that there were no obstacles. He then retraced the distance running flat out, an experience that he too found completely liberating. You might imagine that running without seeing where you are going is an unnatural experience for those who are sighted, yet sports people do it frequently. Running to catch or intercept a ball, one's attention is on the ball, not the ground ahead.

Continuing a similar theme, on another occasion I spent three days blindfolded and in silence. No, I was not holidaying at Guantanamo Bay; it was part of a ten day self-confidence building workshop that I had actually volunteered for. (I can guess what you are thinking, but please don't stop reading this book just yet!). A team of trusted helpers were present at all times, and they would guide us towards the dining room, bedroom or bathroom when we indicated a need by raising our hand. As I knew that this exercise was about to begin, I had familiarised myself with the layout of my bedroom beforehand. When blindfolded I managed quite well in my familiar little room, but on a few occasions I crashed into a wall or a piece of furniture that was not where I thought it should have been. I then had to feel around for the bed, sit on it, visualise the space from memory and regain my sense of direction within the room.

Each day we were taken out for walks around the snowy village, shuffling along in a long chain of people, each holding onto the one in front (perhaps it *was* Guantanamo Bay after all!). Stubbornly I overcame any impulse to cheat by peering past my blindfold, and believe me there were any number of occasions when I wanted to do so, and soon began to enjoy what I was learning from the whole unusual experience. As we trudged in line through the snow I became fascinated by the crunch of every step, by the sounds of the others panting, coughing, (and in some cases complaining out loud). I could hear a dog barking somewhere to my left, the texture of the sound echoing from the hills around us, and a woman shouting at her child somewhere in the distance. As we moved on I began to build a three dimensional image in my mind of the scene around me.

On the second day the image was stronger, it began to be more than a just a picture in my mind, but a physical reality. I could recognise when we were retracing our steps from the previous day. The most remarkable thing was that I began to feel that I could truly see. It was as if I was no longer blind, but when I waved my hands if front of my face they appeared to be invisible. I even found myself thinking "is this what it is like to be a ghost?"!

On the third day the exercise was brought to an end, though we hadn't previously been told how long it would last. Throughout the first two days I had been inhabiting a world that was all grey with a slight brown tinge, and then on this last day, little bits of colour had started to appear in the scene. At this point I was enjoying the experience so much, that I would have loved for it to continue at least one day more. One by one they led us outside, sat us down in the snow and asked us to slowly remove our blindfold. I found myself under the most incredible pastel blue winter sky, sitting amongst a few trees with tiny sparkling snowflakes drifting down from the branches. The beauty was completely overwhelming, and I sat in silence for what was probably an age. I had found an inner stillness in the darkness which has stayed with me. While many of the other participants were eager to chatter and share their relief at ending the experience, I just felt complete bliss, very alive, filled with gratitude for life itself, and for all my senses.

That was some time ago, but I have noticed one significant and enduring change in my behaviour since that experience. If I am engaged in a manual task for which my vision adds little useful information, such as trying to assemble a tiny fiddly nut and bold, or fastening buttons, I now find that I automatically close my eyes until the task is completed, only opening them afterwards to check that all is OK. It is as if my mind wants to minimise any input from my senses that has low value, to focus on the best source of information in that situation. Perhaps the experience taught my mind to trust my non-visual senses more, in this case my sense of touch.

Sometimes we can be too trusting of our limited senses. Imagine a prisoner called John, held in solitary confinement in a dark cell. He was brought to his cell blindfolded and under cover of darkness so never saw his surroundings. One day he hears a tapping noise on the water pipes, he immediately feels less isolated in his little world, realizing that he is not alone. Assuming that it is another prisoner, he listens intently and realises that the taps spell out "Hello" in Morse code.

He excitedly replies, tapping "Hello, my name is John", and so begins a conversation of sorts, through which he learns that this other prisoner, called Ian, has much more freedom and is allowed out of his cell to roam the extensive prison spaces and gardens. Ian can also see the countryside around as the fence is just wire, not a solid wall. Over the weeks, months and eventually years, John builds a more and more detailed picture in his mind of what lies beyond the wall based on Ian's experience. He feels that he really knows his wider surroundings, even to the point that if he ever were to escape his cell, he would know just where to go to try to break out further and find freedom. The rich detail that the prisoner now "knows" about his surroundings have been constructed in his mind's eye, from the small quantity of information he has received from Ian, vastly enhanced by what John already knows of doors, wall, gates, gardens and countryside.

Of course it is possible that John is being deliberately deceived, and that the idea he has of what lies outside is completely false. Those knowledgeable taps may be coming from someone who for whatever reason is deliberately misleading John. I use this example just to emphasise how much we build our idea of reality on what we slowly take in, that this information is enhanced enormously by what we already know, but that we rely so much on trusting our senses. Unlike the poor prisoner, we have multiple senses that help us unmask an otherwise deceptive sensation.

It is even conceivable that there is no one there, that the taps are automatically generated by an Artificial Intelligence program that mimics another prisoner. John might be the only prisoner, kept docile by this program that operates an electronic transducer that taps the water pipe. You may think that John would spot the difference, but in 1966, Joseph Weizenbaum wrote a comparatively simple computer program called ELIZA,[134] which performed natural language processing.[135]

When it was accessed via a simple computer terminal, it engaged subjects in a conversation using open-ended questions, in a similar style to one with an empathic psychologist. The program worked by picking up on specific words within the text typed by the subject (e.g. "I have a problem with my knee"), and reflecting them back in further questions: "Tell me more about your "knee". Programs like this are considered the forerunner of thinking machines, and are now called Chatterbots. Weizenbaum was shocked that his program was taken seriously by many users, who would open their hearts to it. He started to think philosophically about the implications of artificial intelligence and later became one of its leading critics, deriding the Utopian fantasies of his colleagues.[136]

Look into my I's

Many years ago I read a popular book by Gerald Glaskin that described a simple procedure to hypnotically regress people "so they could experience a past life". The method was called the "Christos Experience".[137] My scientific colleagues and I thought it was worth investigating so one evening we took turns to try it on each other, and found the results very intriguing. This particular method allows the hypnotised subject to be questioned throughout the session, and answer freely. The subjects had their eyes closed but were in no way unconscious or asleep, yet they often found themselves experiencing themselves as another person, in a completely unfamiliar place and having remarkable experiences. When my colleagues first tried the procedure on me nothing much happened, so I became the person who did the regressions for other people (but I always refused to call myself a hypnotist!). It worked with more than half of the subjects we tried, and with some it worked very well. A typical session lasted from half an hour to an hour, and we recorded most of them. It was necessary to keep the subject warm using a blanket or duvet, as their body temperature gradually dropped during the session, just as it would if they were sleeping.

Word spread, and various groups of people wanted me to conduct sessions with some of their members, usually in the belief that I would help them reveal their "past lives". However, I would only agree, on the condition that I would explain beforehand why there were plenty of other explanations for what they might be about to experience. What emerged from many of these regressions were very plausible stories, rich in detail, usually set at some time in the past, never anyone famous, more often someone of little importance. However, the subjects experiences felt so real to them, that they were often convinced that they were things that had actually happened "to them" in the past. They could see remarkable sights, smell smells, taste tastes and be aware of the emotional state of the individual that they felt they were somehow connected with, yet without experiencing the emotions physically. Their descriptions were often quite profound. It was difficult to think that they were simply the products of the subject's imaginations.

As always, the scientist in me wanted to get to the bottom of this, so I would often try to extract some detailed information from the hypnotised subjects that I could later attempt to corroborate. As the subject could respond to many of my requests (e.g. "look at your hands and describe them"), it was usually possible to guide them to explore the environment that they were experiencing in their mind. For example one subject when questioned revealed that she was the owner of a bookshop in Victorian London. I asked her to find a newspaper (my cunning plan was to get her to read the front page, especially the date so I could check it out at the library later). She responded that the maid had used the paper to light the fire. I asked her to go out and find a newsstand. She said she could not as it was raining, and so on. I carried out many of these regressions, but never did achieve sufficient corroboration to prove that the subjects' experiences were in any way evidence of their "past lives", however, the experience did impress upon me just how real and detailed an imagined world could be.

It seems that when the subjects were in this hypnotic state, there was no need for them to align the world they imagined with the realities of the world they usually experienced, yet most of what they imagined was very plausible. When I compare the quality of these hypnotically induced experiences with those of our dreams, they appeared to have far fewer incongruities; the narratives were much more plausible, rarely involving the bizarre elements that so often litter our dreams. Occasionally I had the opportunity to regress the same subject a second or third time some years later. The content and differences in those regression experiences suggested to me that they might have been metaphors for what was going on in their daily life around those times.

Strangers

In our awake state, unusual things are difficult to see. Where rare items need to be recognised accurately in visual screening tasks, for example detecting knives in luggage or tumours in mammograms, the rarity of such items leads to disturbingly low detection rates: if observers do not find what they are looking for fairly frequently, they often fail to notice it when it does appear.[138]

When we sense something which is completely new to us, our mind tries to fit the sensations with something that we are already familiar with. Shortly after the first lunar landing in 1969 the BBC broadcast a series of children's programs called "The Clangers", about a community of lovable knitted creatures who lived on a tiny planet somewhere out in space. One programme that I watched with my children made a particular impact on me. A strange creature had crashed onto their planet and the Clangers were puzzled and alarmed because it trying to eat the planet.[139]

Seen from my adult reality it was a Lunar Surveyor type spacecraft which had a mechanical scoop on an extendable arm which it used to collect soil samples.[140] The sympathetic Clangers tried to interact with it, with disastrous consequences. It reminded me just how difficult it is for us to interpret experiences that are completely new to us. Even if we sense something completely new, our mind presents us with a view of something that we already recognise in part.

My fascination with space occasionally leads me to stand outside on a cold night, gazing up into the sky. Most of what we see in the night sky remains constant through the seasons. The stars maintain the same relative positions within the celestial sphere, allowing us to see the same constellations through the centuries. Our view of it all shifts a little from summer to winter, due to the tilt of the Earth's axis relative to the axis of our orbit around the Sun. Then there are the "wandering stars", the Sun's planets that move across our night sky at rates depending on the distance of their own orbits around the Sun, and hence appear in different constellations from year to year. And lastly there is our Moon, which lends its name and the duration of its cycle to our calendar month, but not to its synchronism.

Meteor showers, however, are among the few phenomena that recur around the same precise dates every year. They are usually named after the nearest bright star to where the "shooting stars" appear to radiate from, within the night sky. As the Earth orbits the Sun it sweeps through different regions of space, repeating the same trajectory year after year. Although space is generally empty, comets orbiting the Earth leave an extended trail of dust and debris, and when the Earth passes through one of these trails, the debris is vaporised as it encounters the friction of our upper atmosphere. The larger pieces may take seconds to be annihilated, resulting in the extended bright trail of a meteor.

Can you remember the experience of driving a car with bright headlights into a scene of gently falling snow? The bright snowflakes appear as streaks of light, all radiating out from a single point directly ahead of the car. The reality is that it is we who are moving, not the snowflake, as would be confirmed by an observer standing at the roadside. And so it is with meteor showers, it is just we, the passengers on mother Earth, who are driving headlong around the Sun at great speed, our screen of the Earth's atmosphere intercepting pieces of comet debris, and briefly burning them up.

In our annual journey around the Sun, we bump into these patches of comet debris on the same dates every year. So meteor showers are very predictable in their timing, but less so in their intensity. Back in late 1998, the Leonid meteor shower was expected to peak on the night of November 17/18th as usual.[141] By coincidence, I was due to attend an event at the Royal Observatory, Greenwich, in London that very evening. You might imagine that an astronomical observatory would be the ideal place to find oneself for an astronomical light show, but London had grown vastly in size and illumination since the observatory was built in 1675, and the large amount of scattered light from the illuminated city would have made it very difficult to see the night sky clearly from there.

I was at my home on the preceding evening and although the meteor shower was expected to be only just beginning on that earlier night, I had hoped to catch a glimpse of at least one meteor trail. Unfortunately the sky was completely obscured by cloud, and the weather forecast offered little hope of seeing anything of the night sky. I resigned myself to the situation, read for a while and prepared to go to bed shortly after midnight. Then I remembered the anticipated meteor shower, poked my head outside, only to find that miraculously the clouds had just cleared and there above me was the clear night sky. I quickly put on some warm clothes and went outside.

When I looked up, I was greeted with one of the most memorable visual experiences of my whole life. Large bright green fireballs hurtled across the sky above me, leaving long glowing trails. I was both exhilarated and scared, for I had never seen anything like it before. Over the next hour I probably saw around 100 meteors and fireballs in total, but it was not the number which shook me, but their sheer size. Some were so big that they really scared me! The green fireballs got brighter and brighter as they crossed the sky and suddenly disappeared. For each I expected to hear a bang, but there was none, just an inappropriately eerie silence. The dark smoky trails that they left behind extended across a third of the sky, and took ten minutes or more to diffuse and disperse, so at one time I could count half a dozen that still lingered above me.[142]

I struggled to make sense of it all, partly for the sheer scale of the spectacle, but especially as there was no accompanying sound. My mind expected to hear roars and rumbles to match such visual extravaganza, but there was just an eerie silence. That year's display was far bigger than I had anticipated. Alone I watched these brilliant green orbs pass overhead, anxiously wondering if some other part of our planet was now being bombarded by these solid objects from outer space. I suddenly felt awe for my tiny planet in the immensity of the universe.

I found myself remembering the novel: "The War of the Worlds" by H.G. Wells, in which he described something similar: "Then came the night of the first falling star. It was seen early in the morning, rushing over Winchester eastward, a line of flame high in the atmosphere. Hundreds must have seen it, and taken it for an ordinary falling star. Albin described it as leaving a greenish streak behind it that glowed for some seconds".[143] I wondered if Wells had been inspired by reading reports of previous spectacular and frightening Leonid meteor showers, notably in 1833, it is even possible that my own anxiety was rooted in my knowledge of his story.

The following morning I nervously checked for news reports of catastrophic asteroid strikes, and was relieved and even surprised to find that no humans had been harmed in the making of the previous night's spectacle. The meteor show the following night was much smaller than anticipated and not visible from London due to mist, so I was especially fortunate to have seen it when I did.

I have related this experience because it was one of the few situations in which I have been confronted with a very alien experience, and one of which I wrote down details at the time. Memories of single strange events seem to fade, to be smoothed over to fit other more recent and more repeated experiences. It was only when I read my earlier notes that many details were remembered, and now I wish that I had recorded more detail at the time.

A matter of upmost gravity

Before leaving the subject of space, let me describe a fun way to gain a different perspective on your place in the universe. For this to work, you will need to find a location with a broad view of the night sky and stars. This is not easy for most of us who live in populated places, flooded with light from a thousand sources, street lights especially. So it may be best to remember these instructions and save them for a warm summer night, when you find yourself far from the lights of civilisation, lying on the grass, gazing up into a spectacular night sky full of stars.

Feel your back upon the ground. The pressure you feel on your back is due to gravity, the gravitational attraction between the masses of the Earth and your body holding you down, holding you against the Earth with sufficient force to keep you in place. I use the word "down" but I should more accurately say that the gravitational attraction between you and the planet Earth is a force pushing you in the direction of the centre of the Earth. So someone in Australia experiences this force pushing them in the completely opposite direction to someone in England. Standing Australians do not think of themselves as being upside down, despite the use of the phrase "down under", so from the planet's perspective, up and down are rather arbitrary directions.

So now, instead of comfortably lying on your back under the stars, try to think of yourself as lying on your back on the *underside* of the Earth, and gazing *down* into that same star filled sky! Just remember, that the only force that holds you in place *above* this sky, is the quite modest force of gravitational attraction between your body and the larger body of the Earth behind you. Can you feel the precariousness of your position should gravity suddenly disappear? Can you get a sense of vertigo as you are suspended above this infinite dark star-filled void, just by gravity? You can see that although nothing has changed physically, a simple change in our perspective can make us feel very different. Now as you return to your familiar way of viewing yourself upon the ground below, perhaps you have a new-found gratitude for gravity, and for the affection of mother Earth that holds us close and keeps us grounded.

I nearly forgot: despite the convenient horizontal position, I advise only doing this while sober. You wouldn't want to fall off! Now, back to Earth.

Our Learning and Recognition Bottlenecks

We have two information bottlenecks:

1/. Our Learning Bottleneck - The limited rate of learning something completely new.

2/. Our Recognition Bottleneck - The limited capacity to recognise something that we are already familiar with.

Our learning bottleneck is the constraint on our ability to learn what is truly new to us. It is a system limitation of our brain, rather than a localised limitation of our eyes or ears. When we learn something new it must be integrated into our internal conceptual model, not just stored some place in our brain as a piece of unrelated data. This integration is likely to involve many different regions within our brain, as the novel component of a single observation or sensation may have implications for many different aspects of our knowledge. For example, when I suddenly notice that the date or the time indicated by my watch is different time from what I had expected or assumed, I have to integrate this small piece of information into many different aspects of my life to deduce the consequences (e.g. collecting the kids from school, doctor's appointment, wedding anniversary, end of the tax year).

It is a bottleneck in the sense of a performance constraint in the communication network between the external world and our mind. Using the computer analogy, it is likely to be constrained by both our hardware and our software. This largely unrecognised human learning limitation is important because it is so much narrower than the other constraints which we encounter in the world of information and concern ourselves about, such as the speed of our broadband network or our mobile network data capacity. Later I will reveal the numerical evidence for the narrowness of our learning bottleneck.

Recognising what is new and updating my ideas

Although I am particularly interested in the rate at which we can learn something new: the learning bottleneck, almost nothing we ever experience is completely alien to us. Most everyday situations involve observing things that are already very familiar to us; I see a chair and I already have a model in my mind for a chair so can focus on discriminating details such as the orientation, colour, the style, and what is unusual about it. In this situation the only part of the experience that is new is the difference between what I expect and what I observe. The more accurate my internal model, the greater my sensitivity to differences. Repeated exposure to an experience enables me to continually add to my internal model through a vernier-like comparison between what I anticipate and what I experience, each time learning what is new.

Let's explore a crude analogy of the process: Imagine that I am able to look out of my window at the scene beyond, and could arrange to be able to view the scene through a precisely aligned photographic negative of it that I had taken the previous day. The bright parts of the scene would be dimmed by the dark areas in the negative and vice versa, creating a fairly uniform grey experience over the field of view. But where some part of the scene had changed, (for example, the black car that was parked in front of the white wall yesterday has now gone), today there would be a bright patch within the overall grey image, which would draw my attention.

Now let's extend this analogy to include the process of learning. Imagine that I view the same scene through a glass window, and later that night I paint dark translucent paint onto the glass in precise alignment with what I remember of the scene, but as a "negative", so the brighter the object, the darker I paint it. If my artwork and memory of the scene were perfect, the view I should experience on the following day would be a uniform grey; the darker areas on my window would completely compensate for the brighter portions of the scene.

But my memory was not perfect; I completely forgot to include some objects from the scene, and made errors both in shape and size of others. These areas now stand out clearly from the uniform grey, and I make a note to focus my attention on these when I view the scene again the following day. When I repeat this process on successive days and nights, the accuracy of my "negative" image gradually improves as I successively add more detail. My painted image becomes an increasingly accurate representation of the scene out there, and even when the shutters are closed I can explore the detailed scene I have created. This analogy gives some idea of our learning process, except that our mental model is a replica not a "negative".

What we expect is held within "the mind's eye", our brain, so most of what we see is simply the imaginings of our brain. When our senses observe something out there that our mind thinks it recognises, our attention is focused on the differences between what we expect from our previous experience, and what our eyes are actually sensing. If we notice the difference, we then update our internal model of the thing. Sometimes this is new information, helping to fill in the blanks. Often it is similar to something we have experienced before, and we refine our expectation of further similar experiences in the future. Even if what we sense exactly matches what we expect we still learn something, for our confidence in that knowledge is increased. On other occasions it may be contradictory information which increases the complexity of our internal model, for example when we see a black swan for the very first time.

When we learn more about something that we are already familiar with, our ability to compare our expectation with what we sense is limited by the information capacity of our sensors, such as our eyes and ears; this is our recognition bottleneck. On the other hand, our ability to absorb what is new, what is different, is limited by our much narrower learning bottleneck, which is most likely to be caused by limitations of processing within our brain. So if there is a large difference between what I expect and what I sense, then I will be limited by the rate at which I can learn the newness of the experience. However, even with this low rate of learning, over time I can develop highly complex representations of what is out there.

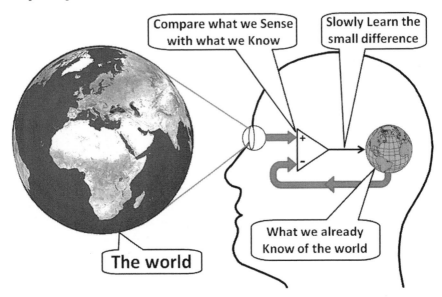

Figure 17: Building our inner world. When we perceive something and recognise it we are comparing what we sense with what we expect from our internal model of it, and use the difference to update our idea of it. The thicker line indicates that the information rate due to "Comparing" is much greater than that of "Learning".

This diagram is not intended to be a representation of the actual architecture of our brain, but is a simple analogy based on what we can observe of our own process of perception. Donald MacKay[144] proposed that the function of the visual cortex is to generate a model of the world, and this idea is consistent with some of what we now know about the anatomical structure of the brain, in that there are ten times as many fibres projecting back to the visual thalamus as there are going in the other direction.

The *visual* cortex was so named because of its key role in vision discovered long ago. However, its activity is much more than just visual: It is a part of our brain that contains a model of our world; not just a *visual* model which is two-dimensional, but everything we know of the spatial configuration of our three dimensional world, whether by touch, taste, smell, sound, or imagined facts. Once one accepts this idea, some otherwise surprising observations can be more readily understood: a) When we imagine performing an action, it causes brain activity in the very same location within the brain as when we actually perform that action. b) Top sports people can improve their physical performance by rehearsing in their minds what they will do prior to their actual performance, visualising the entire sequential performance in their mind, practicing without physical activity.

So our visual cortex is not just associated with seeing, but rather the act of envisioning. Someone who is blind from birth builds their own model of the world within their visual cortex using their white stick, their hearing and their learning. When they listen to a tale on the radio about the Taj Mahal, they build a model of it within their mind. They can even imagine themselves visiting the place, despite that fact that neither they nor the narrator of the story may have ever seen the place.

We can compare quite complex internal ideas with complex sensations, but have a more limited ability to be aware of and learn the difference. We humans with our highly intelligent minds can do this processing within our brains, but do you remember the bird of prey I described earlier? It achieved something similar for the very specific function of detecting moving prey within a static scene using the fading characteristics of its eyes. In some sense it is as if the static scene was subtracted from what was sensed, leaving only a sensation of the difference: i.e. that small part of the image that had changed. Some security CCTV camera systems work in a similar way.[145]

The bird does this processing within the retinas of its eyes, because it is a simpler process and does not require a large energy-demanding brain. It is a simple subtraction, whereas we have to perform a far more complex operation, requiring scaling and rotation in a three dimensional world before we can begin to interpret what has changed in the scene. However, the benefit for us humans in doing this processing within our brain is the incredible flexibility it provides, we can learn from almost every experience, not just from observing movement.

As an analogy, consider the way that the development of the microprocessor and the PC has transformed so much electronics. At one time every piece of electronic equipment was designed for its specific function, and the hardware completely defined its function. Today most electronics uses the ubiquitous microprocessor, and the function is now determined by the programming, the software that instructs the hardware. This has led to huge benefits in flexibility, reconfigurability, system reuse, software updating, all of which have brought down the cost to consumers of electronic equipment.

Our intelligent learning brain is equally adaptable, whether it be learning to make flint tools or building a science of almost every aspect of our world experience. The power of our species does not lie in our senses, for most other mammals have more sensitive hearing, sharper sight and a much more sensitive sense of smell. The key to our success has been our ability to use prediction from learning as a powerful alternative to direct and immediate sensing of our environment. Biological evolution of larger creatures like us is slow, our hardware cannot adapt quickly, but our intellectual software can. We achieve rapid evolution of our capabilities by continually developing our mental software by learning, and by efficiently passing on that learning.

Attention

From a very early age, we have internal models that guide where we place our attention. A baby will have a model of a face, mothers face, and will learn to focus attention on the eyes and mouth as these features carry more valuable information, and this pattern of eye movements will continue throughout the rest of its life. Through the years the model will become more complex and more sensitive to subtle nuances, enabling the viewer to make predictive judgements: "She is happy with me", "He is lying". So this is where vision has a significant advantage over our other senses, our internal model quickly tells us where to look based on its current prediction of relative importance. Unlike a camera, we do not take in a uniform image, but we use our point of gaze to tease out important details. This is somewhat similar to the way that a blind person uses his stick while out walking. He does not use it to build up a pixel by pixel tactile image of his surroundings, but to pose specific questions such as: "Have I reached the kerb yet?" Similarly the sighted man moves his point of gaze to focus on a feature that will help resolve an unknown or an ambiguity: "If he has a beard, it can't be my brother, so does he have a beard? Yes or No".

We have seen how turning our eyes towards something dramatically increases the quality of information we receive (due to the better resolving power of the centre of our gaze), but the same cannot be said for our ears and hearing. However, we can direct our mental attention towards a source of sounds. This is well demonstrated in the "cocktail party effect", where we might superficially appear to be listening intently to the person we are with, but focus our listening attention on one or more people around us (perhaps because we think those conversations could be more interesting!). This effect allows us to receive one communication channel out of several that are superimposed and interfering. Cocktail party effect works because there is redundant information. If we miss a syllable, a word, or even a sentence, we can still get the gist of the conversation (though with increased possibility of errors and subsequent gaffes!). Incidentally WiFi networks work in a similar way, several channels can overlap in frequency, yet still be separately resolved.

In this chapter I have shown that the world that I see and experience is not a clear view of what is out there. Instead, it is only my best guess of what is out there based on my limited previous experience. My only way of knowing the difference is by paying careful attention, and in my daily life I rarely have the time or interest to look that closely. So most of what I experience in the moment, is a rich and convincing simulation of what is out there, built from years of earlier experiences. It is convincing, because it is all that I have got, for I am fundamentally unable to take in the entirety of what my eyes see and my senses sense in each moment.

What I experience in my mind is as real as a vivid dream, yet unlike a dream it is rooted in a persistent external reality. I can use my senses to check for inconsistencies with a mere glance, a brief touch, or an attentive ear, and so immediately update my simulation, my idea of what is out there. I can also use language to compare my idea with those of other people who I trust, and modify my idea to achieve some consensus.

We cannot live every moment of our daily life aware of all that has been revealed to us, we need to use more workable ideas, however flawed. When I stand under the night sky in Australia and gaze "down" into space, I forget that it is only the gravitational attraction between the Earth and my body that prevents me being flung out into space by the planet's rotation. The same is true of our day-to-day perception the world about us; we forget that what we experience is an illusion of reality, and imagine that we all experience the same world. But when we choose to remember these revelations, we give ourselves the tools to explore not just our incredible physical universe, but to venture into the largely uncharted regions of our minds.

Chapter Four

Rules and Explanations

"The most incomprehensible thing about the universe is that it is comprehensible"

- Albert Einstein

Our intelligent mind does much more than simply remembers details of past experiences, hoping to spot a similar experience from the past. This would be very inefficient, and incapable of predicting any situation that was significantly novel. The model that we build within our mind is based on rules, and these rules are developed by our subconscious mind as it finds explanations for what we sense.

Our conscious mind is almost completely unaware of this process, as it only gets to experience the predictions made by our internal model of the world. We perceive the output of our model, not the incoming sensations. If I were to show you a red hot poker and then touch the back of your neck with a piece of ice, then for the first few moments you would probably have the shocking experience being burned.

We develop our scientific understanding of the world by deriving rules and explanations from experience, but in the case of science we are fully conscious of the process. It will therefore be helpful for us to first explore the meaning of rules and explanations in the context of science, before we ask our subconscious to "explain itself".

Rules, our intellectual power-tools

Civilisation provides us with a vast set of rules. The purpose of some rules is to simplify our lives. For example, the rule that in England we drive on the left side of the road makes speedy car travel both possible and safe. Many rules are arbitrary yet give us a sense of conforming and belonging within our society, such as sharing a particular form of handshake when we meet. Others, such as abstaining from eating pork, may have their origins in hygiene and disease but have subsequently been incorporated into religious rules and so now apply to a particular sub-section of humanity. Legal rules and laws are designed to protect the individual and the state, and may be similar throughout much of the developed world, yet none of these rules are considered to apply to absolutely everyone on (or off) the planet.

Scientific rules therefore are different. They are assumed to be ubiquitous, to apply to all that exists, not just to us humans, but to apply everywhere. Though we may be taught them as laws, somewhat like the Ten Commandments, they are deemed to be self-evident to anyone who chooses to do the experiments. As we grow up we learn all kinds of rules, some cultural, some behavioural (e.g. the child learns that it gets detention if it speaks when the teacher is speaking), and some rules that are based in science. When a child grows into an adult and subsequently explores the greater world, it is exposed to different rules, yet the rules of science (the physical sciences especially), are the ones that are most enduring.

By building explanations that are a good match with the world we observe, we develop a set of rules that efficiently describe most of what we experience: When we hold an apple and let it go, it accelerates downward in a direction toward the earth's centre, and we learn to expect this behaviour. There may be occasions when this simple rule seems not to apply, such as when we are on a fairground ride and the apple appears to fall sideways, however, that experience in itself is a new learning. Rules that enable us to predict things make much more efficient use of memory than simply storing the details of all our previous experiences. For example, we can apply the rules for building a bridge to a wide range of structures, and to completely new situations of which neither we nor others have previous experience.

Rules tend to be much much simpler than the rich detail of reality that we observe around us, but do not assume that simple rules can only describe simple systems or can only lead to simple outcomes. The comparatively recent discoveries of fractals, chaos theory and the Mandelbrot set[146] have revealed how incredible beauty and complexity can arise from a very simple process when it is repeated many times (recursively), and can even explain an infinitely complex structure. The Mandelbrot set is a mathematical set of points whose boundary is a distinctive and recognisable two-dimensional fractal shape.

Figure 18: A plot of a tiny part of the Mandelbrot set:

(This incredible beauty and complexity results from successively repeating a very simple equation: $Z_{new} = Z_{old}$ times ($Z_{old} + C$), using complex numbers[147] and plotting the rate at which Z_{new} expands as a colour.)[148]

Though these patterns were originally discovered as a purely mathematical phenomenon, we now know that much of the beautiful complexity that we see in nature and the world around us can be explained by remarkably simple recursive processes, for example the self-similarity of ferns.

Figure 19: This delicate fractal "fern", (Left, and zoomed in on Right) is the result of a simple mathematical equation repeated many times. Note the self-similarity in the leaf structure.

Beautiful though these images may be, we should not be seduced into thinking that the majority of our world's complexity can be fully described by simple rules. We are compulsively driven to try to describe everything in a sufficiently simple way that we can grasp, as this is the way we can gain control over our lives. However, we must be careful; the fact that something *can* be explained in a simple way, may deceive us into believing that it is fully explained and that we have an accurate model for it. The thing itself may be far more complex than we realize, and we may just be overconfident through our ignorance.

There is both beauty and power in seeing the patterns in everything around us, power to plan, to design, to build, to exploit. However, the universe we find ourselves in is incredibly complex, and any simplicity that we see is usually in the mind of the beholder. As Shakespeare said: "There are more things in heaven and earth Horatio, than are dreamt of in your philosophy".[149]

Conscious Explanations

"What we observe is not nature itself, but nature exposed to our method of questioning."

- Werner Heisenburg[150]

Ask yourself: Does everything have an explanation? If so, has it always been so? Did explanations exist before man, before the big bang? It seems that we give explanations rather more credit than they deserve. So what is an explanation?[151]

We often think of explanations as existing "out there", perhaps independent of us. We may even consider a good explanation to be the objective "truth" about reality. But "explaining" is something that we humans do to information, to convert confusingly vast quantities of information into an elegant predictive model, to compress it into the smallest size that will suffice to describe what we observe. Scientists and mathematicians speak of an explanation being beautiful or elegant when the extent of this compression is particularly high. We subsequently use these models to describe our past experiences in a more elegant way, but more importantly we use them to predict future possibilities.

Simplicity is a commonly-praised virtue of scientific theories, though surprisingly there are few arguments that offer a good philosophical reason to prefer it, other than invoking what is commonly known as the principle of "Occam's Razor", "that it is vain to do more when simplicity can suffice".[152]

Isaac Newton similarly stated the rule: "We are to admit no more causes of natural things than such as are both true and sufficient to explain their appearances".

More recently Ernst Mach,[153] Austrian physicist and philosopher, advocated the Principle of Economy, stating that "Scientists must use the simplest means of arriving at their results and exclude everything not perceived by the senses". Ernest is probably most known for his contributions to physics such as the Mach number (the normalised speed of sound)[154] and the study of shock waves, but he was also a great philosopher of science. He understood the profound difference between the simplicity, elegance and ubiquity of a scientific principle on one hand, and the unique and hugely complex nature of reality at any moment, on the other.

> "When the human mind, with its limited powers, attempts to mirror in itself the rich life of the world, of which it itself is only a small part, and which it can never hope to exhaust, it has every reason for proceeding economically."[155]

So for scientists, a useful statement of the principle is: When you have two competing theories which make exactly the same predictions, the one that is simpler is the better. Note that I do not say that simpler is more correct, merely better, better able to achieve a manageable model within a subject of high complexity. Simple is good as it empowers us to make progress, but if the theory is too simple, it will fail to explain all the observations. So that's it: an explanation is just a tool to help us exploit our scientific method, not a statement about the world out there.

However, a good explanation is much more than just an efficient way of describing something of the world we experience, because it allows us to predict the future, to extrapolate, to take men to the Moon, to envision way beyond the totality of our experience, to the very stars. What makes humans so special is our remarkable ability to predict across wide expanses of space and time. Science is a divination tool that has dramatically increased the extent of our powers. Unlike hunches and clairvoyance, the magic of science is based on consistent evidence, the more the evidence, the greater the predictive power. A thousand observations of similar phenomena suggest that a further one is quite likely to occur. For the wizards of science, rules are their powerful magic spells, used repeatedly and reliably to conjure up all manner of previously undreamed of things. If we are diligent in following the rules when we build new bridges or aircraft, they usually stay up!

It is said that science recoils from subjectivity, but physical scientists recoil furthest. In the hard sciences like physics, the basic tenet has been that there is one true explanation for everything, while all others are flawed approximations, since it is not in our nature to settle for multiple simultaneous truths. Conflicting explanations are a rallying call, which quickly attracts enthusiastic research to resolve any ambiguities. Prior to the observation and discovery of quantum phenomena in the last century, this approach had always been successful, but suddenly physics could no longer provide a single comprehensible description of these observations using metaphors from our common-sense world.

One of the biggest ambiguities of this sort encountered by physicists in recent times is that of Wave-Particle Duality. As we dig to the deepest levels of physics, and quantum theory in particular, we find that what we observe is determined by how we observe it. Consider light, for example: It behaves as waves when we look for interference between two beams of light, and as particles when we detect it at low levels, all within the same experiment. This has presented a big dilemma for most physicists who would like a single description what light is (and that includes Albert Einstein).

I have spent much of my life as a scientist working with light, using it to communicate over vast distances. There is plenty of evidence that light propagates or travels as waves, and equally good evidence that light behaves as particles or photons when it is created or detected. Yet there has never been an experiment that proves that photons actually travel. The problem is that we can only measure the presence of a photon once, either at the start or finish of its journey, since the act of measuring it destroys it (by converting it to an electron). So we cannot know that it is the same photon that went from A to B. To say that photons travel, requires an act of faith alone, and hence is not true science. The more one thinks of photons as objects, the more puzzling they appear, as evidenced by the famous Dual-Slit experiment, where the same source of light can be shown to display the properties of waves or particles (photons), depending on how one chooses to detect it.[156]

As Albert Einstein said: "All the fifty years of conscious brooding have brought me no closer to answer the question: What are light quanta? Of course today every rascal thinks he knows the answer, but he is deluding himself".[157] What if our "explanations" are just ideas that we project outward from our minds onto an external reality that is under no obligation to fit our simplifications. Then we can see the wave-particle duality problem, as simply a case where we do not have a commonplace metaphor from our everyday world which can be used as an example. As Nobel physicist Richard Feynman said: "If you think you understand quantum mechanics, you don't understand quantum mechanics".[158]

When it comes to our experience of the world around us, some people are more interested in small differences in interpretations, while others are happy to settle on one interpretation. Most of us like simple ideas because we are lazy, and we can save so much time applying simple rules to complex scenarios. However, the more creative scientific minds tend to be dissatisfied with anything that is a less than perfect match between what is sensed and what is perceived based on their internal models. They can become obsessed with the small discrepancies, believing that behind these tiny chinks of incongruity, may lie some great revelation, and so are more dissatisfied with intellectual discomfort than the average person. They want to "get to the bottom of it", even if the pursuit of understanding seems endless.

It reminds me of the story of The Real Princess (The Princess and the Pea) by Hans Christian Andersen: The fact that she could still feel discomfort from a single pea placed beneath "twenty mattresses ... on top of the pea, and then twenty feather beds on top of the mattresses" and so was unable to sleep, proved her to be of royal blood! So it seems with the great scientific minds throughout history; they cannot sleep, for they are sensitised to the tiniest imperfection in our comfortable theories. Perhaps great creative minds are biased towards dissatisfaction and continue to search for alternative solutions, when the rest of us are happy to settle, and get on with our lives.

Should we expect everything in the universe to be explainable using examples from the point of view of our tiny little place in the vast universe? It is possible that the entire universe is comprised of stuff which is very similar to everything which we earthlings have experienced, but I think it's highly unlikely. If it were so then it would imply that the universe is full of duplications, copies of things we are familiar with, that it is just a patchwork of places similar to those we already know, that everything is made in our own image! The more I think of the vast scale of the universe in relation to our own worldly experience, the more I wonder if we just imagine this similarity, perhaps it is the only way that we can make sense of nonsense. We project this simple model of the universe out there so we feel a little less awed, and a little more in control.

It is interesting at this point to re-examine the meanings of some of the words we use: When we say that we "sense" something it means more than just nerves being triggered in our sense organs; it means that we perceive the sensation, that we become aware of it. To "make sense" of something means to understand it, to make some novel experience comprehensible, to make it fit into our existing logical mental framework. Note that the actual words within the phrase "make sense" implies that our conscious mind can only acknowledge a raw sensation when we can understand it, when we can fit it our pre-existing ideas. When we say that something is "nonsense", we are saying that we personally are unable to fit something sensed or experienced or reported to us by another, with our predicted reality, and so imply that it should be rejected. In contrast when we say something is "common sense", we usually mean that we believe that the experience has been experienced by many individuals or repeated through time, so leading to a future expectation.

In science and engineering we make the distinction between the transducer or sensor (which converts a property of our environment such as temperature or illumination, into a signal that can be communicated), and the subsequent information processing that derives meaning from this signal. When we humans "make sense" of something, we interpret the incoming signals from our nerves in the context of our previous experience, and ascribe "sense" to these signals when we can fit them with our historically based mental predictions of the external world.

When we suddenly recognise something that is nonsense, it can make us laugh. It has recently been proposed that humour evolved as a mechanism to improve the quality of our mental simulation.[159] The idea is that our brain searches to predict the future by building models of the world, and that the brain rewards us when we discover an incorrect expectation by giving us some pleasure. Furthermore, it is suggested that over time we have become addicted to that pleasurable feeling, so enjoy and value comedians who are skilled in triggering this reward mechanism. The idea is plausible as it would be a mechanism for getting out of mental "blind alleys" and correlates well with the strong link between creativity and humour. As Isaac Asimov[160] said: "The most exciting phrase to hear in science, the one that heralds new discoveries, is not "Eureka" but 'That's funny'..".

A single point points nowhere

Though the immense power of science is evident, we often forget that science is impotent when faced with a single completely novel observation. It is fundamentally impossible for us to make sense of a single completely novel experience. Our predictive logic requires two or more similar experiences before a sensation can be considered a true sensation of the external world. With two observations I can note similarities and draw a line between the two isolated points on a graph. I can then extrapolate the line and make a prediction that further observations might well fall near to this hypothetical line. With an isolated observation we only have a single point, with no idea how to draw a line, extrapolate or predict. For example, consider the existence of life in the universe. Are we unique? The one example of ourselves tells us nothing, two examples tell us everything.

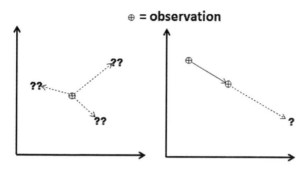

Figure 20: We need two or more observations to make a prediction.

Science as the religion of the explanation

This is why science struggles so much with highly unusual or paranormal phenomena. Science can be considered as the religion of the Explanation, whose fundamental tenet is that nothing exists that does not have an explanation. Those who have a strong *faith* in science can feel threatened by an observation of something that might fall outside science as generally accepted at that point in time. They will generally avoid exploring subjects such as the paranormal or psychic phenomena, fearing discomfort or being ridiculed by their peers, so rigorous investigations of these subjects are rare yet fascinating.[161]

Paradoxes can feel threatening or exciting. When one emerges within the safety of the physical sciences, it is likely to quickly attract bright and energetic minds to resolve it, and encourage them to make more observations, carefully and with prepared and open minds. However, when we encounter one at the boundaries of science, we may rush blindly to annihilate the threat posed by uncomfortable observations that might threaten the foundations of our belief. We can then behave irrationally and deal with our discomfort by uttering the protective mantra: "It's just a coincidence" to deny the potential power of an observation that threatens the current idea. This ritual prayer provides protection. Panic over, now back to work!

Note the power invoked by the word "just". Without it, there is a coincidence, no more, no less. To say it is "just" a coincidence, implies that we should ignore this new observation, despite the fact that it suggests that our science may possibly be incomplete. Of course most observations are made within the context of a vast amount of previous experience, and "Extraordinary claims require extraordinary evidence"[162], or as Laplace put it:

"The weight of evidence for an extraordinary claim must be proportioned to its strangeness".[163]

The big challenge for scientists is to stay open to new and controversial observations and not become heroic defenders of the current faith of science. A single observation counter to everything that has gone before is rightly treated with suspicion, but it is important not to discard the evidence. Who knows, we might have another similar experience at some point in the future, or perhaps someone else who I am currently unaware of has already experienced something similar. The history of scientific discovery is littered with examples of phenomena that long remained unrecognised, yet with hindsight should have been obvious.

We find it easy to discard information that does not make sense to us. The growing hole in the Ozone layer was missed by NASA scientists for several years despite it being recorded in their own satellite measurements, because the software had been designed to reject unexpectedly low values, assuming these were equipment errors. The subsequent discovery of the Ozone hole by the British Antarctic Survey in 1985, using meteorology balloons to carry instruments high into the stratosphere shocked the scientific community, because the observed decline in polar ozone was far larger than anyone anticipated.[164] When the earlier satellite data was subsequently reprocessed to include these previously rejected samples, the Ozone hole was seen to have been detected, yet not recognised, almost a decade earlier.[165]

Resistance to new ideas is very common. Many years ago the research team I worked with were about to install the world's first practical optical fibre transmission system between two UK towns, Hitchin and Stevenage, communicating over prototype optical fibres.[166] [167] When the system was assembled and tested in the lab prior to installation, to our horror it did not work; the received pulses were too noisy and distorted.

I set about investigating the phenomenon, and at the same time asked researchers from other labs if they had experienced anything similar, but they all denied seeing any problems. It turned out to be due to a complex interaction between the lasers, the particular type of optical fibre, and the way these lengths of hair-thin fibres were joined together section by section. Although the core of the fibre that carried the light was far narrower than a human hair, light could travel through it via many different paths, and this created confusion. We were fortunate to quickly find a practical solution, but most people were initially very resistant to this new theory.

One day someone from a neighbouring department marched in, threw a copy of a Japanese technical paper on my desk and said "I told you that you were wrong!" He proceeded to point out that the paper described an experiment that would clearly have demonstrated my phenomenon if it really existed, yet the author indicated no evidence for it whatsoever. But by that time I had become sufficiently confident in my own observations and theory that I had to assume that there was something odd about this Japanese result.

Sure enough, some years later when I had the opportunity to talk with the author of the paper, he confessed rather sheepishly that what he had written was not entirely true. He had omitted a key physical component from his experimental system to save time and money (the optical fibre!), yet his diagrams and description showed this component quite clearly. Based on the prevailing scientific knowledge at the time, he had thought that his shortcut was inconsequential, but it turned out to be crucial. A year later when I published my theory and the evidence for the phenomena, many people then started to reveal that they had in fact observed something similar, but had dismissed what they had seen because it did not make sense to them.[168]

The problem involved the interaction of a large number of different components each of which could only be fully described in great complexity. Subsequently, we spent some years trying to build a more comprehensive explanation, a model that would enable us to predict the performance of each individual system. It was a failure; the overall complexity of the problem in any practical situation left us unable to make usefully accurate predictions. So for a while we made do with a simple model that enabled us to avoid problems almost all of the time.[169]

This complexity problem proved a key reason for abandoning this early type of optical fibre, despite the fact that so much of this fibre had already been installed in the UK telephone network. We quickly moved to a new optical fibre design, one that presented far greater technical challenges, for the tiny light-carrying core was much smaller, only a few microns in diameter.[170] However, the core of this new fibre was so narrow that there was only one unique path through it, so it was simpler to understand. The rest of the world soon followed, and today this fibre type connects all our cities and our continents; it is what made the World Wide Web possible. So this example shows that success of the scientific method sometimes requires us to move towards simpler conceptual territory, so we can exploit the power of our explanations.

The priests of Science

Physics always builds new science on the old foundations. It adjusts, extends and reinterprets the old physics. So too do many world religions, for example, those developed within the last few hundred years such as the Church of Latter Day Saints (Mormon) and Jehovah's Witness', despite having hugely different beliefs, still have their roots in the doctrine of the Christian old testament. However, the "religion" of science is unlike that of other religions, in that it has maintained its ubiquity, its single truth, because we have continued to find common ground through the shared experience of near identical experiments. If one describes a physics or chemistry experiment sufficiently clearly, then scientists in different countries (and differing religions) can repeat the experiment themselves and observe essentially the same result, providing a binding agreement of "truth".

This has been the keystone to much of science, but physics is entering difficult territory now, with String Theory, Dark Matter, Dark Energy and other competing truths, and a failure to unify Physics despite many over-ambitious promises. Different groups of theoretical physicists are asking us to believe different stories, often with minimal or even zero experimental evidence to supporting their ideas.

Today, the vast cost and scale of the Large Hadron Collider ensures that the community around that experiment now have a priest-like authority. No individual can perform their own experiment to check the "truths" that issue forth from this the greatest temple of physics. Furthermore, there is pressure on this new priesthood to come up with the goods, to announce some new magic (accompanied by spectacular and highly realistic computer generated graphics), in order to justify the huge diversion of resources into one experiment with so little practical value that is obvious to the man in the street.

The recent discovery of a blip in the data[171] that corresponds to an energy appropriate to the hitherto undetected Higgs Boson[172] has been a huge relief to all concerned. The fact that the press refer to it as "the God particle" is an indication of the sacred status of modern physics. To explore beyond would require us to build an even bigger "collider", and society may not be able to justify the expense of such a magnificent edifice. So we may now be approaching an era where physical proof of theoretically derived physical beliefs is no longer practical. Perhaps the once unified community of physicists will split off into tribes travelling in different directions each with their own beliefs and community of believers.

Explanations feel good, even when they are bad

I am a compulsive explainer. My wife jokes that I am like inspector Clouseau, the fictional detective. I assume that everything has a reason and I cannot rest until I have found the reason behind some minor thing. Occasionally it is a useful compulsion: When repairing a piece of equipment such as an iPod, I might notice that there is a small gap at one point where the two halves of a unit meet together. I might surmise that pushing a narrow screwdriver into this gap may release a hidden latch holding the two halves of the case together, and voila, the case opens wide and the rest of the repair is easy.

When modern gadgets and equipment are designed, it is unusual for any feature to be included without a reason, even if that is just to make it an attractive object. So it is reasonable for me to assume that each feature has a purpose, a reason for being there. I would often see such features as a kind of puzzle, a challenge to pit myself against to deduce just what that the purpose might be.

I could take the same approach with living things if I could assume that the features were all products of successful evolution. However, we are unlikely to know the evolutionary path of a plant or animal with any certainty, and many features may not have been honed to perfection by evolution, just the result of some chance DNA mutation along the way, or an optimisation for some long-forgotten situation. As for the rest of our universe, unless we believe that it is all the work of an intelligent supernatural designer, we have no reason to expect to find that everything has a clear purpose, (and if we do believe it is all the work of an intelligent supernatural designer, it would be somewhat arrogant of us to think that we could understand it at the same level of the all-knowing designer!).

Perhaps explanations feel good because they are evolution's way of rewarding us for developing our efficient predictive models. I have become aware that I feel comfortable having thought up an explanation even if there is no real proof that it is correct, or even one that I later find to be downright wrong. So my comfort comes from an explanation, and not necessarily from the truth. Members of my family can find this trait infuriating, failing to appreciate that I am usually aware of the difference between an explanation and reality.

Sometimes it can be extremely difficult to find adequate explanations for something. We then have two options; deceive ourselves with some trumped-up explanation that we would normally feel obliged to reject, or admit that we just do not know. The latter is a much healthier approach, as it retains the basic information. For all we know now, we might just have another experience in the future, which in conjunction with the first one will lead to greater insight.

Some years ago I was confronted with the inability of my world of science to explain everything I encountered. I lived next door to a nice guy, salt of the earth type, quite bright, but due to circumstances he had left school early. I had great respect for his ability to weld a pair of written-off cars into one saleable car, albeit the final hybrid vehicle naturally pulled to the left a little. He came to respect me as a "Scientist/Engineer" and occasionally asked me to explain something to him.

One day he asked me a simple question about his own working practice: He worked for a company that laid water drainage pipes in farmers' fields using a big machine (each year farms were eligible for a government grant for this work). When they started work on a new site adjacent to a field where drains had already been laid, they needed to locate the previously laid drains so they could connect to them. The method that the company had taught him to use, was to manually dig a long exploratory trench to intersect and hence locate the buried drains, a time consuming task.

I was happy with his description so far. But then he went on to say that he personally never had to do any of this, because a long time ago an old man had approached him and shown him how to just "dowse for the drains using a hazel twig" ("water divining"). So they then only needed to dig a small hole to confirm that they had indeed located each of the old drains, and that is what he had successfully done for years. I queried whether this required some water to be in the drains, and he replied that it still worked if the field and drains were completely dry.

Now while I was puzzling over all this, he then said: "Can you just tell me how it works, I have always wanted to know?" Frankly, I didn't know what to say, so I mumbled something about us not yet discovering all our human skills, but it was obvious that he was not impressed. He must have seen the look of impossibility on my face though I tried to hide it. From that day on, my status with him was diminished; I was obviously not so clever if I couldn't answer that one simple question.

I never did dare to ask if dowsing still worked for him, fearing that he might not trust it any more. The scientist in me would prefer to forget this whole incident, while the explorer in me feels compelled to remember it.

Medical Science - a second opinion

Because the creed of science is: "Everything that exists has an explanation", the world of science also prefers an incorrect explanation, to no explanation at all. This is particularly evident in the field of medicine, where we are all familiar with the fluctuating opinions of what is good for us and what is not, (whether it be vitamins, aspirin, animal fats, carbohydrates, or sunlight). We tend to feel much more comfortable with explanations than unknowns.

A doctor friend, who had worked in general practice for many years, told me that when patients are first diagnosed with cancer, many insist that it was started by a knock they had received. It seemed to her that many patients needed a story to make sense of what was happening to them, despite the fact that it had probably arisen spontaneously. If we know what has initiated something bad, then we can at least plan to avoid a recurrence. If it appears to be without cause we are powerless to learn from it, and powerlessness can be very frightening.

Those who suffer from depression often relentlessly pursue a physical explanation for their dis-ease. Just to be given a name for what we suffering can make us feel better. This is one reason for the ever increasing number of medically recognised syndromes. If we have had no experience of mental illness, we might tend to consider physical disease as more authentic than psychological disease, but a pain that we cannot explain can be very disturbing, whatever the origin.

The world of medicine is much more tolerant of ambiguity than the world of physics. Pure objective controlled experiments are impossible with complex living organisms, so nominally "identical" experiments frequently yield different results. Multiple explanations can co-exist over long periods of time. In physics, we attempt to refine the experiment to such a simple level that multiple researchers are likely to achieve very similar results. In medicine, it is usually accepted that the complexity of the situation precludes proof of a theory by performing a single experiment. Proof is typically based on statistical averages over many experiments, with little concern when a few individual experimental results run counter to the theory. It is assumed that these are caused by unknown variables which cannot be controlled.

Medical science gets into particular difficulty when dealing with individual psychological experiences. Many years ago I watched a TV documentary about a pioneering a treatment for Heroin addiction. A Scottish doctor had achieved some remarkable results using electrically stimulated acupuncture to block the pain of withdrawal symptoms during treatment, a technique she developed after seeing the success of a similar method being used in China. The funding for her work in the UK was being stopped, yet she was being offered generous funding to move to a post abroad. They interviewed William Sargant, a very senior psychiatrist at the time, who was asked why her work was no longer funded in the UK. His response was that such treatment was of no interest, as "the patients only imagine that they feel no pain".

In his world view, the pain still existed untreated. In the absence of an "explanation" he considered that the effect of the treatment was not "real", despite the very positive responses of the patients. William Sargant is remembered as an evangelist for more brutal therapies such as electro-convulsive therapy and insulin shock therapy (treatments which are now largely discredited), and he had a strong distaste for all forms of psychotherapy. He also rather optimistically predicted that mental illness would have ceased to exist by the year 1990.[173]

Things have moved on somewhat since then, but there is still a difficult relationship between the world of conventional allopathic medicine which requires a "scientifically valid explanation", and the world of alternative medicine that does not. Herbal medicine is based almost entirely on experimental evidence and has been used for thousands of years. Its use has been rejected by the majority of western medics on the grounds that it is generally unacceptable to use methods that have no scientific explanation even with extensive anecdotal evidence for their effectiveness.

It takes time to identify the active ingredients in herbs and to conduct drug trials with sufficient rigour to satisfy the authorities. In contrast, contemporary allopathic medicine is quickly trusted when there is a theory behind it, a predictive model. The necessary clinical trials are seen more as a nuisance, delaying the point at which the pharmaceutical company can recoup its investment.

Sick and suffering individuals often feel that they cannot wait, and resort to alternative treatments. In doing so, they may be pioneering paths to new drugs and future conventional treatments. They personally take that risk. Many alternative treatments may be considered useless or even harmful to the patient, yet if the patient feels that they live a happier healthier life as a consequence of using such treatments, then who are we to deny this? Of course there are plenty of unscrupulous individuals and organisations ready to exploit such people for financial gain, and people who are desperately ill will try anything.

Millions of us trust scientific predictions based on theories. Take the use of vitamin pills: There is good evidence that a deficiency in our diet of specific vitamins can cause serious and even life threatening disease, and there is probably reasonable evidence that it is beneficial to eat foods known to contain these vitamins. The health industry has taken the predictive step of assuming that the many of us could benefit from regularly taking pills containing synthesised vitamins. Remarkably, we have demanded very little evidence for the value of widespread vitamin pill use. The number of vitamin pills consumed is vast, yet the supporting evidence is tiny. The dosage is rarely based on tests on the specific individuals, and most people buy their own vitamins and set their own dosage. The observable effects of these pills on our body are small, and the placebo effect is probably dominant, so it is difficult to self-regulate effectively. Our naive predictive model assumes that if a vitamin deficiency leads to disease, vitamin excess can do us little harm. However, most vitamins are toxic when taken in excess.[174] For example, large doses of vitamin A are known to cause osteoporosis, hair loss and birth defects in babies.

I believe that greater progress will be made in medical science, when we have developed a better understanding of the role of placebos, treatments with no active element except the belief of the patient.[175] Placebos do work; there is little doubt about that. In a large controlled trial of placebos administered to patients who had just developed the common cold, those who received no pills tended to have longer and more severe illnesses than those who received pills. For a subgroup who believed in Echinacea and received pills, illnesses were substantively shorter and less severe, regardless of whether the pills contained Echinacea.[176]

The placebo effect is often the biggest single effect in many clinical trials of new drugs, so is generally considered a nuisance making it more difficult to measure the effect of the drug itself. Placebos have the potential to be one of the most effective tools in our armoury of medicine, with the potential to bring comfort and relief to many sufferers. The dilemma is how to do so without incurring the wrath of the pharmaceutical industry, whose business depends so much on the drug treatment of psychosomatic disorders. Furthermore, doctors are faced with significant questions of ethics when administering a placebo as it requires a deliberate deception.

No one has received a Nobel Prize for inventing a placebo, but Dan Ariely, a behavioural economist at Duke University won an Ig-Nobel prize in 2008 for his study which revealed that more expensive fake medicines work better than cheaper fake medicines. The Ig-Nobel Prizes are a humorous parody of the Nobel Prizes.[177] They are presented by genuine Nobel laureates each year for ten unusual or trivial achievements in scientific research, and usually ones that make you think. Dan's paper on "Commercial Features of Placebo and Therapeutic Efficacy" was one of those.[178]

Dan had previously spent three years in hospital recovering from serious burns. During that time he noticed that some patients who woke in the night in extreme pain went straight back to sleep after receiving an injection from the nurse, but the nurse later confided in Dan that the injection was often just saline solution, no pain killer having been administered. He became fascinated by the power of placebos and later set up a study to measure how their effectiveness was influenced by the perceived financial cost of the pain killing drug the subjects thought they were receiving.

His team administered light electric shock to eighty two subjects' wrists to measure their subjective rating of the pain. They were tested both before and after taking the placebo. Earlier half the participants had been given a brochure describing the pill as a newly-approved pain-killer which cost $2.50

per dose and the other half were given a brochure describing it as marked down to just 10 cents, without saying why. None of the subjects received any active drug, but all were led to believe that they had. Eighty five percent of the subjects in the full-price group experienced a significant reduction in pain after taking the placebo, whereas in the low-price group only sixty one percent said the pain was less. So the higher the perceived cost of the pill, the more effective it is.

Given that the placebo effect is significant in almost every drug trial, Dan's research suggests that a new drug may score higher in trials, simply because it is expected to be more expensive. As Dan Ariely says: "The placebo effect is one of the most fascinating, least harnessed forces in the universe", "When you expect something to happen, your brain makes it happen". It seems that we expect to get what we pay for. This is nothing new to the witch doctors, shamans and quacks, who know too well the downside of free medicine.

From an evolutionary perspective we might ask; if people are capable of healing themselves without medical intervention, why do they need a placebo to do so? Recent research suggests that the immune system has an on-off switch controlled by the mind. Such a mechanism has been measured in Siberian hamsters, when fooling them to believe that it was winter or summer simply by changing the daily lighting duration.[179]

The immune system takes energy to run, so a strong and sustained immune response could dangerously drain an animal's energy reserves. The reasoning is that as long as an infection is not lethal, it pays for the body to wait for a sign that fighting it will not endanger the animal in other ways.[180] Perhaps for today's humans who have easy access to energy-giving food all year round, it would make sense for the healing effect we associate with placebos to be active at all times.

Our Explaining Brain - filled with unconscious explanations

We have seen how explanations and rules are the basis of all our science, and much of the rest of our daily lives, but I will now show you that they are also the very foundation of human perception. Our every conscious moment is based on our mind's unconscious explanations and interpretation of our raw senses and our history. Though we sense information, we inhabit our explanations.

Raw information offers our mind a myriad of possibilities, yet as observers we are only able to experience a single explanation at any one moment. We may be able to consider different explanations successively, but not simultaneously, as you will see with the following example.

The Necker cube is a simple two dimensional drawing constructed from twelve straight lines, yet it reveals a vast amount about the process of human visual perception.[181] The image is flat and two dimensional; however when we observe it our immediate reaction is to see it as representing a three-dimensional wire-frame cube, despite the fact that our eyes should be telling us that it is a flat image.

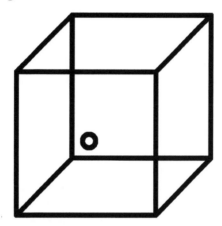

21: The Necker Cube: A 3D idea from a 2D image.
Is the O in the centre of a face of the cube, or in the lower left corner of a face? Is the O on a front face or the back? Notice how your mind oscillates between equally probable explanations.

When you first gaze at this version of a Necker cube image, it appears as a cube with two equally probable interpretations of whether the small circle is located in the centre of a face, or in the corner of a face. With more careful examination, you may notice that there are two further options, whether the circle is on the front or back face of the cube. There may be a natural tendency to assume that it is on the front face, possibly because we are more familiar with solid cubes, in which case a circle on the rear face would be hidden, despite the fact that the "cube" image is a transparent wire frame image.

Now try and see it as it really is: a flat abstract image of twelve lines and a small circle. Notice your resistance to seeing it as anything other than a 3D cube. Our mind urgently seeks an explanation for this abstract image presented to our senses. It makes much more sense to us as a cube, something that we are much more familiar with.

A new-born baby has no experience of cubes, so from its unprejudiced perspective the flat abstract interpretation of the Necker cube image is as likely as anything else. But for those of us who have experienced the world, the cube interpretation jumps right out at us. This Necker illusion is much more than a mere novelty, as it shows us the way in which our mind continually seeks likely explanations for what our senses present to us. It also reveals that our mind cannot hold multiple interpretations simultaneously.

If we stare at the image we typically find that our interpretation switches back and forth between the alternative 3D options. Try focusing on the circle and note how it alternates its position between the centre and the corner of the cube face with a period of a few seconds. Neither option is superior to the other, so the brain continues to search for an optimum solution. If a slight bias towards one interpretation of the Necker cube image is introduced, say by thinning or greying the lines that could correspond to a "back face", we more readily settle upon one interpretation. Now take a moment to try to see it as a flat abstract image again, just some lines in an abstract pattern. It is surprisingly difficult.

It is not just abstract line drawings that we interpret this way. Our modern world bombards us with two-dimensional images that represent solid objects of a wide range of sizes, and we very quickly learn to ignore the difference. When I was 5 years old, I saw my first television picture. It was in colour, but just one colour: Green. The TV had been painstakingly built by my uncle and my father, from post-war surplus radar components. I can still remember my amazement at seeing this tiny flat two-dimensional moving image of "Andy Pandy" (a puppet), for the very first time, an actual moving picture.

In 1953 my great aunt bought a tiny commercial black & white TV, just in time for the whole extended family to crowd into a room and watch the coronation of Queen Elizabeth II. Soon afterwards my grandfather bought one too. It had a huge lens hung in front of the small screen which made the picture appear a bit larger, but more blurred, and the whole thing was housed in a beautifully veneered wooden case.

I soon lost my innocent fascination with a moving two-dimensional picture, as the sensation was replaced by my ability to imagine the three-dimensional scene that the 2D image represented. The ideas represented by the images had overcome the truth of my direct stereo visual experience, of it being flat and small, and only a few feet in front of me. I had learned to see the image of the queen as representing an actual life-size person, and see the tiny flat image of the recently climbed Mount Everest as a huge solid mountain.

About five years later I actually saw the queen "in the flesh" when she visited my home city, and was shocked by two things; she was surprisingly small, and she was in colour too, wearing a brilliant green outfit. This was not the queen that I had learned about and built an mental idea of through seeing her on a small screened black & white TV during those intervening years. Since that occasion, I have updated my idea of the queen, and no longer think of her in black & white, but her size has not been fully corrected in my mind. I only had the one real experience of her, which was very brief compared with all the TV and film experiences that I have had of her. This is the way it is. Our world is created from what we feed our senses.

Today few people grow up remembering a time of discovery such as my own, of seeing a two dimensional moving image on a flat screen. From the earliest age we expose our children to moving 2D images of a 3D world through TV, movies and computer generated displays. The absence of depth clues is incongruous with the other aspects of the visual experience. Because part of our brain architecture is configured by our early visual experiences, it is possible that people growing up in today's world may have some differences in the structure of their visual cortex. They may be less able to observe incongruities between a 2D image of a 3D object but therefore be better matched to the world of flat screens. Whether exposure to 3D TV will change matters remains to be seen, for the depth clues are still not entirely realistic. Recently, enthusiasm for 3D films has waned. Perhaps we prefer to provide our own depth information within our imagination, rather than have the producer's ideas imposed on us.

As we are so familiar with images and screens, it is easy to forget that an image of something is not the thing itself. I heard of an explorer in the Amazon rainforest who showed a Polaroid photo of a particular tree to an indigenous tribesman, and asked him what it was. The tribesman did not see a tree, he saw a strange rectangular piece of card with a pattern on it instead. What he saw was very unusual to him and intriguing, but nothing like a tree, and he knew a lot about trees.

Such confusion is not confined to peoples with little experience of the developed world. On a flight from New York to London, the well-dressed woman in the adjacent seat leaned across to show me a page from the in-flight magazine. It was photo of a piece of Chinese jewellery. She asked "well what do you think that is?" I recognised it immediately and replied "it's a jade necklace", but she simultaneously answered her own question with "Its a million dollars!" probably expecting me to be impressed. We each saw different things.

The more novel the experience, the less well equipped we are to interpret it. During the later stages of the Apollo space programme, I visited the Smithsonian museum in Washington and marvelled at a lunar landing module on display. I was inspired to buy a set of colour slides, wonderfully sharp photographs of the craters on the Moon's surface taken by the astronauts while in orbit around the Moon. When I got home I could hardly wait to see them projected on my screen, and put them in my slide projector, taking care to put them the correct way up, as indicated on the slides. To my disappointment half the images were confusing, the craters appeared as domed lumps, not hollow craters.

With a bit of experimentation, I found that I could solve the problem simply by flipping the orientation of the slides in the projector, then all the craters looked as I would expect them to do. Eventually I understood what was producing the confusion. Here on Earth the source of illumination almost always comes from above, but for the astronaut orbiting the Moon with a camera, there is no absolute sense of up or down, and the direction that craters appeared to be illuminated from was quite arbitrary. The problem was caused by my unconscious expectation that the illumination of the craters came from "above" (and possibly a slight preference for convex objects).

The hollow mask illusion exploits this prejudice: a hollow mask of a face is illuminated from below, viewed from a distance and rotated slowly.[182] What we see is not a hollow mask, but a solid head seemingly illuminated from above that somehow rotates in the opposite direction, all very confusing. We have a strong bias to seeing our 2D impression of a hollow mask as a normal 3D convex face. The bias is so strong that it wins over any competing depth clues we may receive, especially when the direction of illumination is also reversed. These are examples of how our minds have learned to expect certain things, and consequently perceive falsely rather than see things as they really are.

There may be complications

Our own planet Earth seems to be incredibly rich and complex. The closer we look the more we see. Compare that with what we knew until recently about the Moon or Mars, where everywhere seemed quite similar. It appears that Life is what has provided Earth with most of its complexity. However, we cannot be sure that these distant lifeless places are boring, firstly because we have only observed or explored an incredibly tiny fraction of those physical places, and secondly we might not know what we are looking at.

We only have our past experience on which to base our observations. When faced with a new world we may be like the tiny baby, who seeing the world for the first time can only see the simplest of things. It is possible that we are too unfamiliar with what is there to be able to "see" it, and we are left with the comfortable idea that it is a simple place, that a few scoopfuls of Lunar dirt tells us most of what we need to know about this vast object.

Recent images from space probes of the rings of Saturn and the moons of Jupiter suggest that the closer we look, the more we reveal just how much there is yet to know.[183] When Galileo first observed Saturn in 1610 with his rudimentary telescope, he interpreted his blurred view of the rings as a pair of smaller bright objects, "handles" or large moons on either side of the planet. He said: "I have observed the highest planet (Saturn) to be tripled-bodied. This is to say that to my very great amazement Saturn was seen to me to be not a single star, but three together, which almost touch each other."[184]

Subsequent observations gave widely different perspectives, as the angle of tilt of the rings changed with time, providing additional blurred and confusing images. No one expected rings round a planet, and a bizarre range of theories persisted for some time, including one that Saturn had two pairs of satellites, each pair orbiting independently behind Saturn. It was not until 1659 that Christiaan Huygens proposed that all these different images could be explained by Saturn having a thin ring that was tilted in such a way that from Earth we saw it in varying orientations, including edge-on when it would be effectively invisible.

Over the intervening years we have been able to observe Saturn with ever increasing resolution, initially with larger and higher quality ground based telescopes, next with the Hubble space telescope from earth's orbit, and now with space probes sent to the planet that can actually fly through gaps in Saturn's rings. With each step we have learned more about the detailed structure of the rings. What started as a pair of "handles" has become a set of beautifully thin rings of dazzlingly fine structure, containing and interacting with numerous small moons in a highly complex manner.

Similarly, the recent Mars landers (autonomous mobile robots) are beginning to reveal the complexity of the Red Planet's surface.[185] While our knowledge of Saturn has been almost entirely sensed optically, the mobile robots on Mars' surface provide us with additional physical and chemical insights through their complex set of tools and experiments.

I once heard a famous British astronomer[186] state that we understand so much more about distant galaxies than we do about the Earth. Hearing his words, I immediately found myself imagining some intelligent life-form in a distant galaxy far far away making a similar comment while gazing in the rough direction of our own planet. It is easy to deceive ourselves into thinking that when we understand something, we have revealed the truth of its complexity, but it really means that we have found an economical set of descriptive rules that will suffice until we look closer.

Someone who clearly understood this was Sir Bernard Lovell.[187] In a BBC interview on the 50th anniversary of his famous Jodrell Bank radio telescope in 2007, he said; "I thought 20 years ago … we knew all that we wanted to know about the structure and evolution of the universe, and now we know almost nothing", a reflection on the fact that we now need new ideas such as dark energy and dark matter to explain what we now observe as we look more closely. So the more we learn, the more we know of our ignorance, so paradoxically our sense of ignorance comes from our knowledge. As the great physicist John Wheeler cautioned: "We live on an island surrounded by a sea of ignorance. As our island of knowledge grows, so does the shore of our ignorance."[188]

If you work in science it is easy to think that almost everything can be described through science. Well yes it can, but just as a map is not the place, a scientific description is not the whole thing, it is a reduced thing, reduced to simple rules, rules that work because they tell us nothing about what is subjective, even if that part might be most important to us as humans. "Does my bum look big in this?" is not a request for a rigorous objective observation, as I and many other scientists have found to our cost.

"How it Works" books and TV programs generally confine themselves to describing things that man has created. If we made it, we should know how it works, if we didn't, we are just surmising. It is true that we see descriptions of "how the human heart works", but note that the descriptions have become more and more complex throughout history as we have delved deeper and deeper into the mystery of this evolved biological organ. The heart used to be described as a simple pump, now with the aid of high resolution scanners we can describe the complexities of its fluid dynamics as the blood is pumped through its chambers, and the possible reasons why each part is shaped the way it is.

This is similar to our use of reverse engineering in espionage, where we analyse something such as a captured soviet jet engine, and try to deduce the reasoning behind every feature. The problem with biology is that the design team (i.e. biological evolution) has had many thousands of years of development experience, much longer than that of our recently educated scientific minds that are trying to understand it.

Big Headed

"I used to think that the brain was the most wonderful organ
in my body. Then I realized who was telling me this."

- Emo Philips[189]

If you want evidence that we confuse our personal explanations, with an objective reality of the universe we inhabit, just consider the following claim: "Of all the objects in the universe, the human brain is the most complex".[190] It is a nice punchy statement to begin an article on neuroscience or on the evolution of Homo sapiens, and many writers have used similar words to great effect. Note the certainty in the statement, no inclusion of the word "possibly" or a question mark. It is usually followed by more words describing the vast numbers of neurons and synapses in the human brain, and often comparing these numbers with the numbers of stars in the Milky Way. It is all aimed to imbue a feeling of: Wow! Isn't that incredible, aren't we just amazing! All very flattering, but wait a minute, it is *literally* incredible i.e. not to be believed!

What might be meant by "complex"? The dictionary offers an objective definition: "composed of many interconnected parts", and so "most complex" implies the greatest number of interconnected parts. So how about the brain of an elephant or a sperm whale? We don't even know how our own brain actually works, so we are guessing that the larger brains of other mammals are less complex, simply based on what we observe of their intellectual performance. If a system can be considered an object, then the rain forest can be considered an object, that must be pretty complex, especially when including the brains of the many tribal people and loggers, and what about the Internet including all its users, surely that must be a pretty complex object.

What about "in the universe"? Given how little we know beyond our own planet, it takes incredible arrogance to assume that there is nothing more complex out there in the infinities of the cosmos, since we cannot possibly know. Well, I hope you get my point: to suggest that the human brain is the most complex object in the universe is a completely meaningless statement.

The dictionary offers another definition for "complex": "So complicated or intricate as to be hard to understand or deal with". Now this is more useful, as it reveals that complexity is in the mind of the beholder, however much we may try to project complexity onto some system out there. When we complain that something is "too complicated", we really mean that we personally do not understand it, while still recognising that someone somewhere probably does (the tax return form for example).

While some writers constrain the statement to include only that which is currently known to mankind: "Human brains are the most complex objects in the *known* universe",[191] they still fail to take personal responsibility for their part in the perceived complexity. It is their (and our) failure to "understand" the human brain that makes it appear to be the most complex. We just assume that it is very complicated because we don't know how it works yet. The architectural complexity revealed to date by brain scans is relatively simple, due to the poor resolution of the techniques. We might even find it to be deceptively simple some day. Do you remember the incredible complexity of the earlier Mandelbrot image? If anyone had seen this image prior to the discovery of fractals, they would have assumed that it was the result of a highly complex process, whereas we now know that it was created by a very simple process repeated many times over.

Understanding involves conceptual models at many different levels. We can reduce the complexity of our problem solving by choosing an appropriate level. If I say that I understand something, it does not necessarily mean that I can control it or predict its behaviour. I may understand the Physics behind how my car works, yet still be unable to diagnose the problem when it refuses to start. Suppose that I was very very clever, and knew the details of the position and condition of every atom that my car is made of, would that help? Almost certainly not, as the sheer quantity of information would almost certainly prevent me finding a conceptual model at a suitable level within a reasonable time. Meanwhile, the garage mechanic who understood my car at a much simpler level, simply dried the car's ignition distributor and it started immediately.

Can we explain everything? Many people happily assume that given sufficient time our human minds will fully understand the (physical) universe. This view is common among us scientists, (especially physicists), who believe that we are entitled to know how the universe works. However, the complexity of any system is limited by the number of elements and the number of possible states of those elements. Consider the relative scale of one human brain with respect to all that exists within the universe: Our brain is infinitesimally simple in comparison! Any internal model of our universe cannot be more complex than the contents of a single skull.

Current estimates of the information capacity of our human brain are almost meaningless as we really don't know how it works yet. However, based on what is known of neurons and synapses, estimates range from a few Terabytes to a few Petabytes (which are a trillion Gigabytes). This last figure can conveniently be expressed as 10^{16} bits. This might seem quite large, but the information content of the universe has been estimated to be around 10^{120} bits of information, that's 10 followed by 120 zeros (so you can see the value of the maths shorthand!).[192] [193] So if we were to estimate the maximum theoretical fraction of the universe that we could know, it would be the ratio between these two figures, less than one part in 10 followed by more than a hundred zeros. I hope I have made my point.

Now it is just possible that the universe is an incredibly boring place with massive duplication and redundancy, such that the entire universe is no more complicated than my head. It is an attractive idea because it would mean that my mind could in principle contain a completely accurate representation of the universe, not just a grossly simplified model. The idea is certainly appealing to my ego as I might then be as smart as the creator! It is attractive to us scientists who would like to think that we will in due time be privy all of nature's secrets, but it is obviously wrong. If we are correct about the great scale of the universe, then it is likely that the complexity of the physical universe exceeds that of our puny minds, by a factor so large that we cannot even imagine that factor within our own minds.[194]

Throughout the history of science many have confidently predicted that in time all would be revealed, and even that we were approaching that point in time. I used to be intrigued and perplexed by this confidence, and then in an Aha! moment I suddenly realized the truth in their position. As each of us inhabits our own simulation of external reality (the world, the universe), then the specific universe that we have access to and inhabit, can contain no more information than can be contained within our single brain. The universe that we experience appears to be understandable because it is just our personal model, not the universe itself.

Whatever sensory experience we have derived from our contact with the external reality, must be integrated into a model whose size and detail is limited by the complexity of our human brain. Now to us the human brain seems incredibly complex, but it is trivial compared with the sum of all brains and all atoms in the known universe. Any predictions about the external universe must therefore be gross simplifications.

So the entire universe that I can "see" and experience, is a simulation running within the confines and limitations of my human brain. The universe I inhabit is no wider than my skull, or as the poet Emily Dickinson expressed it:

The Brain -- is wider than the Sky -
For -- put them side by side -
The one the other will contain
With ease -- and You -- beside.[195]

Throughout history there has been debate about the location of our Mind. Is it confined within our brain, bounded by our skull? Or does it extend out into the world around us and perhaps include things we interact with? If our entire experience of reality is "only" a simulation of external reality within our own brains, then this question completely disappears, as the concept of our Mind is then contained within this simulation. As such, our concept can extend to the limits of the universe (as the universe is a simulation running within our skull), or be confined within our conceptual model of our brain. Either way it all resides between our ears!

How much of the Universe should we expect to know?

Through careful observation we have developed a science of the universe. We then use this to confidently describe wide ranging aspects of space and time as predicted by our physical models. It is easy to imagine that we nearly understand it all, but our science has only been developed sufficiently to explain what we *have* observed, and *can* observe. We would like to believe that the fraction of the universe we have observed provides us with a reasonable description of everything that is. It is as if we are peering through a tiny keyhole in the doorway of a huge mansion, and making rash presumptions of what lies outside of our line of sight.

What fraction of the universe have we actually observed? Although we might think we can see it all, we are limited to a very narrow view of the universe. To see it all we would need to make observations from many different points in the universe. Most of our instantaneous observations of the cosmos have been through the limited "keyhole" of the Earth's diameter, around 13,000 km across. Because we orbit the Sun, throughout a year we sweep out a much longer baseline, 300 million km, giving us a somewhat wider "keyhole". This may sound wide but we need to compare it with the estimated diameter of the (visible) universe, roughly 5 times 10^{23} km.[196] So our "keyhole" is more than ten million million times narrower than our "mansion". Furthermore, our keyhole extends both vertically and horizontally so this ratio needs to be squared, making the fraction a hundred million million million million times smaller. Oh and I nearly forgot, this is only using the diameter of the universe that we can see! You get the point I hope. We ain't seen it all!

Secondly, what fraction of time have we observed? Man has observed the heavens for several thousand years, but we have only observed it with any accuracy within the last few hundred years. If we assume the age of universe to be 13.7 Billion Years, then we have only been able to observe the universe for about a tenth of a billionth of its span so far.

Now you might argue that we are able to observe times throughout our entire history, from shortly after the proposed "big bang", simply by looking at celestial objects over a vast range of distances. We can exploit the fact that light travels over vast distances at a the finite speed of light, so greater distance means earlier time, and we can measure the velocity of stars through the red shift in colour, due to the source of light moving away from the observer.[197] True, but for any one object that we observe, we have only been able to observe it for a comparatively short time. So we have only a very brief snapshot of experience of those recent "deep field" Hubble telescope images from the dawn of time.[198]

Nearer home there is still a lot that we have not explored of our own planet. Thanks to satellite imaging and Google Earth, we now have considerable visual knowledge of the Earth's surface, albeit with limited resolution. However, we remain largely ignorant of what lies beneath our oceans, and almost entirely ignorant of what lies beneath our feet, the body of the Earth itself.

Occasionally discoveries are made that reveal the magnitude of our ignorance. In 1901 an extraordinary geared mechanism was found by sponge divers in a wreck on the sea bed near the island of Antikythera. It is estimated to date from around 100 BC and it precedes any other known geared mechanisms of similar complexity by four thousand years. Only recently have we had the x-ray tools to investigate the internal structure in detail, revealing a highly complex mechanism which has 30 gears, and probably originally had more. It now appears to be a mechanical analogue computer, pre-programmed with the collected astronomical knowledge of the Ancient Greeks designed and built to predict future astronomical events.[199] [200]

The body of the Earth itself keeps more ancient secrets deeply buried. We know from drilling, that much of what lived on the surface now lies hidden beneath more recent rocks. Where buried strata returns to the surface, we are able to learn about long-extinct lifeforms from fossils, but the number of fossils and ancient skeletons yet to be discovered is likely to be vast compared with those we have found so far and built our historical theories upon. So our comfortable theories of the precise evolutionary path of man and mammals are always under threat of modification by new discoveries. We have limited evidence and construct a story that makes sense of what we have got. Sometimes a single fossil discovery demands a major shift in that story.

Recently, we have dived deep into the building blocks of human life: DNA. We used to think that the human 20,000 protein-coding genes which make up just 2% of the genome, fully described the human life-form, calling the rest of the DNA "Junk DNA" as it appeared to have no biological function. Having looked closer, we can now see that the so-called regulatory elements of the DNA, the non-gene sequences of DNA appear to have a major influence on how our genes act. It is now claimed that 80% of our genome performs a specific function, and I wouldn't want to risk disposing of any of the remaining 20%.[201]

So we must retain our humility in science. Every generation likes to think that they are close to getting the complete picture. But we can never know all that there is, we are simply constructing the best model we can, and it may not be complete truth, just the story so far, the best we can do based on what we do know.

Increasing complexity in technology

When we build something from component parts, the more parts we have and the greater the variety of parts, then the greater the possible complexity of what we can create. For example, if we have a small set of Lego building blocks,[202] which has only two different types of block and only a dozen of each, we will be quite limited in the variety of models we can construct with them. Conversely, we can construct almost anything we imagine provided we have very many blocks and/or a wide variety of types of blocks. The fewer the number of elements the greater the skill required to achieve a solution. If very many elements are available to us there are almost infinite ways that the goal can be achieved. You have probably seen large and highly realistic Lego models of all sorts of things.

In electronics and computing the growth in complexity over the last few decades is quite staggering. There are now a myriad of ways to achieve the same objective. When I was a teenage geek, transistors were a recent invention and hence were the dominant cost of many electronic construction projects. I marvelled at circuits which used a single transistor over again for multiple functions, such as the circuit for a "self-oscillating super-regenerative receiver" that I found in a book by the now famous Clive Sinclair.[203] [204] Nowadays multiple transistors in integrated circuits are incredibly cheap; a thousand million of them cost less than a pound, enabling the complexity of solutions to rise enormously. Simplicity is no longer a virtue in electronics, there are a myriad of ways of achieving a single design objective.

As an engineer, I always found great beauty in simple elegant solutions to problems. Throughout my career I practised electronic engineering and optical physics, yet felt that mechanical solutions to problems were the often most elegant. A single three dimensional piece of material could be formed in a way that performed a host of functions, such as the head of a Supadrive screw.[205] I knew that the design had been optimised to maximise function and minimise cost, and that every part of that shape was there for a reason. Perhaps the beauty of more complex solutions is more difficult for us to see because we cannot hold a conceptual model of it within our mind's eye.

In the world of software, early code writers had to be efficient. Three decades ago I had a home computer (BBC Micro) that could only address 16k (16,000) bits of memory. Charles Moir wrote a word processor for it called Wordwise. The design had to be highly optimised to be squeezed into such a small memory space, but the result was a word processor that worked as fast as my word processor today, and was essentially bug free. The whole program resided in just 16K of memory (EPROM), and Charles alone wrote it all, so he knew exactly what was in it.

Today, no one person knows what is in any current word processor or operating system. Extensive bits of old code persist in newer operating systems because no-one can be sure whether they perform some useful function or not. Many large computer programs are like cities built on the architectural ruins of a poorly understood bygone age, we readily conceal function with a facade, whether by the Mac or Windows computer interface, or the smooth plasterboard that covers the walls of a house built out of recycled rubbish.

Perhaps we will begin to view old software as important archaeological artefacts, concealing stories of those who built the foundations of today's huge towering edifices like Microsoft Office. We may suddenly realize that Windows 95 is almost extinct, and become interested in its family history. While today's archaeologists excavate ancient rubbish dumps, our future data archaeologists may "dig down" into old "waste" data in search of lost treasures from the past, piecing together fragments of code to try to reconstruct what no-one thought important to preserve.

Science and other Religions

We have explored rules and explanations from a scientific perspective, but how do they relate to religious ideas? Both science and religion offers explanations for the unexplained, but only science demands logical consistency. They all offer hypotheses for reality, but the various religions provide differing answers for some big existential questions. Science on the other hand, has little to contribute when we ask: "What do we experience after we die?", or "What is the point of our existence?"

Religious explanations are most often derived from interpretations of specific religious texts, and to be accepted through the faith of the follower when in conflict with others views. The extent of believers' acceptance of what is taught covers a wide spectrum, from being entirely metaphorical, through to the other extreme of a fundamental and literal interpretation. There is plenty of opportunity for interpretations to vary through the centuries, as very old texts are rarely unambiguous.

Because religions can provide answers to questions that are unanswerable through scientific method alone, they are able to provide comfort and certainty in an otherwise uncertain world, in times of grief for example. Conflicting ideas can be profoundly disquieting within religion, while those within science are exciting as they offer the possibility of yet greater enlightenment. So when science does not know something, it merely speculates and offers theories to be challenged. Science wields its surgical blade of reason, yet has no comforting bedside manner.

Mystery is the very essence of religion; while believers may claim to "know God", they would never claim to know all that is God. The few mystics that are found within most religions appear to have more in common with each other, than they do with the average religious follower. Perhaps, by focusing on the mystery and basic principle of spirituality, they avoid the clash of more literal ideas that come from their own religious creeds. In contrast, the ultimate aim of science is to annihilate mystery. Mystery is seen as only a temporary ignorance, a rallying sign to attract bright minds to dispel mystery through logical effort, or occasionally as a "Danger do not enter" sign when the mystery is too challenging.

Scientific hypotheses differ from those of religions, in that experiments shared between unbelievers and believers, can quite quickly bring consensus. Science is based on that key ritual; Experiments repeated by different observers lead us to the same result. However, that consensus can only be achieved by constraining what is observed through a formal language which assumes objectivity, and through the ritual of scientific method. While scientists from widely different fields can agree on the most things such as the observed physical laws, the only uniting consensus between all the various world religions is that there is a spiritual reality beyond science.

Consensus is a powerful force within society, both within science or religion, having the potential to eliminate conflict. The holy books of different religions contain many common philosophies when their texts are read as metaphors. Similarly, the teaching of science uses metaphors to convey the idea of things that are unimaginable. We happily talk about radio waves travelling through space using the metaphor of water waves, despite the fact that there is nothing waving (it is just empty space). Occasionally one dogmatic scientist argues that light is only particles (photons), while another that it is only waves. But these fundamentalists are rare, since most scientists realize that both these descriptions are merely metaphors that describe different aspects of light's behaviour.

Science progresses by stripping away all the superfluous detail in order to achieve consensus, but this kind of simplification is of less benefit to organised religions, which often compete by emphasising the differences between their creeds and beliefs. For evidence of this we need look no further than the recent bloody conflicts between Christian Protestants and Roman Catholics and between the Shi'a and Sunni Muslims. From an outsiders perspective it is difficult to understand why the greatest conflict should be between people with the closest and most similar religious teachings, as seen in the Irish "Troubles", and in the "Arab Spring". From the outside we see what both sides have in common, while those within see only the differences.

When ancient religious texts are interpreted literally, fundamentally different ideas can emerge, even from texts that are nominally derived from the same source. In the extreme, these ideas can lead to religious fundamentalism, where followers learn only their own religion's unique and narrow view of the world, with the consequence that they live in totally different worlds from other outsiders, and when these worlds collide there is considerable friction.

Throughout history, religions have provided many things of value to their followers; a sense of belonging and purpose, a physical place of community, and a stable structure for their lives. Religion also provides followers with a set of moral rules, to guide civilised behaviour. Indeed, some religious people believe that our moral sense comes *only* from religion, having been taught that immorality is the inevitable consequence of ungodliness (ignoring the history of violence perpetrated in the name of their own religion). However, if we only avoid sinning for fear of punishment in the afterlife or in anticipation of a great reward, we have no need to develop our own innate moral sense. Consequently, we might fear that a loss of God would lead to loss of control, with unimaginable consequences.

Evolutionary biologist Marc Hauser suggests that a moral sense is innate to humans, a direct consequence of our ability to predict what might happen in the future.[206] So we modify our behaviour now, in anticipation of a long term benefit, such as having a neighbour return a good deed at a later date, or going to heaven when we die. The "Ethic of Reciprocity"[207] is a cross-cultural ethical precept found in almost all world religions, the Christian version of which is: "Do unto others as you would have others do unto you".[208] So even without a religious creed, caring for our fellows is probably a reasonable investment strategy for any individual wanting a future within their community.

It is easy to associate so much of the world's suffering with religious intolerance, yet we should not forget that science has provided the tools: the nails, the knives, the guns and nuclear weapons. As for all the difficult human relationship problems, whether between individuals, religions or nations, science has yet to provide effective solutions. Over millennia science has transformed our material world, dramatically reducing physical hardship through technology. But what has it achieved in the field of human relationships? It has certainly made us more efficient spectators; we read novels, watch plays on TV, all exploring the same old relationship stories told throughout history. Is mankind making equal progress in relationship skills? Perhaps social networking via the Internet is bringing us closer? It is true that Facebook is shrinking our world, but as it shrinks we are losing sight of our physical neighbours. If a strong solar storm were to suddenly wipe out all electronic communications across the entire globe, we might suddenly remember where our bodies live, and rediscover our physical neighbours.[209]

This book reveals that our experience of the world in almost entirely a simulation in our own mind, and that we have a very restricted access to the reality that surrounds us in each moment. These are difficult ideas for many of us from the world of science, but they are surprisingly paralleled in some Eastern religions. Buddhists teach that everything is illusion, not meaning that nothing exists, but rather that we are living with what our minds have projected onto the world, rather than seeing the way things truly are.

Now from the scientific perspective of the learning bottleneck it seems that *almost* everything is illusion: If we take Jim Crowe's estimate of the information rate of our visual experience of 16 Terabits per second,[210] and compare it with the information rate that we can actually experience the reality around us (which you will see later is little more than 10 bits per second), we might claim that all except one part in 1000,000,000,000 (10^{12}) is illusion! So you see that Buddhism and Bottlenecks are closer than you might expect.

Buddhism is not the only Eastern religion that entertains such ideas. While exploring the ideas behind the bottleneck, I chanced upon "The Cosmos" by Swami Vivekananda,[211] and was shocked by the close alignment between the teachings of this Bengali intellectual, and the purely psychological and scientific ideas behind the bottleneck. Swami Vivekananda (1863-1902) was an Indian spiritual leader of the Hindu religion and a key figure in the introduction of Hindu philosophies of Vedanta and Yoga to Europe and America. He advocated basing religion on experience, scientific method and not creed, and taught that all religions are equal and God is inside everyone. His words reveal a remarkable insight into the psychology of human learning:[212]

"......Suppose I go into the street and see a dog. How do I know it is a dog? I refer it to my mind, and in my mind are groups of all my past experiences, arranged and pigeon-holed, as it were. As soon as a new impression comes, I take it up and refer it to some of the old pigeon-holes, and as soon as I find a group of the same impressions already existing, I place it in that group, and I am satisfied. I know it is a dog, because it coincides with the impressions already there. When I do not find the cognates of this new experience inside, I become dissatisfied. When, not finding the cognates of an impression, we become dissatisfied, this state of mind is called "ignorance"; but, when, finding the cognates of an impression already existing, we become satisfied, this is called "knowledge". When one apple fell, men became dissatisfied. Then gradually they found out the group. What was the group they found? That all apples fell, so they called it "gravitation". Now we see that without a fund of already existing experience, any new experience would be impossible, for there would be nothing to which to refer the new impression. ...."

Also:

"I, as I stand here, am the effect, the result, of all the infinite past which is tacked on to me..."

These statements of his are beautifully succinct descriptions of the consequence of the bottleneck on our experience of reality. So some Eastern religions seem to be open to these ideas. Judeo-Christian religions tend to be based around authoritarian priesthoods, with each religion rooted within a single doctrine, whereas some Eastern religions are more individual, more personal, so perhaps more accepting of a subjective reality.

Enlightenment contemplated

Throughout this book, I explore various ideas that we have about ourselves using a scientific approach, and in places I make comparisons with religious ideas. Most of the world's religions include the practice of meditation or prayer. Some teach that it is a way of transcending the ego and a key practice towards the ultimate goal of enlightenment.

In everyday life, a conscious and aware adult understands the many shades of emotions, and interprets what they are sensing in the present moment as part of a narrative with a remembered past and a possible future. In contrast, when someone is in contemplation they focus entirely within, to explore insights from what they have learned before. They withdraw attention from their senses to avoid distraction, so temporarily cease to learn anything new of the world around them. Nevertheless, they are open to learning new insights from whatever information is already within.

The state of enlightenment is sometimes described as a state of stillness in which the individual is fully aware of what their body senses in the very moment, yet does not judge these sensations in relation to what they already know. Within religions there are many who seek this rare state of quiet mind, with no past, no future, considering it to be the highest state a human being can achieve. But is it not also the everyday mental state of most animals? for we have no evidence that they concern themselves with yesterday or tomorrow.

Perhaps the state of bliss sought by humans on a spiritual path is simply the silent stillness of a mind taking a break from its daily chore of endlessly predicting the past and the future. Perhaps it is a way to experience the innocence of the new-born child, with everything to learn and no internal prejudged ideas of what to expect. If so, it offers a unique glimpse into the very root of the personal narrative that we otherwise inhabit in our daily life. Or maybe we are just parking up and switching off our noisy engine, our relentless predicting brain that takes so much of our energy, leaving us free to just breathe and take in the scenery.

We too were Gods for a brief time

Early humans had little expectation of being in control of what was around them, since they were at the mercy of more than just their fellow man and other predators, but also of flood, drought, pestilence, famine and other natural threats. It provided a fertile time for worship of deities that might provide protection.

As our civilisation developed, we have gradually gained more and more control over our lives. Our manual dexterity has enabled us to create complex solutions to problems, initially over problems whose size was of similar scale to ourselves. We went on to develop the tools to extend the scale our problem solving, both towards the microscopic (bacteria, transistors) and macroscopic (the pyramids, dams). Our progress continued towards the pinnacle of the Moon landings in 1969, when it seemed that science had given us the power to do anything we chose: Today the Moon, tomorrow the Stars.

In the '60s many of us bought into this vision. Anything seemed possible, with mankind leading the way to a beautiful future, building space cities on colonised worlds, spreading our western ideology across the universe. We had become intoxicated with our own powers and had a naive confidence in our ability to fix global problems such as famine and disease. In 1971 President Nixon declared war on cancer, promising that it would be won within a decade, hoping to mirror the success of President Kennedy's earlier programme to put men on the Moon.

But we had forgotten just how many major Earth events such as earthquakes, tsunamis, volcanic eruptions, and asteroid strikes had occurred in our planet's recent history. Today we have come to realize that we are not in control of our planet. Those major cataclysms, floods, droughts, tornadoes and human conflicts do not disappear at the sight of our science or the might of our financial resources. We may fantasise about deflecting an asteroid, or colonising another world to escape what we have done to this one, but if you do the sums there is little chance of either. So we have now gone full circle. We briefly tasted the heady authority of being Gods of all we surveyed, but now are back to our rightful place on this planet; doing the best we can on an uncertain world, a world that we fundamentally cannot control yet still have the power to screw up.

Throughout this chapter we have seen that there is a fundamental human drive to create rules and explanations in all areas of our lives. We convert what we sense and learn about the world into useful rules and explanations that enable us to predict things. These rules and explanations are the most powerful tools we humans develop, for almost everything else that we do depends on them.

In fields such as medicine and religion, we allow multiple conflicting explanations to coexist, while in sciences such as physics, differing explanations ruthlessly compete to extinguish all other competition. The unique nature of our scientific explanations has frequently led to ambitious claims that we nearly understand it all. Such overconfidence is easily understood when we remember that we cannot create an idea of the universe that is any more detailed than the complexity of our much simpler human brain.

Rules and explanations allow us to simplify unmanageable complexity, and enable us to predict beyond what we have experienced so far. Yet there is a paradox in that simple rules can themselves create incredible complexity and beauty. However, we must be cautious with perceived simplicity, for it is often merely a measure of our ignorance, and old explanations can easily blind us to what is new. We may come to trust explanations so much that we forget that the explanation is not the thing itself. However much we might feel impelled to do so, we cannot develop a useful rule from a single unique experience, we need sensations to be repeated.

We may be familiar with the idea of *conscious* rules and explanations; however, our mind also *unconsciously* creates explanations for absolutely everything we sense, as demonstrated by the earlier figure of the Necker cube. This is the principle mechanism behind many visual illusions. These unconscious explanations are simplifications of what our senses detect, yet may be sufficient to predict and hence anticipate most future sensations.

Through the first part of this book I have described the many ways in which our rate of learning is limited, and suggested that our learning speed can never ever exceed a few tens of bits per second as an absolute maximum. I have also shown how our sense of vision is based within our imagination, as is equally true of all our senses. I have primarily focused on vision, as this is the sense that we usually assume provides us with the greatest information. It is also where my journey began, when I explored the possibilities of the ultimate HiFi television display.

You may by now be thinking that this is all mere speculation, that the solid reality that you see before you is real, not a figment of your imagination. If like me, you need solid evidence for a wild idea, then in Part Two, I will reveal the hard scientific evidence for the bottleneck, and explore some of the immediate practical implications.

Part 2

The Objective Evidence

Chapter Five

The evidence for what we take in

*"The great tragedy of Science,
the slaying of a beautiful hypothesis by an ugly fact"*
- Thomas. H. Huxley[213]

*"For me, it is far better to grasp the Universe as it really is
than to persist in delusion, however satisfying and reassuring"*
- Carl Sagan[214]

I have revealed the idea of the bottleneck, the observation that the rate at which we can learn is very constrained. Now let us examine the evidence in more detail, look at the actual numbers expressed in bits per second.

The human mind is an incredible thing. However, we have such respect for it, that we often credit it with capabilities far in excess of reality. For example, it is commonly believed that we have photographic memories: that we memorise everything that our eyes see, every image that falls upon our retina in great spatial and temporal detail, and that under appropriate conditions (for example, under hypnosis), we might retrieve any of this information.

There is no real evidence to support this idea, yet many people still believe that every experience that our senses have ever sensed is accurately retained somewhere inside our mind, even if we have not yet been able to access it. One reason for this delusion is that when asked to recall a recent event, we often remember it in great detail, but most of the detail we recall is derived from many much earlier experiences, and may be largely erroneous in the context of the recent event. Eye witnesses to a crime often strongly disagree about major details of the observed suspect, e.g. whether or not the suspect had a beard, or what they were wearing.

The development of information theory in the late 1940's inspired many to try to apply more quantitative ideas to human perception and communication. At last we could measure the performance of many diverse human tasks in terms of an equivalent information rate, using a single unambiguous measurement unit of bits per second. When subjects were measured performing a range of tasks and the results converted into bit rates, most researchers were surprised at just how low the figures turned out to be, especially when compared with what was known about the intrinsic capability of our eyes and ears themselves.[215] [216] Indeed the measured bit rates were about twelve orders of magnitude smaller than the estimate referred to earlier (That's a million, million times smaller!).[217] Nevertheless, there is considerable evidence to support this surprisingly low figure as you will soon see.

There are two directions of human communication: Outward transmission of information such as when speaking, typing, or playing the piano, and inward when we are a receiver of information, such as listening or reading, and measurements suggest that rates for transmitting or receiving information are remarkably similar. The literature contains several estimates as follows: Quastler and Wulff measured various human skills: Typing: 15 bits per second, Piano playing: up to 22 bits per second, Speech typically 18 bits per second (but can be as high as 26 bits per second), Silent reading was estimated as high as 44 bits per second.[218]

Karl Küpfmüller published similar estimates of information-rate including proof-reading at 18 bits per second (corresponding to a record speed of 200 Words Per Minute).[219] He observed that "All the instances in the human organism that take part in processing messages seem to be designed to the upper limit of 50 bits/sec". Why should this be? That is a very good question and one which is explored in this book. The fact that transmitting and receiving rates are similar to each other might be explained as a simple consequence of evolution, there being no advantage in one being any faster than the other, but why so slow?

All measurements of information rate that involve language, are subject to errors in estimating the degree of redundancy involved, therefore measurements that do not involve language are likely to be more accurate. Klemmer and Muller performed experiments where they could vary the applied information rate and measure the response.[220] They provided stimuli consisting of 5 lights arranged in an arc, and a corresponding set of telegraph keys was arranged under the subject's fingers. The subject was asked to press the keys corresponding to those lights which were on. When the stimulus rate was varied from 2 to 5 per second, the "transmitted" information rate peaked at about 10 bits per second, but fell off rapidly when the lights were switched faster, due to the increased proportion of errors.

This experiment is neat in that it measures data-in and data-out together with the errors, to determine the maximum information capacity of the human subject, their "throughput". The limiting mechanism might be due to any, or all of the processes in the chain: observing the position of the illuminated lights, deciding on an action, or pressing the key, but what is notable is that they show a limited throughput, a bottleneck, similar in value to that achieved in many very different experimental situations.

Around the same time, Helmuth Frank proposed that there is an information capacity of consciousness of 16 bits per second.[221] His estimate is based the idea of the smallest space of time that we can experience, which he called a "subjective time quantum" or a "psychological moment". He suggested that this is related to the minimum frequency that we can hear sounds, and the maximum image frame rate to achieve fusion of flickering images.

While I am very prepared to accept the ideas of a limited rate at which our brain can integrate new information, I have found no evidence that this limit is in any way caused by our sensors. Furthermore, as we are far from being clear what is "consciousness", or where its boundaries are, it seems fruitless to discuss its information capacity in bits per second.

In 1948 Claude Elwood Shannon published his now famous paper on information theory.[222] His work was so pivotal that he is now recognised as "the father of information theory". He defined information in mathematical terms and how it can be communicated in the presence of noise. What until then had been considered as quite distinct modes of communication, the telegraph, telephone, radio and television, were then unified in a single theoretical framework.

Though his work was focused on methods of electrical and electronic communication, it immediately inspired others to explore its implications across a wide range of fields. Psychologists were initially excited by this new tool and much of the published work on human bit rates followed shortly after Shannon's publication, but enthusiasm for such investigations gradually waned.[223]

The reasons I believe are twofold: Firstly, to those who simply wanted to attribute the richness of perception to our moment by moment experience, the tiny bit rates that they measured made no sense so were ignored. Secondly, to the more broad-minded researchers who were trying gain insight into the internal processes of the human mind, these low figures merely emphasised that they needed to direct their efforts towards developing new models of the perception processes within the brain such as "Chunking", hoping to provide insights into our brain architecture.

Chunking is the process whereby our short-term memory appears to be constrained to process information in chunks of a quite limited number of items, around half a dozen. When faced with multiple choices, the delay in responding increases whenever the subject is faced with more than this approximate number of options. This effect was described in the notable paper: "The magical number seven, plus or minus two: Some limits on our capacity for processing information", by Miller.[224] For these kinds of investigations, Shannon's methods were too simplistic, however, for people like me who are determined to learn about actual human learning performance, rather than the internal architecture of the human brain, these early measurements remain as valid indicators of a fundamental limit to human learning.

Some have tried to explain away the low bit rate figures that have been measured by suggesting that they may conceal a much larger information capacity because the human subjects have more choices than those set by the experimenter, such as being able to "respond to a knock on the door". But this is a misunderstanding, the measured bit rates may be low, but even these rates can only achieved when the subject gives the task their full attention. Any distractions cause the measured rates to fall dramatically, and recent work on inattentional blindness (described in chapter two) has revealed just how blind we are to other stimuli in such highly focused situations.[225]

In Tor Nørretranders' fascinating book: "The User Illusion: Cutting Consciousness Down to Size"[226], Tor makes the case for a limit to the *conscious* bit rate of around 16 bits per second (as suggested by Helmuth Frank). However, there is one absolutely crucial difference between Tor's conclusions, and mine in this book. He softens the impact of this shockingly low information rate by asserting that we have a very much larger *subconscious* human interface capacity, such that "A million times more bits enter our heads than consciousness perceives".[227] He proposes that much more information is pouring in unnoticed, to reside somewhere within our memory, information that we might access at a later time.

This is a seductively attractive idea, allowing us to maintain the illusion that we are intimately and immediately connected with the present world around us, even if our conscious mind is not aware of it. However, despite searching far and wide I have failed to find any evidence for this assertion that stands up to scrutiny. Yes, it is true that we absorb significant information while our conscious attention is distracted, but I cannot find any evidence to suggest that it ever adds up to more bits per second can be than achieved by giving something our full conscious attention, i.e. no more than a few tens of bits per second.

How narrow is the language Bottleneck?

Language is key. It is the way we package information in order to communicate from one human mind to another through some physical communication channel. While simple creatures have little detail to communicate, we humans need a channel that can communicate a wide variety of ideas without significant errors. Evolution has provided most of us with the basic equipment for communicating, using hand gestures, by speaking and by making music. Once the information is no longer just our thoughts but is within the physical domain, the channel may be further encoded to optimise communication over some humanly devised innovation, such as smoke signals, heliograph, written text, braille, telegraph, telephone, radio, satellite, fibre optics, or the World Wide Web.

Early innovations in communication technology had far lower information capacity than that of human language and so presented us with an "information bottleneck" due to the technology itself. For example, it was impossible to express and therefore communicate a complex message using a signal fire. Messages had to be brief and succinct. However, the last century has brought incredible progress in communication technology; today a single hair-thin optical fibre can carry many millions of people's phone conversations simultaneously on a single beam of light. Now we can be as verbose and long-winded as we like. All this progress has been made over an extremely short timescale when compared with that of human evolution.

Human language has evolved to contain a high level of redundancy, meaning that the information is in some sense duplicated. This enables us to maintain effective communication in the presence of noise and other distractions including competing voices. Because of this redundancy, we can accurately predict missing letters and even words in most messages.

Claude Shannon applied his information theory to calculate the information content of printed English text.[228] His work provided great insights into redundancy and the statistical nature of communication languages.

He used the following examples to illustrate that our use of letters in language is very predictable: This next piece of text was generated using random letters, but where the frequency of use of the letters was adjusted to be the same as the average of their use in the English language, so the letter "E" is the most frequent:

OCRO HLI RGWR NMIELWIS EU LL NBNESEBYA TH EEI ALHENHTTPA OOBTTVA NAH BRL

The following text was generated in a similar way, but in addition the selection of each letter was based on its likelihood depending on the two preceding letters:

IN NO IST LAT WHEY CRATICT FROURE BIRS GROCID PONDENOME OF DEMONSTURES OF THE REPTAGIN IS REGOACTIONA OF CRE

This looks more like English, and is actually easier for an English speaking typist to type, yet it is no more a piece of English text than the first piece. It just has similar statistics for the numbers and positions of letters. Incidentally, I note that as I typed this, my spell-checker was happy with almost half of the words!

Some English words are much more frequent than others. For example, in a collection of a million words of text in general use in the USA in 1961.[229], the word "the" is the most frequently occurring word, and alone accounts for nearly 7% of all word occurrences. The second most commonplace word "of", accounts for slightly over 3.5% of words, followed by the word "and". (I just did a quick analysis of the text in this book and it shows that the most common words I have used are "the", followed by "of", "to", "a", "and" in descending frequency of occurrence.)

The following piece of text was randomly generated by simply applying knowledge of the statistics and positional rules of English words:

THE HEAD AND IN FRONTAL ATTACK ON AN ENGLISH WRITER THAT THE CHARACTER OF THIS POINT IS THEREFORE ANOTHER METHOD FOR THE LETTERS THAT THE TIME OF WHO EVER TOLD THE PROBLEM FOR AN UNEXPECTED.

This almost looks like intelligent text yet it nevertheless has still been generated automatically from a completely random input, but with extensive use of knowledge of English language.

All this shows that written text contains a high level of redundancy. Shannon measured the ability of human subjects to guess successive characters in text, and from this estimated the information content to be somewhere between 0.6 and 1.3 bits per character of the alphabet. Later work refined this figure to 1.1 bits per character. This is far less than the 4.7 bits required to define a single character out of an alphabet of 26 characters plus a space.[230] So here is an explanation of Predictive Text half a century before it became commonplace on our mobile phones.

Predicting what is likely, becomes more accurate as we extend the number of characters and words that are considered. In the previous example, we know that "FOR AN" is more likely than "AN FOR", though the text generated did not use any knowledge of likely relationships between words. Shannon's figures for bits per character could be even lower if the total context of a message were taken into account. You can probably think of times when you struggled to understand many words in an overheard conversation, until you recognised the context, and then suddenly it made sense. Equally when we are trying to read some almost unintelligible handwriting, recognising one word can lead to an unravelling of the whole sentence.

When we use an eye tracker to monitor our point of gaze while reading, we can observe that our point of gaze jumps from word to word along a line of text. We skip over most of the simple words like "the" and "of", as the text can be understood without them; they can be inferred. But every so often our point of gaze jumps back along the line, back several words enabling us to re-read a difficult word. It is likely that our mind has suddenly realized that it has failed to make sense of the sentence and goes back to correct a misread word (mostly subconsciously). So we can read faster if we allow ourselves to make a few errors that can be picked up later and corrected. The task of reading random words is very significantly slower than with regular prose as we do not know what to expect.

Let us now use this 1.1 bit per character figure to calculate the speed of human communication as an information rate in bits per second. This is typically characterised in Words Per Minute (WPM), with an assumed average of five characters per word.[231] So for example, a speed of 120 WPM would be 120 x 5/60 = 10 characters per second, and using the above estimate of 1.1 bit per character, this would be 11 bits per second.

Although the first examples above were based on the characters of the written alphabet, the latter example comprised of English words could equally well be written or spoken. Similar information rates have been found to apply to verbal language. So what information rate can we absorb through listening to speech? Audio-books generally "speak" at around 150 WPM, which corresponds to about nearly 14 bits per second. People can read text aloud at twice this rate, but it is very difficult to determine the degree of redundancy and the real error rate when reading material in which much is familiar to the reader. Pierce & Karlin of Bell Labs concluded that 43 bits per second can be transmitted under certain conditions and that the speed of word recognition appears to be a more severe limiting factor than the physiology of articulation.[232]

Some of these information rates for language are somewhat faster than those measured for other tasks that I will discuss later. This might suggest that our brain is more highly optimised for language, as it has been such a key factor in the development of modern humans. However, it is more likely that the estimates of language redundancy used in the calculation may be too low. Of course the redundancy we describe only applies when we are familiar with a language. When we first encounter a language that is foreign to us, the communication rate becomes very low, and if we are multilingual, we must spot which language is being used before we can apply our knowledge of redundancy.

Many years ago during the time of the Cold War, I attended a big technical conference in California. It was one with several concurrent sessions of lectures on different topics running simultaneously in adjacent conference rooms, each with a tight programme of fifteen minute talks. Sometimes it was necessary to duck out of one session and quickly transfer to another room to hear a talk of particular interest. On this occasion a Russian speaker was due to give a talk in a different session from the one I was in. It was to be one of the highlights of the conference for me. It was rare for Soviet scientists to get permission to present at western conferences at that time, so I was keen to hear his talk. I rushed between conference rooms and took my seat just as the Soviet speaker was introduced by the chairperson as "bla bla bla.......from the University of Moscow".

As he started talking, I sat there for several minutes completely failing to understand a word he said. I made allowances for his unfamiliarity with English, and used all my experience of Russian accents (acquired from dialogue in recent spy films), but all to no effect. Then my attention was drawn to his appearance; he had long curly red hair, very unusual for a Russian I thought. In truth he looked remarkably like the Scottish comedian Billy Connolly!, and then the penny suddenly dropped. The Soviet speaker I had expected was a "no show" as usual (he hadn't managed to get his family out I guess). The chairperson had therefore moved straight on to the next speaker in the programme, who was from the University of Glasgow (the chairperson had pronounced it "glass cow" not "moss cow"). Suddenly as if by magic I could understand almost every word despite the speaker's broad Glaswegian accent. It was a remarkable lesson for me. I had engaged the wrong decoder in my head, used the wrong language redundancy information. As soon as I had correctly identified the language, it was easy to understand.

Sometimes language is misheard, but in a way that still makes sense to us. This phenomenon is known as a Mondegreen, the mishearing or misinterpretation of a phrase in a way that gives it a new meaning. It is most commonly applied to a misheard and subsequently misremembered line in a poem or a lyric in a song, many of which are particularly hilarious for all except the person who naively repeats one.

Speed Reading

Many of you will have heard the claims of "Speed reading". Does it really work? My favourite quote on Speed Reading by Woody Allen suggests that speed is often at the expense of accuracy; "I took a speed reading course and read "War and Peace" in twenty minutes. It involves Russia". However, inexperienced readers will often read at a rate significantly slower than appropriate to the material being read, so for these people a little training can improve their performance without losing accuracy. Research on reading rate indicates that reading for comprehension is best achieved at 200-350 words per minute (WPM), and has been found to be constant for all competent readers.[233] When the reading rate is increased to 400 WPM, comprehension drops to below 50%.[234] Research conducted on rapid reading courses, indicates that they are actually teaching a limited kind of skimming, and that speed readers are poor at judging their own level of comprehension.[235] Skimming can be learned easily and involves reading at a rapid rate for the purpose of searching rather than comprehension, and there is evidence that skimmers had a higher rate of comprehension than trained speed readers when reading difficult material.

Reading by touch

For those who are blind, Braille provided one of the only ways that they could read until recently.[236] Our sense of touch is potentially quite powerful as it has the possibility of sensing several simultaneous sensations in parallel. The Braille alphabet and language is an example of information communicating with our conscious mind via touch. It was first developed in 1824 by a fifteen year old blind French student named Louis Braille, who wanted a better way to read and write. The raised dot system that he invented grew out of another code; "night writing", a code which had been invented to let soldiers share secret information on the battlefield without having to speak.

The average Braille reading speed is about 125 WPM, and some Braille readers develop a speed of 200. This compares well with the average reading rate for English text in print of between 200 and 250 WPM. Braille readers can read faster when using fingers from both hands, but it appears that they are rarely using both simultaneously. For most Braille readers, when one finger was on a letter, the other finger was on the gap between letters or a space between words. With the advent of voice synthesis as an alternative to Braille, most blind people report that they can read much quicker with the synthesised voice, and of course it saves them having to learn the Braille language.

Measure for measure

When we consider how we might accurately measure the width of our learning bottleneck, the maximum information rate that we can absorb from the world around us, we find that there is an experimental problem. Ideally we would want to monitor and measure what happens inside the brain, but for our purposes that is impossible: We need to monitor what reaches our conscious mind but there is still much debate about what consciousness is and where it resides, and we certainly don't know how to connect any instrumentation to it. Furthermore, whatever we might use as a measurement technique must have an information capacity greater than that which we want to measure (otherwise it would artificially limit the measurement).

Modern brain imaging techniques are providing ever greater insights into the large scale architecture of the brain, but they do not provide a means of measuring the rate at which we acquire new knowledge. They are neither sufficiently localised nor fast enough. We just don't know how to make a meaningful connection to the information contained within the brain.

However, our language provides us with a means of reporting back, to tell just what has reached our conscious mind. But if we provide a continuous stimulus and use language to report back continuously, then language itself might then be the bottleneck of that experiment. However, we can use a burst mode: Expose the subject to a burst of stimulus of limited duration, and subsequently get them to report back, but over a longer time scale (assuming that the stimulus itself is not language).

As we have seen, the maximum information rates associated with communicating via language are not that dissimilar to the maximum rates measured for other tasks. This suggests that there is a fundamental limit to the rate at which we can integrate new knowledge into our internal model, and that there has been no benefit for language to have evolved to exceed that limit. Could this explain Karl Küpfmüller's earlier observation that 50 bits per second appears to be a general limit? There is also an alternative possibility: that all novel tasks require the process of language, and that language itself is the constraint. However, in the next chapter I will show similar evidence from activities that are not dependent on language.

The speed that people speak does vary from place to place (Farming country versus New York), but not by a huge amount, and it is interesting to speculate whether speaking speeds have increased to any significant degree over a thousand years. There might be other reasons for its comparative constancy, such as physical constraints of the jaw, and tongue. Smaller lighter jaws could move faster due to their lower inertia, but we see little evidence that people with smaller jaws are able to speak faster and hence communicate faster.

So let's explore how we might measure this learning bottleneck experimentally. We might use the human subject as an information translator, where we measure the information rate by passing information In and Out of the human mind. If we ensure that the task requires a change of format, then we can avoid the possibility that it is simple "parroting". However, if the format change is complex and requires significant mental processing, then we might expect the overall speed to be slowed. Simultaneous translation would be an example of fast continuous format change.

So to make a meaningful assessment of the human capacity for learning new information, then we need data from tasks that meet the following criteria:

1. One in which we can measure the novel component of the information flow unambiguously, i.e. distinguish what is truly new, from what was learned previously.

2. It must be quantifiable, e.g. in bits per second, not just hearsay. It should exclude tasks that include unquantifiable redundancy.

3. One that requires the involvement of the conscious mind (as that is what we are trying to reach), and is not just a simple reflex.

4. Where the task of the unconscious mind is sufficiently simple that the resulting performance is limited by our human input / output interface, and not dominated by delays caused by the complexity of the associated intellectual task.

5. Sufficiently long duration that it is representative of our long term learning capability (there is evidence that memories of very short exposures to information are stretched by persistence of vision and mental "buffering", as we will see later).

6. One in which we are not just measuring the limited information rate due to language itself.

The first two requirements are difficult to quantify for normal spoken and written language, because we do not know what is novel and what is already known. We would expect large errors in estimating the amount of redundancy in the content. If the message were just a string of random words, we would expect all the measured rates to fall dramatically.

Bring on the champions

If you want to discover the extreme limits of human performance, make it a contest, a competition. World Athletics Championships and the Olympics bring out the very best in competitive people. Individuals devote enormous time and effort training for these events and exploring different techniques. As a consequence the achievements of the top performers are usually very closely matched - often within just a few percent - reflecting some fundamental properties of human beings and their physiology. For example, here is a graph I plotted of the fastest human running speeds versus duration, derived from published men's world athletic records.

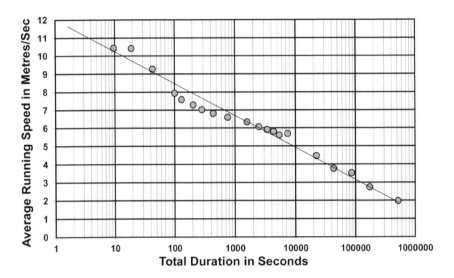

Figure 22: Record running speeds versus event duration.
(Male athletes, from 1 second to 6 days!)

It is interesting to note that between the fastest ever sprint, and a full marathon, the record speeds vary by less than a factor of two, so it would appear that we have evolved to be able to run remarkably long distances. Although the data points fall along a smooth curve, they correspond to many different individuals. The performance of one such individual will only be a curve peaking at the duration of their speciality, their trained event. Sprinters don't make good marathon runners!

The limits we see here are primarily those determined by the human physique, optimised by training. Over the years, record running speeds have improved through better training and diet, but not by a large percentage. Indeed, if a single physical athlete claimed to have outperformed their peers by a big margin, it would immediately raise suspicion of cheating or error, and as we will see later, the same is true for record breaking *mental* athletes.

So much for physical athletes, but what about competitive events for *mental* athletes? We already have many such events: TV is full of quiz programmes such as Mastermind. These test the speed of recall but not the speed of learning. A participant is generally allowed unlimited time to learn a large amount of information, and then competitively tested on how fast they can retrieve some fact.

The events measure the subjects' ability to access their mental database, and recall information which may have been acquired over many years. The quantity of information traversing the human interface is usually small in either direction: Question: "What is the capital city of France?"...Answer: "Paris". The mental database size is usually vast. Many exams are of similar format, as they are far easier to mark or score than exams which measure abilities such as creativity or comprehension.

So how about a contest to see who can absorb the highest information rate? One might imagine a set of Olympic style events, in which participants compete with each other to prove that they are the fastest at learning novel information, measured by testing how many bits of information they can learn in a given duration. These would be the requirements:

1/. Information In (made available to the senses).

2/. Integration with the subject's internal model (easiest proved by a change of format)

3/. Confirmed by subsequent information Out, recalled over a longer duration.

One might allow competitors a wide choice of formats: numbers, binary, random text, perhaps even images that are random matrices of squares, but whatever format is used, the scores must be capable of being unambiguously characterised in bits per second.

Such events might serve a useful purpose, quite apart from enabling us to achieve a valid estimate of the limits to how much information humans can take in. They could exploit people's competitive nature to find techniques for optimum "learning" and observing, based on results for different time scales and information formats. As with running events, there might be a range of events with different durations allowing competitors to choose their optimum duration, which would reveal something of the sensitivity to time scales.

Record Breakers

I was delighted to discover that a community of mental athletes already exists, and that they regularly compete against each other in professionally organised meetings such as the World Memory Championships. In various events competitors memorise as much information as possible within a given period of time.[237] What these people can do with their minds is all the more amazing to me, as I find it difficult to remember a single phone number that I have just been told. In this arena I am merely a fascinated spectator, and would not dream of being able to compete.

The most popular format in these championships is for the competitor to memorise a sequence of information within a fixed duration. This is then followed by their subsequent recall of that information from their memory over a longer more relaxed period of time to confirm the accurate completion of the preceding memory task. Many kinds of information are used in a range of different events: numbers, text, packs of playing cards, and random patterns.

The organisers and competitors merely need events that present the same degree of difficulty when they are re-run on different occasions, whereas I am specifically interested in the performances that can readily be characterised in bits per second. I need figures for bit rates that are beyond dispute. As it is difficult to precisely calculate the bits per second for either words or images, I have focused on the world records for the events using decimal and binary numbers, and packs of cards.

I can readily calculate the number of bits required to describe each symbol as follows: In information theory, information is related mathematically to uncertainty; it takes more information to specify an item from many possibilities, than from a few possibilities. As the number of alternatives increase, more bits are required to select one of them. The number of bits required is the logarithm, to the base 2, of the number of alternatives. So for dice, there are six possibilities for a die, and the number of bits required to identify each face or number on the die is $\log_2 6 = 2.58$ bits/symbol. For identifying one card within a pack of 52 playing cards is: $\log_2 52 = 5.7$ bits/symbol. Thus, for the die three yes/no questions will unambiguously determine the number, and six yes/no questions will identify a playing card.[238]

So the number of bits per memorised character is the binary logarithm of the number of possibilities (= $\log_2 N$), where N is the number of different symbols in the set. For binary numbers, just ones and zeros, only a single bit per symbol is needed, while 3.3 bits are required to specify each decimal number.

Now you may be thinking, how can we have fractions of bits? You are right; we do need a whole number of bits to define a single symbol. Rounding this up to 4 bits would work for numbers 1-10, (and would also allow us to specify up to a total of 16 possible symbols (2^4)). However, if we are calculating the information content of a large number of symbols, we can average out these fractions to produce whole numbers of bits. So a ten digit number has an information content of 37 whole bits (10×3.7). Knowing how many symbols are memorised in the time allowed enables me to calculate a bit rate corresponding to each record.

I collected all the appropriate records data (See Appendix 2), and plotted their corresponding information rates versus memorising duration, on a single graph as follows:

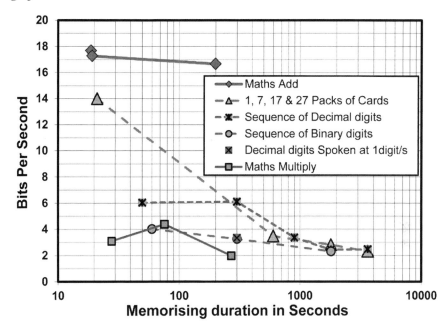

Figure 23: Bits per second calculated for a wide range of world record memory contests, plotted versus duration. Note that highest bit rates were achieved for shorter durations and for simpler tasks.

When I first plotted this data I was astounded to find that the points for many different events and symbol types fell close to a smooth curve, especially for the longer durations. This is where it helps to use data from competitive athletes, as it allows us to see the limits of human biology, beyond the laziness and boredom that impedes mortals such as myself.

My primary goal is finding evidence of the ultimate limit of absorbing novel information, so you might expect the only records of interest would be the ones with the highest bit rates which also happen to be for short durations. However, we will briefly explore the other records because they provide insight into the more commonplace scenarios in life, where the process of learning information from outside competes with an internal mental process, in this case memorising.

Our memory athletes perform a sequence of tasks: First; taking in information, Second; storing it in memory, and Thirdly; subsequently recalling what was memorised, but under less time pressure. Compare the difference in difficulty in memorising a continual sequence of numbers over just 1 minute with a similar task over 30 minutes. It is obviously much harder to remember a longer sequence of numbers. As the duration increases, the total number of symbols to be remembered increases proportionately and hence so does the complexity of the mental storage task.

We do not know the relative proportions of the workload of the two parts of the task, but the increased burden of the memorising is likely to compete for mental resources with the basic learning process (via the bottleneck), and hence reduce the measured bit rate for longer durations. (In other words, while the competitor is thinking about memorising, they are not observing what is before their eyes). This is exactly what we see in this graph of various world records in bits per second versus the event duration. The speed of human learning falls with duration, (as does the maximum human running speed), but not to a great extent. For example for the task of memorising binary numbers, the difference between the bit rates for the 1 minute record and the 30 minute record is less than a factor of two. These figures clearly show that the rate that we can learn, falls with the duration of the "lesson", as every teacher knows.

We also see a trend towards a record value of between 10 and 20 bits per second as we look at shorter durations. The figure of nearly 15 bits per second for memorising a single pack of playing cards stands out well above the tasks of memorising digits. Perhaps we have evolved to recognise complex images faster than we can recognise numbers, a comparatively recently developed skill in our evolutionary history. It is worth noting that Ben Pridmore one of the world's fastest card memorisers achieves slightly faster performance by memorising 2 cards at a time.

The surprising fact revealed by this graph is that competitions to memorise very different types of information produce such similar results when expressed in bits per second. This is especially true for the longer duration events where the memory task becomes huge. There we see the information rates tightly clustered around 2.5 bits per second. So for similar durations the maximum number of bits of information that can be remembered is similar whether the task is memorising playing cards, decimal or binary digits. This may be a consequence of competitors using a similar memorising technique for remembering these different types of symbol, as we will see later.

We should not forget that these competitions demand an error rate that is extremely low or zero. It is likely that the bit rates achieved would be higher if more errors were allowed. It is also likely that for zero errors this constraint would become more significant for the longer duration tasks, simply because the accuracy required would be correspondingly greater.

There is one data point that I have deliberately not plotted: In 2006 Andriy Slyusarchuk claimed to have memorised 5100 decimal digits in just 1 minute 57 seconds. This gives a figure of nearly 145 bits per second for a duration where we would expect a maximum of 6 bits per second, so 24 times faster. That is equivalent to a runner claiming to run a mile in ten seconds, so one would require a well monitored result before including it in any scientific study. It is reported that he refused to participate in the supervised World Memory Championships despite being promised $40,000 if he broke the officially ratified memory record.[239] [240]

Memorising a sequence of symbols is not a trivial task and one that becomes progressively more difficult for longer sequences, but there are easier competitive tasks that can be done with the mind. The competitive field of "speed maths" provides us with a few record results which I have also plotted on the graph. Here the task requires a mental calculation, such as adding together a sequence of digits, but only the result, the sum, needs to be memorised and carried forward as new information comes in. So for example the task of adding 100 random decimal digits only requires a number of value around 500 (on average) to be memorised, i.e. just three decimal digits, (and for the majority of the successive steps of adding another digit, only two of these digits will change).

The record bit rates achieved of around 19 bits per second for adding 100 random decimal digits, suggests that it is a significantly easier task than the straight memory tasks discussed previously. A second maths task of adding ten ten-digit numbers ten times, gave a result of 18 bits per second - only 1 less - despite taking 10 times longer. The fact that these figures are relatively independent of task complexity makes it likely that they are close to the fundamental limit of learning, the learning bottleneck, at least for this kind of information, numbers. The top two records (for adding 100 random decimal digits) were achieved by different people on different occasions yet lie within just 2% of each other, which suggests that we are seeing something of a fundamental limit of human brain physiology. The more difficult task of *multiplying* pairs of numbers together, understandably gave much lower figures.

Remember these figures suggest the maximum possible information rates, so we should not assume that our own learning performance throughout our daily life will match those of the world's best mind athletes, any more than we might expect to be able to sprint at world record speeds on a daily basis.

It's a walk in the park

While this may be an indication of a common bottleneck in all these processes, we should remember something about the methods employed by the champions for memorising large quantities of information. Almost all of them use a similar memory technique, called the "journey method" or "method of loci"[241] also known as the "memory palace". Long before any actual competition, they devise a system whereby symbols to be memorised are each substituted with an image or idea (a number 4 might be represented by a chair). They establish a strong memory of a journey with a sequence of landmarks, and practice familiarising themselves with it.[242]

During the competition they mentally move successively from landmark to landmark, at each location imagining something that represents the next item to be remembered. When asked to recall what has been memorised in the event, they retrace the journey in their mind, remembering the implanted associations. This has the advantage that they can reverse their steps if they miss something.

The fact that this journey method works so much better than others that have been tried, suggests that memorising a complex sequential journey is a human skill that has been key to our survival over evolutionary time scales. Hunters needed to be able to precisely retrace their path through the forest or across the desert via the waterholes if their dependent offspring were to survive and carry their genes forward.

The earlier figure of running speed versus duration showed that humans can run a marathon distance at more than half the speed of our fastest sprint, suggesting that we have evolved to be able to cover tens of miles in a day in pursuit of prey. That would require a lot of landmarks to be remembered, so might explain our ability to remember very long sequences of images.

It may also be significant that for many thousands of years (from the development of language until the invention of books), verbal storytelling was the primary method of transferring acquired knowledge forward in time, from generation to generation. Passing on stories through songs and rhyming poetry made them even more memorable, and probably reduced errors. Both songs and rhyming poetry introduce additional redundancy in the text through the rhythm of a song and the rhyming of words, making some words more predictable.

We have seen how the champions perform; but how does an enthusiastic amateur compare with the top memory athletes? In a recent BBC TV documentary Michael Mosley was coached by world memory champion Ben Pridmore as he trained himself to memorise the sequence of a shuffled pack of playing cards.[243] After 3 days of practice, Michael could memorise a pack of cards in 30 minutes, which would correspond to about 0.1 bits per second. With further practice he achieved it within 10 minutes. So his performance improved significantly with practice, but peaked at only 0.3 bits per second, far slower than Ben's own record speed of 12 bits per second (21.68 seconds). This is not surprising as this task is not part of our everyday experience.

It would be easy to assume that the champions of this sport possess an innate talent for memorising information. However, the evidence is that the key to success is practice and dedication (probably bordering on the obsessive). The process by which memory can be improved is described by Chase & Ericsson, in "Skill and working memory".[244] Ericsson measured the number of digits that can be held in memory when presented at a rate of one per second, and which can then immediately be recalled in the correct order, what he called Digit Span. He measured the digit span of several naive subjects over a period of time during which they consistently practised the task.

One subject could initially memorise just 7 digits which is fairly typical, but after two years his span had increased to 82 digits. Over the 264 sessions he achieved this by gradually devising more sophisticated ways of mentally encoding the digits. It was noted that subjects digit spans typically increased by one digit for every two hours of practice. Note that because the decimal numbers were always presented at one per second, the information rate was constant (at 3.32 bits /sec). The world record for memorised digit span, is 300 digits and is currently held by Wang Fen of China (in 300 seconds).

Seeing for the first time

These record breaking figures for our learning speed suggest that our ability to see what is new to us is severely limited. Now that we have some accurate figures, we can explore what they might mean for other novel experiences. What if we were to suddenly encounter another living creature, one that we have had absolutely no previous experience of (for example a Yeti or an alien life-form from another world)? How much detail could we take in during our initial sighting?

We would try to make sense of what we have just sensed, constructing an image in our mind of what our eyes have just seen. We might try to determine what we were observing by looking for a match, however weak, with something that we are already familiar with. However, if it is completely alien to us and nothing like anything we have previously experienced, our ability to see what is before us will be completely limited by our learning bottleneck. The chances are that we would absorb information somewhat slower than the highest record rate, as we would probably spend a significant fraction of our precious observation time wrestling with an internal dilemma: "What the **** is that?", "Should I stare or run?"

To give you some idea just how inaccurate an impression we might get, I have created a sequence of images corresponding to successively longer observation times, based on a learning rate of 10 bits per second.

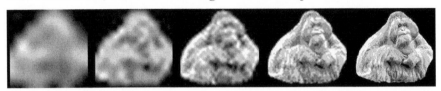

Figure 24: Five images of a creature, showing that the clarity increases the longer we observe it. The images were created using 128, 512, 3072, 16384, and 65536 bits of information respectively. For 10 bits/second learning rate, the corresponding viewing times required would be: 13 seconds, 51 seconds, 5 minutes, 27 minutes, nearly 2 hours.

I couldn't provide an image of something completely alien, so I used an Orang-utan. Assuming that you are already familiar with something similar, you probably recognised the images on the right almost immediately. This highlights the huge difference between learning something completely new, and recognising something that is familiar to us.

You will also have some initial idea of its size. Learning the size of completely alien objects is more difficult. Objects naturally look smaller when they are further away, and we generally make a correction for scaling with distance by knowing what we expect for a familiar object. So our idea of its size may be way out. This is a common problem when Unidentified Flying Objects (UFOs) are reported (perhaps meteorological balloons, the planet Venus, clouds), even when observed by experienced pilots. A visual observation of something strange does not tell us its size, only the visual angle over which it extends, its size is often inferred with little evidence.

This is a particular problem with objects seen against a backdrop of sky, as there are no clues from adjacent familiar objects. You may have noticed that jumbo jets often appear to fly slower than smaller aircraft, such as executive jets. Seen at an uncertain distance, all we have to go on is the rate at which the object traverses its own length. A larger longer aircraft takes a longer time to do so.

Brief Encounters

There are a few world records for very short duration memory tasks (from 0.5 to 4 seconds, by World Record holder Ramon Campayo).[245] However, I did not plot these on the previous graph because something rather odd appears for very short durations. When I plot these records as the *total* number of bits memorised versus duration, the number of decimal bits remembered does not tend to zero for zero exposure time, as we might expect, but towards a finite value (~50 bits).

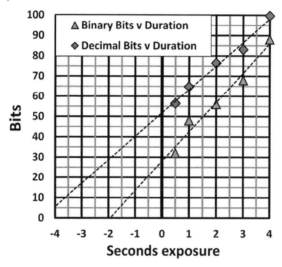

Figure 25: Record number of bits of information memorised during very short exposures.
Extrapolating these sets of measured points suggests we can memorise a finite number of bits for nearly zero observation time.

At first this may appear to make no sense, as it is obvious that no information can be absorbed in zero time! However, we need to remember that for durations of only a few seconds, the allowed recall time is much longer (typically half a minute) and probably includes time spent still absorbing the "snapshot" of the information, either as a result of simple persistence of vision induced within the retina of the eye, or perhaps by a mental stretching of the observation time occurring within the very early stage of visual perception.

Linearly extrapolating to zero observation time gave around 50 bits when memorising decimal numbers, and 30 bits when memorising binary digits. The difference may be due to our greater familiarity with decimal digits than binary, allowing us to take in more information in that format, or that the greater number of bits per symbol is more compatible with the way we "chunk" information. Remember that champion Ben Pridmore performed better when memorising two playing cards at a time.

So it appears that the briefest glance can capture around 50 bits of information, provided that sufficient time is given for subsequent introspection and storage. It is worth noting that Averbach & Coriell at Bell Labs found a near identical figure in short term memory experiments memorising letters.[246][247]

In the context of the learning bottleneck, I have chosen to ignore these very short duration records as I am interested in continuous bit rates, rather than occasional bursts of information. However, this figure of 50 bits is interesting in itself, as it may provide an estimate of the limit to the amount of information that anyone can absorb in a brief glance. Witnesses to a novel event would only be able to absorb a limited amount of information, depending on the duration. Consider a witness to a crime who has a clear view for 5 seconds: the briefest initial glance could provide 50 bits, and if we assume a learning bottleneck for continuous observation of say 10 bits per second, that could provide a further 50 bits giving a total of 100 bits of information.

This approach might allow us to estimate the maximum plausible accuracy of someone's observation based on its duration, and might offer a way of defining the limits to the accuracy of eye witnesses. Knowing the length of time that a witness has observed an event would allow us to put limits on the amount of information absorbed. When the testimony contains more information than that limit, it must be being supplemented from the witness's previous experience, not the event itself.

It is important to remember that our powers of observation are dramatically reduced when our attention is directed introspectively, such as when we are thinking about what we have just seen. If our first glance has aroused our interest, we are likely to use the subsequent time to observe more carefully and take in more detailed information, but if it has not, then we just "don't give it a second glance". As experienced adults, we comfortably assume that we can refer to our internal predictive model, rather than reality itself. We have a lifetime of well-developed internal models to refer to, which are usually simpler and require less effort, sometimes blinding us to the reality of what lies before us in the very moment.

Over the years, while exploring the idea of the learning bottleneck, I have become ever more aware of the strength of my prejudged ideas based on the briefest glance. I have observed this especially while driving and glancing at passing drivers. The duration of my observation may be very short, yet I immediately have an idea of their facial appearance, one that I imagine I could recall if required. The evidence provided by the mental athletes suggests that no more than about 64 bits of novel information can be absorbed in a brief second long glance, yet the subjective experience is of far, far more. Without any prior knowledge of faces this is equivalent to a 64 pixel one bit (black or white) image (e.g. 8 x 8 pixels), or a 4 x 8 element image with just 4 brightness levels (black, dark grey, light grey, white, needing 2 bits per pixel).

Back in the introduction you saw a reasonable quality image of me wearing spectacles. I will now show how little visual detail we could resolve if the same image were created only with the information we can absorb from a brief half-second glance:

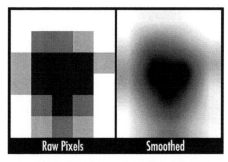

Figure 26: A version of the earlier image of the author, but this time using just 60 bits of information (30 pixels (5x6), each pixel described using 2 bits, so giving 4 brightness levels).[248]

If I had never seen a face before, I would learn almost nothing about faces with so little information. Many more bits are required to provide us with an informative image. Note that even the cheapest digital cameras today provide images of a million pixels, each of which has 256 possible levels of brightness. So how is it that we seem to know so much from just a glance?

Sixty four bits may be insufficient to provide an image that is of any use, but in complete contrast, 64 bits is sufficient to describe any number from 1 to 18,446,744,073,709,551,616 (that being 2 multiplied by itself 64 times).[249] That is a lot of possibilities. But what if we had studied different faces for years, and had a huge mental database of facial types and orientations. Then our meagre 64 bits of information might in principle allow us to choose from eighteen million, million, million possible recognised faces.

This is of course ridiculous, as this is far greater than the number of people on the planet. Not only that, but if we learned a new face every second continually for thirty years, it would only add up to a thousand million faces. However, I use this example to demonstrate the huge potential of a relatively small number of bits when used to identify one of many previously learned experiences.

From birth we learn about faces, not by simply remembering each face we see. We start with recognising the important features of "face" (eyes, nose, mouth, all of which appear on a head), and then learn to differentiate between familiar faces (Mom, Pop). Next: those faces in various orientations (Mom side on), different emotional messages (happy Mom), Grandma, other children etc., each time absorbing and remembering the differences, learning how to differentiate.

When we move outside our home environment we experience a wider diversity of faces, but only need to remember the differences that are important in enabling us to predict behaviours. Growing up in a ghetto community (black or white) we might lead us to ascribe very little information to people of unfamiliar race or colour. If we are taught that "the other people" are to be feared or hated, we may be able to allocate them just a single bit of information: Bad.

When we glance at something that our mature mind expects to be broadly familiar with, our mind quickly tries to match what is sensed with one of our many previous experiences. We readily find some kind of match, the closest match, and imagine that we are seeing what lies before our eyes, while actually we are seeing what lies closest within our mind's eye.

Experienced adults are capable of quickly recognising a large number of familiar faces. Earlier in this book we saw that our eyes are capable of sensing raw information at around 6 Megabits per second, nearly a million times more than the rate at which we can learn something new. Now that is sufficiently fast to convey quite a detailed image to our subconscious, but we cannot absorb this amount of raw information into our *conscious* mind, because we cannot learn this fast. However, there is no reason why our mind cannot subconsciously compare this detailed image with its huge remembered collection of similarly detailed faces. This is where the parallel processing power of the human brain probably comes to the fore, enabling it to simultaneously explore many possible matches and present the closest match to our very much slower conscious mind.

Our mind then "sees" this nice clear image from our memory and tells us that this is the face that we are actually looking at. In the previous chapter, the Necker cube image revealed that our conscious perceiving mind is decisive, opinionated, and reluctant to admit that it is unsure. So when we glance at a face, our mind confidently tells us that we know that type of person. It immediately associates much more information with the face we have glanced at, such as their age, intelligence, habits, family, history, how friendly they might be. A longer observation allows us to refine our match, and we conveniently forget the errors in judgement we made a moment ago.

If the face we glance at, only weakly matches two different faces from our memory, our mind constructs a single hybrid between the two faces, and associates this new idea of the person behind the face with a hybrid of the associated information. In that brief momentary glance we "see" a clear face, and immediately believe that we know so much about the person. I explore this process in more detail in the later section on the science of prejudice.

Big brain, narrow Bottleneck, slow reactions

You may find it surprising that we, the most intelligent species, have such a low bit rate bottleneck, but the key goal of survival makes different demands on creatures of different intelligence. A simple creature may depend entirely on its rapid reflexes for survival, whereas intelligent predictive creatures such as humans benefit from longer timescale plans and need to outsmart other smart predators (sabre toothed tigers, salesmen). I believe that the bottleneck constraint results from the complexity of the process of integrating our sensory experiences into our ongoing predictive models.

For every prey or predator there will be a trade-off between their reaction speed and the complexity of their predictive capability. It is likely that the overall performance of each species will have evolved to balance these two factors to maximise their ability to survive; survival of the fittest physically and intellectually. We humans believe that we have the most sophisticated mental processor, capable of the most complex predictive computations. However, our brain is built on a similar biological technology to many other species, yet is called upon to "compute" many more implications from what we sense. So it would not be surprising if we had one of the lowest rates of learning when expressed in bits per second. Complex simulations take a long time to calculate, a longer time before an answer is available.

Less intelligent creatures can generally respond quicker than humans. We have to use our guile to outwit them when competing head to head, whether we are catching a fly, a rat or a wild horse, and may be reliant on our technology. Experiments that accurately measure the speed of human learning are difficult to apply to other creatures, being mostly based around language, and often involving concepts that only humans can appreciate such as numeracy. However, there is evidence to support the idea that intelligence comes at the expense of speed.

When chimpanzees are provided with a good private education from a young age, it appears that they can perform as well as, or even better than humans at some mental tasks.[250] There are some very smart chimpanzees at the Primate Research Institute, at Kyoto University in Japan. Professor Matsuzawa and his team have worked closely with some of them for more than thirty years, trying to understand the similarities and differences in the way humans and chimps think.[251] [252]

Several chimps have been taught to memorise the sequence of numbers one through nine, a fairly impressive feat in itself. Various touch screen computer activities were devised that enabled the chimps to demonstrate their prowess. One of these activities tested their short term memory ability as follows. Numbers 1 to 9 were briefly displayed in random grid positions on a computer screen, but immediately after the participant touched the first number, all the numbers were obscured with white patterned squares.

The challenge was for the subject to touch all the squares in ascending order, one to nine. To do this, they must memorise the position of each of the nine numbers. Chimps were trained to do this by automatically dispensing a treat to them every time they correctly remembered the location of all the numbers on screen and selected them in the correct order. It was found that the best chimps completed this task much faster than human students, and with the same accuracy.[253] [254]

Next, instead of allowing the chimps all the time they wanted to look at the screen prior to touching the first number, they only displayed the numbers for a fraction of a second. One startling result occurred when the star chimp Ayumu was competing against the human memory champion Ben Pridmore, who I mentioned earlier. When just five numbers were displayed for a total time of 0.6 of a second, Ben and chimp Ayumu's performances were quite closely matched. But when the numbers were displayed for only 0.2 of a second, chimp Ayumu correctly identified the numbers in sequence 90 % of the time, while Ben Pridmore was only successful for 33% of the time.[255] Ayumu's success rate, like those of other chimps younger than about 10 years, is better that of her mother Ai[256], and other older chimps. It appears that young chimps, like human children, have better eidetic memory (the ability to take a mental picture of even a complicated image) than their elders, and it was found that chimps outperform humans when the numbers are displayed very briefly.

More recent experiments with Ayumu proved even more startling. He could even recall 9 numbers in the range 1 to 17 with an exposure time of just 60 milliseconds.[257] This task is completely impossible for human subjects as the exposure time is so short, and only becomes easier with a much longer exposure, but why? Sally Boysen of the Ohio State University suggests that "Chimpanzees may have a perceptual advantage that is slowed down in humans, whose knowledge of counting may interfere".

The chimps see the numbers as symbols, and have merely learned the sequence of those symbols as they appeared on screen. The task may be more difficult for a human because we cannot avoid seeing the symbols as actual numbers, and we know that numbers are inherently part of a numerical sequence. Furthermore, when we see "17" we see "1" adjacent to a "7" and know that it represents (1 x 10) +7. So we cannot choose to look at a number and see it merely as a member of a set of symbols. We cannot avoid this additional processing step in the same way that we cannot avoid thinking of the person behind a face when we see a face. It does raise the interesting question: Would a bright but innumerate human perform better at the task?

Is this evidence that the human learning rate limit is lower than for the chimpanzee?[258] It might be, but I suspect that the fact that our human record breaker performed similarly to our star chimpanzee when given a long enough exposure, may indicate the same rate of learning when large amounts of information must be remembered. However, the fact that chimps demonstrated better performance for short exposures, suggests that they are faster at this type of simple spatial task.

So much for humans versus apes, but what about comparisons between apes? At the Lester E. Fisher Center for the Study and Conservation of Apes at Lincoln Park Zoo in Chicago, the ability to memorise sequences of up to 5 symbols was tested in three Gorillas and three Chimpanzees. They found that Gorillas were better at remembering longer sequences than Chimpanzees, but they exhibited longer delays in their response.[259] This would support the idea that intellect comes at the expense of speed.

Reaction Time

There is a significant delay in our conscious reaction to a stimulus, and by the very nature of consciousness we are unaware of that delay. Our minds manipulate our experience to make the experience tidy, it closes the gaps. A child runs into the road ahead of us, and we instantly hit the car brakes, or so we think. Yet the truth is that we are paralysed for a significant fraction of a second.

For short duration athletic events, the inherent delay in responding to the starting gun is a significant fraction of the overall time. It can be precisely determined by measuring the time between the firing of the gun, and the moment that the runner's foot applies force to the starting blocks. Due to our physiology there is a minimum reaction time, and a competitor starting to move within 100 milliseconds is judged to have "jumped the gun" and made a false start. A movement in such a short time after the sound of the gun would indicate that they did not start in response to it, and under the new rules any false starting athlete is immediately disqualified.

This had a dramatic impact at the 2011 world championships, when current world record holder Usain Bolt was disqualified. He was more fortunate in the London 2012 Olympics where he won the Gold medal with the world's second fastest overall time of 9.63 seconds. On that day Usain's reaction time was 0.165 seconds, with Silver and Bronze medal winners managing 0.179 and 0.178 respectively.

Simpler creatures such as insects have faster reaction times than humans. It takes only 30-50 milliseconds for a House Fly to leap into the air and start beating its wings in flight after sensing a threat, which is why they are so difficult for us to catch. A small fly will only survive among predators if it can respond quicker. If a fly had a brain that considered at length how to respond to its senses, it would be too slow and soon perish, so its responses are simple hard-wired fast reflexes. In its evolutionary niche it has evolved to be quick witted rather than thoughtful. If it had a significant brain, the extra weight would impair its flying performance. Its fast reactions may also be helped by that fact that its nerve impulses travel over much shorter distances.

When we investigate human reaction times for more complex decisions, we find yet more evidence for a processing bottleneck. Fermín Moscoso del Prado Martín analysed subjects reaction time delay for both word naming and various word recognition tasks over a range of degrees of task difficulty. When he interpreted the results as mental processing speed in bits per second, he found they reached a maximum of around 5.5 bits per second for the more difficult tasks[260].

Subliminal Perception

A subliminal sensory stimulus is one that is below an individual's threshold for conscious perception, (as distinct from supraliminal ones that we are conscious of). The press frequently raise the spectre of our vulnerability to subliminal messages, such as a brief image flashed with in an advertisement on the TV, but there is little evidence that we are readily influenced this way.[261] However, there is evidence that our mind can register things of which we are not consciously aware.[262]

The fact that our brain can *recognise* what we sense, far more rapidly than our consciousness can learn (6 Megabits per second versus a few tens of bits per second), may give a fresh insight into the process of subliminal perception. The world memory records for short duration exposures showed that we can learn more from a briefly sensed experience if we are allowed to digest what we have sensed for a few moments afterwards. However, if we are bombarded with a stream of sensations such as successive frames of a movie or a TV image, then it is likely that our rate of learning is no faster than

10 bits per second. It follows that our conscious mind can learn no more than a single "yes" or "no" within one tenth of a second.

But the minds ability to *recognise* familiar sensations corresponds to an information rate almost a million times greater, so it follows that we will be able to register quite complex sensations or images subconsciously when they are flashed up briefly, provided that we already have some familiarity with it. It is well-known that such subliminal messages do register with our mind at some level, but now our understanding of the learning bottleneck suggests that we can only subliminally register something which we already have experience of, not something entirely new to us. This is why brief subliminal messages have to be repeated many times to have any significant effect.

Savants Asperger's & Autism

When discussing the human learning bottleneck, I am often asked "What about Savants? surely they can learn much faster?" It has been suggested that individuals with autism are biased towards detail-focused processing and that this predisposes them towards savant talents.[263] An autistic savant is a term used to describe a person who has both autism and another condition known as Savant Syndrome[264], a rare condition in which people with neurodevelopmental disorders, notably autism spectrum disorders and/or brain injuries, demonstrate profound capabilities far in excess of what would be considered normal. These skills may include exceptional memory, arithmetical abilities, or extraordinary skills in art or music.[265]

Do savants have a less narrow bottleneck? Do they exhibit higher data rates for learning than other people? The answers depend on what is learned. Many savants have an amazing ability to memorise detail exactly as it is presented without analysing it, and are able to recall the kind of detail that the rest of us would find mind numbingly tedious to have to remember. Equally, they seem to do less "conceptual encoding" that reduces the information to a more flexible form, and they cannot handle metaphors.[266] Recent research confirms that some of these savants operate by directly accessing low-level, less-processed information that exists in all human brains but is normally unavailable to conscious awareness.[267]

This fits with the idea that the narrowness of the bottleneck is a consequence of the mental processes involved with integrating sensations into a broader conceptual model. We who are not savants are preoccupied by this integration, while the savant is able to quickly record simple details. We see a human face and immediately substitute the idea of the person behind that face. We may be preoccupied by what emotion might be indicated by the features, and be busy predicting this person's behaviour towards us. The savant on the other hand, is unlikely to be distracted by such issues, and may quickly notice that the face has five small spots on its left cheek. Incidentally, Dr Temple Grandin, a woman with high-functioning autism herself, has suggested that the related condition of autism is associated with a lack of connectivity between different processing regions of the brain.[268]

While savants are credited with amazing mental feats, I have failed to find any evidence for them having a wider bottleneck when doing intelligent tasks. If it were the case, then I would expect most of the world records for memory, to be held by savants, and they are not. It is worth noting that savant Daniel Tammet holds the European record for reciting pi from memory (to 22,514 digits, in five hours and nine minutes on 14 March 2004). This corresponds to an information rate of 4.2 bits per second, but is less than half as fast as the world record of nearly 10 bits per second for an even greater number of digits. However, as you will soon see, records for fast recall may simply be limited by the rate that we can pronounce text, so are unreliable as measures of the conscious communication bit rate.

In this chapter I have revealed the direct evidence for our learning bottleneck; the rate that information enters our mind from the world around us. I have explored the challenge of acquiring precise numerical data to support our claims. When we compare the abilities of mind athletes with their physical counterparts we find that the performances of mankind's best are very similar, suggesting that both these limits are dominated by our biology.

We have also seen just how limited are our abilities to see anything completely new to us. Now that we have precise data for the maximum rate that we can we can absorb any new experience, we have a greater understanding of our brief encounters, and can speculate upon the precise information content of a mere glance. This reveals the fragile nature of witnesses' ability to recall events.

Much of the evidence I have presented involves language; indeed it might be tempting to suggest that the process of language itself is our bottleneck. However, in the next chapter I explore the ways in which our learning bottleneck reveals itself through the things we choose to do in the world, when information flows from our mind into the world around us. While some of these involve language, others such as physical skills do not, and you will see that these provide some remarkably clear numerical evidence for the bottleneck.

Chapter Six

The evidence from what we do

"What matters is how quickly you do what your soul directs."

- Rumi

Information projected from us to the world

So far we have only considered the flow of information from the external world into our selves, but we are not passive observers, for we shape the world around us based on what we have a mind to do. We speak, write, dance, we play computer games, musical instruments and tennis, we drive cars, pilot planes and do a myriad of other wonderful things with our bodies when our mind reaches out to the world around us.

Speaking Out

What do we know about the information rate of verbal communication? Speaking speed is usually specified in Words Per Minute (WPM), but we want to characterise it in bits per second. An average word is standardised to five characters for the purposes of WPM measurement, and we can use the earlier estimate of 1.1 bit per character. So for example 120 WPM (= 2 words per second, = 10 characters per second), corresponds to 11 bits per second.

Fast talking may be a valuable skill for salesmen and in the debating room, simply in terms of its force. But when we communicate through speech we generally limit our speaking speed so we can be heard and understood, so the same bottleneck that Shannon estimated also applies to the act of speaking. There are people who claim records for remarkably high speed speaking, approaching 600 WPM, however, I do not consider this useful data as we cannot determine the information content.

The reason is that we have no receiver for these spoken words that can provide an accurate measure of the error rate, (which might be 90 %!). The speaking rates are inevitably judged by listeners who are insufficiently fast thinking to determine errors and information content. To clarify this point, consider the effect if the text provided were an unfamiliar list of random words. There is no way that either the speaker could read them as fast, nor could the judges take in ten words that fast. This reveals that the listeners only think they are hearing language at 600 WPM because they are hearing familiar content. Very high word rates are used in situations such as livestock auctions, but the context and expected vocabulary size are constrained far more than in normal speech, so we would expect the bits per word to be much less than Shannon's estimate.

In principle, one might measure speaking rates using an automated speech-to-text computer program. Today's speech recognition system programs can interpret clearly enunciated words spoken at average speed very well.[269] However, they cannot handle unusually fast speech without generating a large proportion of errors; 170 - 200 WPM being about the maximum speed (corresponding to 16 - 18 bits per second). Improvements in recognition speed have not kept up with speed increases of the processing computer.

This may well be one of those difficult problems that humans have evolved to deal with very effectively, and so make look deceptively easy. It is just conceivable that automated speech recognition systems will be improved sufficiently in the future that they could interpret spoken speech faster than we humans can. In this case there would be value in being able to speak faster than we can listen. Given their current performance, it may be a long way off, but perhaps not impossible. However, it is not obvious that our mind is capable of communicating useful information from our mind to our lips at a faster rate than we can listen, even if we can rapidly recite a memorised sequence of words

All automated language recognition systems exploit knowledge of the inherent redundancy within the language. The ultimate recognition speed would be achieved by taking the entire message into account, not just probabilities of words and word sequences, but probabilities of words and sentences with respect to topics. This would result in huge processing delays; in the extreme, no text might emerge until the last word of the message has been spoken. Such delays would be fine when leaving a message on an answer-phone, but no use in an automated bidding system listening to a fast talking auctioneer.

Among the world memory records there are many for the rapid recall of the value Pi (π); the competitor having previously learned Pi to a vast number of decimal places over an extended period of time. The world record is held by Rajan Mahadevan who correctly recalled the first 31,811 digits of Pi over a period of nearly three hours at a rate of over three digits per second.[270] This corresponds to a rate of about 10 bits per second. There have been several slower records previously, but for much shorter durations, so this is certainly an impressive demonstration of memory. (See Appendix 3)

However, I do not think that this is an unambiguous indication of the limiting rate at which we can recover numbers from memory, more likely it is just an indication of the speed of speaking memorised text, like singing a song. Why? Well, just try saying "3.14159…" (π) quickly from memory. You almost certainly aren't thinking of the numerical meaning of the individual numbers as you say it, but reciting a string of text instead, which might equally have been: "freep oin twonf or wonf ive ny …."!

If this is the case, then we cannot hope to estimate the number of bits per second accurately. With perseverance, people are able to learn huge tracts of text in an unfamiliar language and subsequently recite or sing them without any comprehension of the meaning of the text. For example, some Islamic scholars are able to learn the entire Quran by heart in Arabic, and can subsequently recite it despite being unable to read or understand the Arabic language to any extent.

The speedy type

While fast talking has limited value, being able to type or write faster than we can read might be very useful. However, there is no evidence that we can type novel information faster than we can form the ideas of the message in our own mind. So what information rates can we attribute to text? An average professional typist achieves around 60 WPM, and a very fast typist can achieve 120 WPM, and as we calculated above, this corresponds to 11 bits per second. The fastest reported typing speed ever, 216 words per minute, corresponds to 20 bits per second.[271] Very fast typists might be operating at a higher information rate than more typical typists. The other possibility is that the text they are typing has greater redundancy, due to the typist's greater familiarity with the language style or topic.

Slowing to a scrawl

As for handwriting, mine is poor, but I can write quite fast. However, as neither I nor others can subsequently read most of what I have written I have no reason to be smug. This exposes the problem of estimating the information rate for handwriting. When the doctor hurriedly scribbles a prescription, the patient is relying on the familiarity of the pharmacist with both the script and the context. Doctor Jones never dots his "i"s, and usually prescribes Prozac!

The average person handwrites at 22 WPM while copying and 31 WPM for memorised text, corresponding to only 2 and 3 bits per second respectively. Shorthand was invented to enable fast speech to be recorded, and Charles Lee Swem holds the world record for this at 282 WPM or 26 bits per second.[272]

These figures suggest that we can generate language through our hands at rates varying from a few bits per second to a few tens of bits per second. Despite the widespread availability of these figures, it is difficult to estimate the bit rate of human communication in everyday language, because we do not know what the recipient already knows and expects.

Reaching out to touch our world

Sometimes we discover things in unexpected places. In my search for evidence of the learning bottleneck, I had focused on communication tasks. Then one day a friend[273] drew my attention to some experiments by psychologist Paul Fitts at the Laboratory of Aviation Psychology, Ohio State University.[274] He was exploring ways of measuring how subjects performed various manual skills. At first sight the only connection with my learning bottleneck seemed to be that several of the experiments reported results yielding figures of around 10 bits per second over a wide range of conditions.

Paul Fitts headed a team whose objective was to improve worker efficiency, whether piloting aircraft or performing physical tasks on the shop floor. He had been intrigued by studies of handwriting movement that showed that the total time required to write individual letters is essentially the same when the size of the letters is varied.[275] Fitts was smart; he approached the problem using the information theory that Claude Shannon had just developed to provide an estimate of the fundamental limit to the information capacity of a communication channel based on the ratio of its Signal to Noise.[276] Though Shannon's theory had been developed for completely different purposes, Fitts cleverly reinterpreted it to describe the information capacity of a manual task with a given degree of difficulty, when performed in a measured time. He considered the required movement *amplitude* (displacement) as the Signal, and the *dimensional accuracy* required to complete the task, as the Noise.

Earlier I explained how the precision of a signal or something sensed can be described in terms of the minimum number of bits to define it. When we are discussing information, it is more useful for us to describe a measurement as having 7 bits accuracy than simply stating that the accuracy is say: 1% (or 1/128 to be precise). Fitts recognised that he could also describe the accuracy of a physical skill in terms of the number of bits required to define the spatial precision, so he used bits to describe the degree of difficulty of various physical tasks.

It may be clearer if I give a couple of examples: Making a physical movement of 128 mm to reach a target only 1 mm in size, corresponds to 7 bits accuracy ($2^7=128$), and likewise, a displacement that is 8 times the target size would be a difficulty of 3 bits ($2^3=8$). The degree of task difficulty can be thought of as the relative precision of an action. When expressed in bits, it is the Logarithm to base 2 of the ratio of these two dimensions, so each additional bit is a doubling of accuracy.

In Fitts' ground-breaking 1954 paper, he described a set of three different experiments to measure the speed of response in simple human manual tasks, while exploring a wide range of degrees of difficulty. These were:

1/. "Reciprocal tapping": Repeatedly moving a stylus back and forth horizontally between two targets.

The experiment consisted of two metal strips of various widths, separated by various distances. Each subject was asked to repeatedly move a stylus back and forth between these two target strips as fast as they could manage, while minimising errors. Errors were monitored by additional metal strips either side of the targets.

Different experimental configurations were explored in separate experiments as follows:

The distance between targets was varied (Amplitude of the movement).

The target size was varied (Exploring different required accuracy of movement).

Two very different stylus weights were tested (exploring dependence on muscle force required).

2/. "Disk Transfer": Moving disks from one peg to another.

With various movement distances.

With various hole-clearances (Exploring different required accuracy of movement).

3/. "Pin Transfer": Moving pins from one hole to another.

With various movement distances.

With various hole-clearances (Exploring different required accuracy of movement).

All the tasks were repetitive: his subjects were instructed to repeat the same task over and over again as quickly as possible.[277] As he used male college students, I expect they readily responded seeing it as a competition. He instructed them to "emphasize accuracy rather than speed. At the end of each trial I shall tell you if you have made any errors". For each condition of target size and distance to the target, he measured both the total number of movements, and the total duration. He was then able to characterise his subjects' performance (their information capacity in bits per second), by simply multiplying the number of actions per second by the degree of difficulty expressed in bits.

The results were very surprising. Tasks requiring greater precision took longer, but only in proportion to the information implied by that precision. When he changed the comparatively lightweight one ounce stylus for one weighing a pound, it had almost no effect on performance despite being sixteen times heavier, nor did the overall distance of the required movements. He also noted that one or two days of training had little effect on performance.

In the next figure I have re-plotted his published data for the Reciprocal Tapping task as information rate in bits per second versus degree of difficulty (expressed in bits). It reveals that the maximum bit rate is remarkably similar for a very wide range of experimental conditions. Furthermore, his other tasks that involved moving pins and disks with various clearances, yielded almost identical results (as can be seen in Appendix 4), despite having very different goals. What a coincidence, the limiting information rate he saw was almost the same figure as our learning bottleneck!

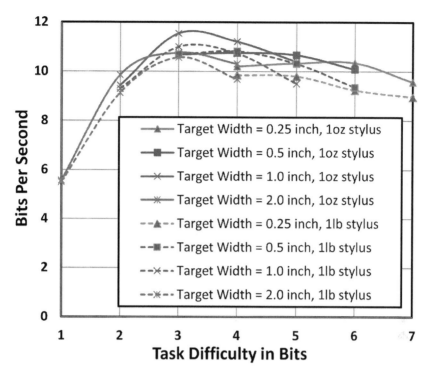

Figure 27: Information rate versus task difficulty plotted for Fitts' reciprocal tapping task. Task difficulty was determined by the ratio of the target distance (2-16 inches), to the target width.
(e.g. a ratio of 8 would be a task difficulty of 3 bits as 2x2x2 = 8).

Remarkably, the maximum rate of performance expressed this way, fell close to 10 bits per second for all the subjects and over the wide range of conditions he explored.[278] He wrote that "The results show that the rate of performance is approximately constant over a wide range of movement amplitude and tolerance limits. This supports the thesis that the performance capacity of the human motor system plus its associated visual and proprioceptive feedback mechanisms, when measured in information units, is relatively constant over a considerable range of task conditions."[279] [280]

When I first read about his experiments, I was surprised by two aspects: First, the remarkably tight distribution of the bits per second figures for a wide range of experimental conditions, (remember that these are human beings being measured), secondly, by how close his bit rate figures were to the learning bottleneck figures that I had derived from memory competitions, and also to Shannon's analysis of the information capacity of language. However, I could not immediately see why a manual task concerned with information flowing outwards, should be subject to a similar constraint on information capacity as an inward learning task.

My preoccupation had been with the acquisition of novel information: the inward flow. I then realized that the tasks set by Fitts required the subjects to use their internal conceptual model of the experiment "out there" in order to complete the task. In the reciprocal tapping task, every time the subject attempts to hit one of the two targets with the stylus, they can only continue when they consciously know that they have hit the target.

But in order to know they have landed on target, they must be able to interpret the 2-dimensional information they sense through their eyes, as a 3-dimensional model of the experiment, and they do this by continually updating their internal simulation of the external scene. If our brain were a computer performing this complex task (which it may well not be), we would expect there to be a significant processing delay or latency due to the finite rate at which it can perform the mental transformation and subsequently produce the output confirming that the target had been hit, thus allowing the subject to continue and now move the stylus back across to the other target.

Every back and forth step requires this complex interpretation because the subjects have been asked to perform the task with minimum errors. The information rate is limited by the continual need to learn what the stylus is doing out there in the 3D world, so it is my belief that the ~10 bits per second that Fitts measured, represents the maximum throughput of our internal simulation.[281]

My own particular interest in Fitts' experiments is because they reveal an information rate limit that is suspiciously similar in size to our learning bottleneck. However, his work is widely recognised for its impact on the design of interfaces between humans and machines. In short, "Fitts' Law"[282] has become one of the most successful and well-studied models of human motion. It has provided the rules for optimising the layout of computer screens, rules that are still used extensively today to optimise the size and layout of on-screen buttons.

Others have successfully replicated his results many times since.[283] His basic ideas have subsequently been developed for situations with more spatial dimensions.[284] In 1978 Card, English and Burr at Xerox PARC in Palo Alto used Fitts' law to compare a variety of computer input devices including keyboard keys, joystick and mouse.[285] [286] They found the mouse was close to optimum when compared with finger pointing or stylus, and this was a major factor leading to the commercial introduction of the mouse by Xerox (and the rest of the world has followed). So Fitts' Law has helped define the way most of us interact with computers today.

Fitts observed that the highest bit rates were consistently achieved for displacement amplitudes of around 4 to 8 inches. It is interesting to speculate whether this might be related to the size of human hands and manual dexterity. Whilst Fitts' Law has been successfully applied in the field of human computer interaction, many have struggled to explain Fitts' observations through low level mechanisms. The observed facts are counter intuitive: We might expect that using a stylus of 16 times the weight would slow the speed of movement and hence lower the information rate. Similarly, we might expect larger displacements to take a longer time and hence also lower the information rate. If the speed were indeed limited by muscular strength, we might expect a factor of 128 times difference between the extreme test cases of weight and displacement, yet Fitts found a difference of just 5%.

Scott MacKenzie comments: "despite being robust and highly predictable, Fitts' Law remains an analogy awaiting a theory."[287] Fitts' Law is merely a description of empirical data, so does not provide an explanation for the underlying mechanisms. The only hypothesis that comes close to explaining the result in terms of properties of the body (as opposed to those of the mind) is the assumption that a move is realized by a sequence of sub-movements each taking a constant time to complete. While this would go some way to explain the near constant information rates observed, little experimental evidence has been found to support the idea.

The experimental truth is that the derived information rate in bits per second hardly varies at all with physical parameters such as length, mass and difficulty. This suggests that none of these parameters are involved in the limiting mechanism, and that there is another narrower constraint. I believe this is the complex mental signal processing required to incorporate what is sensed, into our internal model of what is "out there". This constraint is determined more by what is in our head, than in our arm and hand.

To reinforce this point, we might have expected the hand to be much more dexterous than the foot, but Drury investigated Fitts' Law in a study of foot pedal design.[288] Using their preferred foot, subjects tapped back and forth between two pedals for 30 taps. When six different amplitudes were explored for two pedal sizes, he measured a similar information rate of 12 bits per second. It has also been found to apply to head movements. All of which suggests that the figure is determined by something other than the speed, strength and agility of our limbs.[289]

A learned skill

Earlier we considered the very significant difference between observing something that is completely novel to us, and observing something that is broadly familiar to previous experiences we may have had. Similarly, when discussing our actions in the world, we need to be clear whether these are based on familiar skills, or on skills that are significantly novel. Fitts' stylus tasks were essentially novel; when presented to his subjects, they were unlike anything that they would do on a daily basis. Indeed their performance showed little improvement when repeated over several days, suggesting that increased familiarity was of little help. This is not to say that a dedicated subject would not improve over a period of months if given sufficient incentive.

There is a "knife game" performed in bars by men trying to demonstrate how macho they are. They place one hand face-down on the table with their fingers splayed apart. Then with a knife in their other hand they stab successively with the sharp point at each of the gaps between their fingers as fast as they can. If the movements are not accurate there is a serious risk of stabbing one's own finger. The challenge is to do it fast and impress the other guys in the bar.

When one does this while consciously watching and controlling where each stab is aimed, the process is very slow, since the mind has to monitor the correct destination of each stab in real-time. However, there are a few people who consider this feat of such importance that they practice extensively (perhaps on the kitchen table at home) and in time are able to perform this skill remarkably quickly without damaging themselves too much.

These movements are not that dissimilar to those required in Fitts' stylus experiments, so it is reasonable to believe that with practice a subject might significantly increase their performance in Fitts' experiments, at least when focused on one specific task. It would mean that they were moving the stylus back and forth by dead reckoning, without observing for each step whether they fell on target or not. Maybe Fitts should have tried his experiment in a bar using a sharp stylus and offered a few drinks to the winner!

It is tempting to ask why Fitts' subjects did not develop the skill over the several days of the experiments. I suggest that they did not, because they were discouraged from making mistakes, and learning a skill is usually associated with a gradually increasing accuracy. So by simultaneously demanding accuracy in their movements, and maximum speed of performance, Fitts probably suppressed any tendency of his subjects to develop the action as a skill, so it remained an equally difficult task despite many repetitions. But what about the man stabbing the tip of his knife between his splayed out fingers? If you see a comparative beginner practicing this task, you will observe that they stab at a distance beyond the length of the fingers, so even a serious error misses the fingers. They are not penalised for low accuracy during the learning phase, unlike Fitts' subjects.

This has wider implications, for it is a scientific explanation for why errors are fundamentally vital to the process of developing skills. If we expect someone to learn a skill we must encourage them to make mistakes. Obviously there will be situations where errors cannot be tolerated in a fully realistic scenario such as learning to fly a jumbo jet, then we can use simulators or co-pilot instructors to avoid disaster. However, it is worth remembering that if we expect perfection of a trainee, we may block their skill development process.

Most tasks fall somewhere between two contrasting extremes of problem solving versus skilled behaviour.[290] Problem solving requires us to be attentive (as with the Fitts' tasks described earlier), whereas skilled tasks are largely automatic. Performing a skilled task consumes negligible cognitive resources when compared with problem solving, so is less susceptible to interference and can even be performed simultaneously with other tasks. An experienced driver can hold a conversation while avoiding parked and moving cars, even to the point of not remembering most of the journey home. Sometimes a skill feels as if it acts completely independently of ourselves, and is experienced as "the inner game".[291]

Those of you who have learned to drum will know that our reactions are far too slow to be able to strike each individual beat of the drum consciously in time to a tune, for it requires responses that are faster than our normal consciousness can act. If we think too much about what we are doing, then by the time we have thought that we should strike the drum, we are too late. Our rhythmic drumming collapses leaving us sounding and feeling foolish.

We must disengage our overzealous supervising consciousness and trust our body to do what it knows how to do. Through past experience the body and subconscious mind of a skilled drummer have learned a vast array of possible repetitive patterns, which their conscious mind then mixes like a skilled DJ in the present.

One of the attractions of the practice of drumming is that it forces us to drop into a less intellectually controlling mental state, and this can be a blissful experience, especially for those who are caught up in too much thinking. Nobel Prize winner and physicist Richard Feynman certainly found it most useful.[292]

Private Practice

Humans have an incredible facility for learning new skills, both mental and physical, whether it be chipping a flint to make an axe head, precisely hitting a tennis ball into the far corner of the tennis court, or performing complex mental calculations. Those at the top of their game often perpetuate a myth that their achievement is almost entirely the result of their innate talent. Of course the competitor, who pretends that they don't need as much practice as their peers, has a distinct psychological advantage. The key is to keep the sheer scale of practice a secret. Those of us who are not experts can watch the apparently effortless performance of experts, and think of them as particularly fortunate individuals who have been born with a special gift, so have less need to practice their skill than the rest of us. For us, long hours of practice seem a tedious activity, a waste of valuable play-time.

However, in 1985 Benjamin Bloom examined the critical factors that contribute to talent.[293] He looked retrospectively at the childhoods of 120 elite performers who had won international competitions or awards, in fields ranging from music and the arts to mathematics and neurology. He found no early indicators that could have predicted the virtuosos' success. Subsequent research has shown that there is no correlation between IQ and expert performance in fields such as chess,[294] music, sports, and medicine. The only innate differences that turned out to be significant were height and body size, and they matter primarily in sports. In addition, psychometric tests on these individuals revealed no general superiority, just superiority in the area of their expertise.[295]

While an innate propensity towards a particular skill is an important factor, studies have shown a surprisingly strong correlation between the number of hours of practice and the level of achievement.[296] Ericsson discovered that continued improvements in achievement are almost entirely the consequence of deliberate practice.[297] For example, he found that the key difference in the level of solo performance attained between expert musicians was the amount of time they had spent in solitary practice during their music development.[298] This totalled around 10,000 hours by age 20 for the best experts, around 5000 hours for the least accomplished expert musicians and only 2000 hours for serious amateur pianists. More generally, the accumulated amount of deliberate practice is closely related to the attained level of performance of many types of experts, such as musicians,[299] chess-players, and athletes.[300] This fits very well with the idea of an intrinsically limited rate that we can learn, our bottleneck; there is just no way to rush it.

The one factor that does correlate with expertise is competitive determination, and what else would enable one to sacrifice so much of one's young social life for 10,000 hours of solitary practice? There is a current fashion in TV programming for competitions where successful celebrities across a wide range of fields compete against each other in a completely different field.[301] It is very evident that the participants are far more determined to win than the average person. It seems that an intense drive to succeed in one field is easily redirected. We might think of popular comedians as easy-going individuals, but for those at the top of their profession the opposite appears to be the case. In 2009 comedian Eddie Izzard ran 43 marathons in 50 days, and in 2006 another comedian David Walliams swam the 35 km wide English Channel, both of them to raise money for charity.[302] Neither of them had any previous sporting history. Such feats of endurance are beyond almost all of us, not just physically, but psychologically too, revealing the remarkably high level of drive in these individuals.

So practice is the key to developing physical skills. I can slowly build my internal model by repeating an action while observing the effect through a precise comparison between what I anticipate and what I experience, each time learning what is new. Repeating something while focusing on the difference between what we envision, and what we achieve, is what we call "practice". If the difference is large then we are limited in the rate at which we can learn the newness of the experience (to a few tens of bits per second), but even with this low rate of learning, with practice over time we can develop very high precision. We may think of practice as a simple tool used consciously in the pursuit of excellence, but it is the same process by which we learn anything as we develop an internal model of the world, whether consciously or unconsciously, a successive homing in to minimise the error.

When we perform a skill, the information required to define the action in three dimensional space and time with sufficient precision is very large, but we are acting as a pre-programmed machine. The amount of information attributed to our conscious choices around our action is far less. A top grade pianist can play a long piece of Beethoven's music with incredible precision. A piano playing robot would require quite a high information rate to play a piano with equal precision.

But what if the piece of "music" to be performed consisted entirely of random piano notes and of random timing and intensity? Suddenly the human performance would be incredibly difficult, being slow and probably flawed. However, the robotic piano playing machine would achieve the same performance as with the piece by Beethoven. What if I gave the pianist ten years of practice with many different "random" pieces? I suspect it would be of little help, for there would be no familiar, chords, note sequences and structure to assist the pianist, indeed no patterns to learn that would help in the future.

All this suggests that when a pianist plays a familiar piece of music, the amount of information flowing from the pianist's consciousness is quite small: Obviously the title of the piece, plus deliberate small variations from what the pianist had previously rehearsed. Similarly the audience's experience of hearing it will be largely what they remember of the piece from previous experience, plus some of the variations introduced by the pianist.

Sports skills

The more I have learned about human perception, the more amazed I have become at human sports skills. We see the tennis champion loosely spin the racquet in their hand, and a moment later return the fast sliced serve so accurately that the ball bounces just a few centimetres within the back corner of the opponent's court. Because we are familiar with seeing players do this, it seems quite natural - that is until one considers that they achieved this accuracy just moments after spinning their racquet. To me it seems almost miraculous when I consider the angular accuracy required of the racquet head with respect to the court. The potential sources of uncertainties include: the angle and stiffness of their grip, the angle of the wrist, elbow, shoulder etc. etc., the direction of the eyes gaze, orientation of the head with respect to the torso and many others.

A scientist designing a robot to play a fast game such as tennis would endeavour to maximise the rate at which visual information can be acquired, and to minimise any processing delays. This maximises the robot's ability to respond in real time. However, the human response to any stimulus is measured in significant fractions of a second, and as we have seen, our consciousness is unable to quickly take in large amounts of new information. Our first attempts at skilled tasks often involve delays in response that make the task almost impossible. Observe an intelligent child's very first attempts to catch a ball, or strike a ball with a racquet, you will see that initially they find it impossible to respond sufficiently quickly to what they observe.

Skills are learned. No one is born skilled, though some may be born with a greater talent for learning new skills. A skill is an accurate predictive faculty that we develop through gradually building an increasingly accurate set of internal simulations of the action. We do this through practice, through repeatedly rehearsing similar conditions over an extended period of time. The human process, in which our detailed internal simulation slowly learns over years, eventually provides us with rapid responses despite the inherent slowness of what we sense. However, it fundamentally depends on the rules changing only slowly.

We might consider our inability to perform such actions based entirely on what we sense in real-time (in the very moment) to be a handicap, in that it may take years of practice to develop a skill. However, a real-time control system will inevitably lag behind the action as it can only follow what is sensed, but a predictive skill derived from past experience enables us to track something perfectly, which, if you remember, is what exactly our eyes do when following a moving object. Furthermore, a predictive skill even enables us anticipate what has not yet been observed. Acquired skill is the basis of our civilisation; think how many years of skill acquisition occur before we consider someone to be ready for adult life.

Now back to the game. In the absence of imparted spin or the wind, a served tennis ball will follow a simple trajectory. The rules of this trajectory are defined by simple Newtonian mechanics, so it would be possible to predict the entire trajectory of the ball from as few as three discrete observations. Measurements of players' eye movements (using eye-trackers) have revealed that we do not "keep our eye on the ball" throughout its flight, but only track its initial trajectory and anticipate the rest.[303]

A highly skilled tennis player has a vast experiential database of possible scenarios built through endless hours of practice against skilled opponents. This experience includes a wide range of spin and wind conditions and enables him to anticipate what he must do with his racquet to return the ball. So the receiving player performs a comparison with a set of internal predictions, covering the range of likely trajectories. While the raw information content of the scene is huge, the information required to describe the possible options is quite small. Of course none of this occurs consciously, for to involve higher level mental processes would result in a catastrophic delay in judgement. The ball would have sailed past the defending player before he decided what to do.

The responses of expert tennis players were measured when returning serves from either another live player, or from a ball throwing machine.[304] Their response to the machine was 50 milliseconds slower. This showed that being able to observe the servers actions prior to the ball being served provides a very significant advantage. For the fastest serve on record, 163 miles per hour, the served ball travels a distance of twelve foot in 50 milliseconds, a significant fraction of the size of the court.[305]

With the top players, the serve is so fast that there is insufficient time to take in significant information about the actual flight of the ball. However, the receiving player is able to carefully observe all the movements of the serving player, right up to the last moment of hitting the ball, and compare this with the outcome of a vast number of previous serves to predict the best action to take. By accurately comparing the predictions from our internal simulation with observed behaviour of the ball and player, we can refine the simulation specifically in the areas where it makes a difference to our performance (whether we win the point). Note that for this to work well, we must focus intently on the tiny things that seem to be important (the angle of the opponent's racquet head, the position of their foot etc.), and completely ignore other information (the colour of the logo on their shirt, the spectators behind etc.).

When the eye movements of the very top sports champions are compared with the other competitors who are near the top, some significant differences are seen. When skilled performers play a stroke, whether with a racquet, club or bat, kicking or throwing a ball, there is a period of time during which the target (e.g. the ball) is fixated or tracked steadily. This period has been called "the quiet eye", and typically lasts a few hundred milliseconds, but may even last several seconds for example in target shooting. Measurements across a wide range of sports have shown that the "quiet eye" duration of elite performers is significantly longer than that of near-elite, or lower skilled performers, meaning those who consistently achieve high levels of performance, have learned to fixate or track critical objects or locations for longer durations, irrespective of the conditions encountered.[306] Observations show that the eyes of those less skilled spend more time flicking back and forth. It is therefore suggested that a steady period of observation enables the elite players mind to more accurately simulate the activity, and so increase the chances of success. These insights are now being used to train competitors.[307]

It is interesting to compare human skill development with what we expect from robot technology. At present, we require our robots to display their skills from the moment when they are first switched on without needing years of practice. We have assumed that by providing them with very fast cameras and computing power, they can achieve comparable performance without prior learning. However, although robot technology may be vastly improved in the future, it is possible that some robot tasks will be fundamentally impossible without some skill "training" or embedded "experience". There is no reason that robots couldn't be designed to learn skills in a similar way to humans. Watch a robot football match and you will see that there is a very long way to go before a team of robot footballers become competitive with a human team.

Recent developments in the field of robotics are beginning to mimic the way we humans perceive. Systems are being developed that gradually build an "imagined" environment using a camera to scan the scene for things that its computer can recognise. It does this by comparing the images with its own internal database of possible objects, representing objects out there, such as a chair or a desk. This learned environment can then be anticipated in real time, leading to more optimum strategies for negotiating paths through the actual environment.[308]

It is well-known that by rehearsing a response to an emergency, we ensure the fastest response to it, and with the minimum distraction. Not long after I had learned to fly, my instructor sent me off to practice some aerobatics: barrel rolls in particular. I was nervous as I kept getting it wrong, finishing the manoeuvre having to pull out of a dive which subjected me to unpleasantly high G-forces. So I took a break and decided to entertain myself by experimenting with flying a zero-G parabola, like NASA's "vomit comet" aircraft that is used to provide the experience of weightlessness for trainee astronauts, but in my case only briefly as it was a small light aircraft. The procedure is as follows; dive down to get some airspeed, then pull back into a fairly steep climb, then push the control column forward just until you feel completely weightless going "over the top". After a few moments of weightlessness the aircraft is now going down again quite fast, so you pull back, feel the G-force and can then level out. This was good fun and less scary than my defective barrel rolls, so I performed the manoeuvre several times in succession. All of a sudden the engine cut stone dead! Silence!

Before I knew it, my mind had switched into automaton mode, gone right through the emergency check list procedure memorised in case of an engine failure, levelled out and even picked out a suitable field below to try to land in. And then the engine restarted, just as suddenly as it had stopped. It had probably only cut for a couple of seconds, but in that time I had carried out the procedure that I had been trained to do, and now everything seemed back to normal. I was no longer acting as a robot and had the time and intelligence to wonder what the hell had happened. It then dawned on me that this plane had a carburettor that required gravity to keep it supplied with fuel. My extended zero-G manoeuvres had been long enough to temporarily starve the engine of fuel. It had been an interesting afternoon, one that impressed me with the value of rehearsing for emergencies.

Learned skills give fast reactions

When I first left college, I played the racquet game Badminton at a very amateur level for a few years, then for various reasons didn't play again for another 30 years. When I resumed playing my body was older and considerably less fit, however, I was surprised how my earlier practised skills seem to have been preserved over the intervening years. One of my opponents complimented me on the speed of my reactions (when compared with those of my younger colleagues), and I returned home feeling quite smug. I went on the Internet and took a reaction test that I found there, fully expecting to confirm it.[309] However, I was horrified to find that my reaction time of 240 milliseconds was significantly slower than the average (215 ms), and hence probably slower than all my fellow players. So what looked like faster reactions was probably entirely due to more effective predictions based on my more extensive experience, enabling me to respond earlier. The fact that our simple reaction times slow with age is well documented, so I should not have been surprised.[310]

Many top sports people find that they can improve their performance by rehearsing what they will do in their minds prior to their actual event, visualising the entire sequential performance, practicing without physical activity.[311] A world class high jumper will visualise the whole process of the next jump, including clearing the bar at a height higher than they have yet to physically achieve. This not only prepares their body for what is about to be demanded of it, but also acts to counter the natural belief in the impossibility of going beyond the best height that they have previously achieved.

Formula One drivers, while waiting for the key qualifying practice run (which will determine their starting position on the grid) will sit in the cockpit of their car with their eyes closed, mentally rehearsing a complete perfect lap in real time and realistic detail. They imagine all the physical motions of their hands on the wheel and their feet on the pedals for every corner on the track.

The mental workload of a top racing driver has been measured while driving a racing car round a race circuit. Electrodes on his head enabled the ratio between his Alpha and Theta waves to be measured as an estimate of his mental workload.[312] Remarkably no change in mental workload was observed when the driver applied opposite lock to correct a sudden and unexpected loss of grip from the rear wheels.[313] This suggests that the driver's skill had been developed as a reflex response.

Most popular spectator sports provide moments of intense action, such as the action around the goal in football, the finish of the 100 metres sprint or the unravelling of a crash in Formula One. When we watch a sports event in real life or on TV, we only see the portion of the action that is focused around where we are paying attention, where we expect the most interesting bit to be based on our prior experience. If we are able to watch a slow motion replay of these moments, there is so much more that we can learn, even when viewed from the same camera position. Furthermore, replays of the same event taken from several different camera positions can reveal a very different "truth" of what actually happened, whether the goal scorer was offside, who crossed the finish line first, or who really was to blame for the crash.

More and more sports are recognising the limited ability of human observers such as referees or track stewards, to take in what has happened in real time. In some sports the photo-finish evidence has been an essential tool for years, other sports bodies such as in football (soccer), are still debating whether technology should be used to assist the referee in making decisions. Now with our insight and understanding of the learning bottleneck, it is clear that a single observing referee will often be unable to judge the truth as observed by the collective audience.

In the last decade automated ball tracking and prediction systems have been developed to the point where they now are a valuable adjunct to many professional sports. The technology was developed from the science of tracking missiles and is now applied to the slightly more benign area of umpiring competitive professional sports. It is useful to compare tennis and cricket ball tracking systems such as Hawk-Eye with the process of human perception, as there are many similarities and a few significant differences.

Hawk-Eye provides an invaluable tool in tennis championships for judging whether a serve falls in or outside the service area, and is used to resolve line disputes between players and the umpire. In the game of cricket, Hawk-Eye offers an additional power; to predict what would have happened if the ball had not struck the leg of the batsman. The rules say that the batsman is judged to be "bowled out" if the obstructed ball would have hit the wicket if unobstructed and allowed to continue on its path. Hawk-Eye uses its computing power to predict what this theoretical trajectory would have been, and reveals whether or not it intersects the wicket.[314]

Hawk-Eye "observes" the ball using between 4 and 10 cameras spaced widely around the tennis court or cricket ground (whereas we have just two eyes with almost the same point of view). The raw information provided by the cameras is a sequence of discrete snapshots (the successive image "frames"). Software interprets the ball's position and timing from each image, and deduces a continuous trajectory and any impact points. This is achieved by prediction, using a set of rules that have been pre-programmed into the system using the programmer's knowledge of ball dynamics. It is also programmed with the rules of the games as it is required to generate judgements. It is able to calculate the precise position of the ball at specific locations such as the white line on the tennis court, the edge of cricketer's bat or the cricket stumps. Currently it can do so with an accuracy of approximately 3 millimetres, the thickness of the fluff on a tennis ball!

Measurements of eye movements of professional tennis and cricket players have revealed that the human eye observes the ball in flight, by similar brief fixations or snapshots, from which our mind deduces the trajectory.

However, we humans must learn the "rules" of the ball's behaviour by repeated observation and trial and error. Furthermore, the limited speed of our human responses may allow time for only 2 or 3 fixations during the ball's flight, limiting our own judgement accuracy when compared with that achieved by the Hawk-Eye system. However, the player's responses are remarkably fast when compared with the processing speed of these automated systems, which can take several seconds before they finally deliver a judgement.

These ball tracking systems predict something that has not actually been observed, and may not even have happened. They achieve this using an accurate model of the trajectory, just as the human sportsman does. The human umpire at a cricket match has to decide whether a ball that strikes the batsman's leg would otherwise have continued unobstructed to the stumps and so bowled him out. Hawk-Eye predicts an alternative future in a remarkably similar manner.

The difference between a human observer and Hawk-Eye is that Hawk-Eye is given its rules by its programmer, while we have to learn all of them. But a system that learns from its mistakes is capable of continually improving with experience. For most of life's activities this currently gives skilled humans an advantage over computing machines. However our sports activities are intrinsically designed to explore the limits of our abilities, both physical and mental, but systems such as Hawk-Eye have the potential to out-perform a skilled umpire, for the technology can continue to be developed further and is not constrained by human biology.

When time stands still

We have all watched slow motion replays of key sporting events on TV, but very occasionally some of us have a direct personal experience that appears to be in slow motion in real time. For most things that happen to us in adult life, we have previously experienced something very similar. We have seen that the more we learn, the less our experience depends on what we sense in the moment itself, but very occasionally we might have an experience which is almost entirely novel. For example, when we have a rare accident we may have no mental model of anything similar with which we can compare our sensations.

A biker friend of mine tells me: "When you fall off, time stands still. Everything seems to be in slow motion".[315] Assuming that he doesn't make a habit of it, he will have had very little similar experience to call upon during his accident, so must construct a new predictive simulation in real time. He probably struggled to build a conceptual model of what was happening to him, from scratch, so to speak.

In such situations our usually fast internal model has little or nothing to offer, almost everything is a new experience. So it's possible that the experience of slowing of time is a consequence of having to rely entirely on information derived at a much slower learning rate due to the bottleneck. We have to create a new model "on the fly", quite literally in my friends case. Something similar may occur when performing skills that demand very high levels of attention. Some professional ball game players report the feeling of the ball "slowing-down" before hitting it.[316]

Now we have numbers

At the very beginning of this book, I described how the richness of the world that we experience would require vast bit-rates of information to faithfully recreate through our technology, with some estimates suggesting we would need more than 10,000 Gigabits per second.

In the second chapter I showed that our eyes are *physically* incapable of sensing most of what we think we are experiencing, due to the biological limitations of the retina and optic nerve. I showed that the eye has very poor resolution across most of our field of view, and is only capable of resolving detail at the very centre of our vision. Experimental measurements of the performance limits of our eyes reveal a raw information capacity of around 6 Megabits per second.

Our eyes are our highest capacity sensors; similar estimates of the raw information capacity of our ears provide a much narrower figure of just 10 kilobit/s. These figures represent the ultimate limit in our ability to recognise sensations from the world around us that we are already familiar with. The implication is that our hearing is a thousand times less capable of comparing and recognising complexity. It is evident that an audio description of something such as a map is a poor substitute for a visual image.

Subsequently I showed that we are *mentally* incapable of absorbing even a tiny fraction of what is new within this sensed information. These last two chapters have revealed the hard evidence that the rate at which we can learn anything new is no more than a few tens of bits per second at most. Although our capacity to recognise familiar detail is far greater for vision than for hearing, our much narrower learning bottleneck appears to be the same for all our senses.

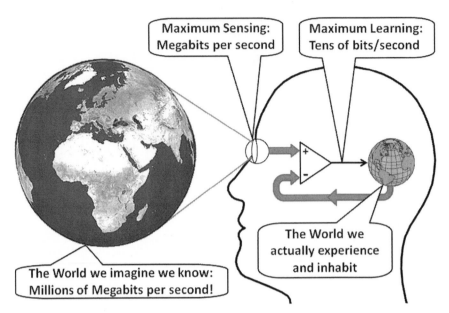

Figure 28: Information rates associated with sensing and learning.
The world we experience is based almost entirely on our past experiences.

Our ability to recognise the present is limited significantly by our sensors, and our ability to learn from the present moment is further limited to just a few tens of bits per second.

So there are two bottlenecks that limit our ability to experience the world in the present moment: First, our incredibly constrained ability to learn whatever is completely new to us, and second, the considerably wider recognition bottleneck that limits how fast we can compare what we expect with what we sense. Although this second recognition bottleneck is almost a million times wider, it is still surprisingly narrow when compared with what we imagine we experience.

In this chapter, I have described the surprising evidence for our learning bottleneck within the things we do, such as speaking, typing and our physical skills. Unfortunately, we cannot determine the maximum information rate of the spoken human voice, as currently no automated voice recognition system is sufficiently fast to follow it. Nor can we determine it using human listeners, as their own learning rate limits their listening capability, and they cannot differentiate between what they expect and what they sense. Similar problems occur when assessing the information rate of rapidly typing text whenever the information being typed is familiar language.

However, perhaps the most remarkable evidence for the bottleneck comes from experiments that measure the information rate associated with carrying out skilled physical tasks. We can do some physical tasks without sensory input, for example with our eyes closed, such as pedalling a bike. However, there are many tasks that can only be continued by observing the completion of various successive steps. This act of observation requires the subject to learn that they have achieved each step before continuing, and this learning part of the sequence dominates the speed at which fast skills can be performed.

The difficulty of performing a task such as moving a mouse pointer across the computer screen to click on a button can be characterised by the ratio of the size of the button to the distance required to be moved. This ratio can then be expressed as a number of bits of accuracy. We have seen that when such tasks are performed at the fastest possible speed, they correspond to an information rate of around ten bits per second, our learning bottleneck. Furthermore, similar rates are found across a variety of physical skills despite varying the amount of physical force required. This clearly demonstrates that the speed of these physical processes is limited by our mental learning capability.

When we examine sports skills from this perspective it is immediately obvious why practice is such a key requirement for human participants. This situation may be contrasted with that of a robot, possessing much faster sensors and information processing, yet without history. The inability of today's robots to compete with humans in our sports, suggests the future of skilled robots will lie in the ability to rapidly provide them with experience, whether taught (pre-programmed) by other experienced robots or humans, or learned during their normal operation. By comparing the processes used by sophisticated ball tracking technology at top sports events, with the process of human perception; we gain further insights into our ability to predict the future from the past and the present moment.

We now have a more precise understanding of the difference between recognising what is familiar, and learning what is new. In the next chapter I explore some of the implications for the process of education and our communication technology.

Chapter Seven

So What?

- The Objective Implications

"There is no such thing as an insignificant life, only the insignificance of mind that refuses to grasp the implications"
- Laurence Overmire

Let's now explore how knowledge of our learning and recognitions bottlenecks might impact our practical lives. So what if we can only absorb a few tens of bits per second of information?

Education and learning

Throughout our history it has been an advantage to learn at the fastest possible rate, so that our dependent young can become skilled knowledgeable adults at the earliest age. At its deepest level education is a poorly understood process. In the past, copying and repetition have been a major part of that process, whether learning how to put an edge on a flint, or memorising the seven-times table. Today, pupils have ready access to information through books, computers and the World Wide Web, so there is less emphasis on memorising facts, and more on learning how to use this information. Whether we are learning raw data or complex ideas, all require information to be communicated to our receptive minds, and the speed at which we can do so is of great interest. If there really is a learning bottleneck we would expect it to be most evident in childhood, when there is most to be gained by learning rather than by introspection.

For the first two decades of our life most of our learning is quite closely synchronised in time with our peers. In infancy, skills like walking and talking occur at broadly similar ages, and parents may get anxious if these stages are delayed relative to other children of a similar age. There can be many reasons why some fall behind in their schooling: a difficult home environment, poor physical or mental health, unskilled teachers. My grandmother was thought to be an unintelligent child in school, so her teacher made her sit at the back of the class. She was intelligent, but was also profoundly deaf, so putting her at the back where she could hear nothing simply confirmed the teacher's misdiagnosis.

Where conditions are far from ideal we see large variations in children's development versus age, and in extreme cases a child may remain almost completely uneducated. However, for the fortunate majority of children who are healthy, of average intelligence, and are supported by their families, we see much less variation, especially when they are provided with formal schooling in an environment supposedly optimised for their education. Learning rates then seem to be more closely aligned with age, in that we are happy to describe a pupil's academic level as "year 8" for example. In my own school, a few pupils were sufficiently bright to be considered capable of being taught two years ahead of their age, hence my classmates included some who were two years younger than me, but this is not a common practice.

It would seem therefore, that the innate *maximum* rate that young individuals can be educated does not vary by a large amount, certainly not by a factor of two. There is one exception to this: subjects such as maths show less correlation between age and ability, perhaps because maths education is almost entirely about understanding concepts, and much less about acquiring information. The speed of progress is probably limited more by the pupil's ability to manipulate very abstract ideas within their mind, than their rate of absorbing information. For all other subjects "education" seems like filling the fuel tank of your car, in that you can't do much to hurry it. You might argue that this synchronisation is just for the convenience and efficiency of the educational establishments, but even when pupils are individually tutored they rarely get significantly out of synchronism with their age. Where we see apparently gifted children acquiring particular skills at an unusually early age, it is often at the expense of other broader aspects of education, such as the development of the child's social skills.

It is too simplistic to imagine that we are only becoming more knowledgeable during the time when we are being taught. The process of integrating what we have taken in with what we already know seems to involve significant time when we are attending to other things. Insights and comprehension often comes when we are distracted from our studies. Furthermore, children who are privately tutored for a small fraction of the equivalent school day do not seem to suffer significantly. Yet those who are privately tutored for a similar duration to a normal school day do not show a dramatic benefit over those who receive a good but conventional education.

Is the process of education optimised? Is it likely that we could find a way of halving the number of years of formal education, or halving the number of term days? Who knows what the future might hold. However, this synchronisation of education with age may be a small piece of additional evidence in support of the idea of a learning "bottleneck".

We have seen that there is a fundamental limit to the rate that we can learn new information when expressed in bits per second. Could we use this insight to help us speed the process of education? When we examine the information rate of successful methods of learning within university education, we find that the process is already highly optimised. The process of formal education in universities typically consists of listening to spoken text in lectures, and reading written text, as typified by the phrase "to read for a degree" in law for example. The use of this phrase implies that the study of written text has been considered an efficient and effective strategy for learning.

In an earlier chapter, I showed that the information rate of language corresponds to the maximum learning rate bottleneck. There is obviously much more to education than this, for tutorials, workshops and projects all help the student integrate the information they have absorbed through lectures and reading, into effective conceptual ideas. However, for new information, language forms the primary conduit to the student's mind. So unsurprisingly, it seems that in the context of our learning bottleneck, universities already use an optimised process.

What about images? It is often said that "a picture is worth a thousand words", but if this were really true of their learning potential, shouldn't we ban *text* books from our colleges and Universities? When communicating graphical and spatial material, pictures can be a more effective than words, especially for ideas that are best expressed in two or more dimensions. A car repair manual would be quite ineffective without illustrations, but the majority of serious educational books used by our universities are "text" books.

You may be surprised at how little information is contained in a typical book when expressed in bits: From Claude Shannon's estimates of redundancy in language, the entire text of this book could be described using less than a Megabit of information. It is worth noting that the same total number of bits would only provide a few illustrations, so perhaps it is more accurate to say that a picture costs as many bits as a thousand words.

For adults, illustrations find their niche in publications whose purpose is for pleasure and entertainment, rather than education (my wife finds it amusing how I always enjoy a good map or a graph!). Newsagent's racks are dominated by magazines on food, fashion, hobbies and of course porn.[317] Though high resolution accurate colour images may not be ideal teaching aids, they are perfect for "coffee table reading", such as books on art, travel and interior design. Images can be easy on the eye, while text needs our attention. We can relax our gaze upon most images and still enjoy the view, but a defocused view of text yields nothing.

For the very young or illiterate, images are the preferred language; a child can recognise the image of a cat long before they can read the word "cat". Children's comics are an intermediate stage; mostly illustration, but with supplementary text, both of which contribute to the story.

The great power of words, is that they can convey a much wider variety of ideas than can a picture: "the ten year old dog smelled of freshly mowed grass, and barked with a high pitched wheezing sound for no apparent reason". A picture has to communicate everything visually, even if the ideas to be communicated are non-visual. In addition, while a picture can offer great detail, it is less effective as a guided teaching mechanism, because although a skilled painter or photographer will try to manipulate our gaze on a trajectory of their choosing, the viewer's point of gaze can choose from a multitude of possible journeys through the image.

From facts to theories

Education teaches us a whole range of things, from simple information, right through to highly complex ideas. In daily life those who know a lot of facts often command greater respect than those who know theories and have "grand ideas". The attitude is: a fact is a fact, and a theory is just someone's opinion. Indeed, someone who is full of ideas may be suspected of knowing little of practical use. The situation is completely reversed in academic institutions and places of leadership, where people with ideas are valued, especially if they have a track record for having used them to bring about useful change.

There are numerous TV quiz shows such as Master Mind[318], or Spelling Bees,[319] where the participants ability to recall information from memory is tested. Someone studying for such a quiz might read extensively and rehearse their ability to recall it. The extreme case is learning information by rote, which enables us to replay facts on demand while doing little to integrate this information into our mental models. Those who are highly "detail conscious" excel in such memory tasks, and our memory champions would probably perform well in such activities.

Our memory champions repeatedly demonstrate very high learning performance when they have trained themselves in the "journey method" that I described earlier.[320] So why do we not teach this method to pupils in schools so they can maximise their learning speed? It would certainly have helped me when I was required to memorise the names and dates of all the Kings of England in my History lessons at junior school.

However, nowadays we want our pupils to become much more than just efficient list memorisers. Healthy brains need to interpret incoming information on the fly, to integrate it with what they know already, enhancing their models of understanding and enabling them to steer attention towards the most valuable information. In contrast, those people with severe autism have a disability that impairs their ability to interpret details, but as a consequence, leaves them better able to remember every detail.

Today our potentially huge memory for detail is becoming a less valuable resource. Text books are now allowed into some examinations, and grades are now partly based on course work where students have ready access to Google and electronic databases. In the world outside educational establishments we have ready access to huge amounts of data via our mobile phones. We humans probably need to focus on the things we still can do better than machines; recognising familiar things and working with ideas.

When a teacher complains: "How many times do I have to tell you this?" they express their frustration at the pupil's inability to memorise something despite being exposed to it several times. The memory champions can do this, so why can't the average pupil (assuming that they are paying attention)? The most valuable things we can learn are concepts, but they are also the most difficult, taking the most time. When we have conceptually understood something we have an explanation that links the information we have absorbed. We have built a mental model that not only describes what we have already learned, but enables us to predict additional things that are probably true, yet have not actually experienced. Furthermore, our conceptual model can predict information forward and backward in time, to describe situations that we have no possibility of learning about through observation, being in a different place or time.

Here are a couple of examples of what I mean: In the UK people's weight has often been measured either in stones and pounds or just in pounds. I might be able to tell you that my current weight of 12stone and 13lb is the same as 181 pounds. If I was running a weight watchers group and were particularly detail conscious, I might simply learn a wide range of such pairings. However, if I learned the simple rule for converting stones to pounds and adding the pounds, I could convert absolutely any weight without any prior experience of those values; a rule may take a little longer to apply, yet is often far more valuable.

There is a well-known saying that it is better to teach a man to fish than to give a man a fish.[321] In a similar way, it is generally more valuable to be taught a rule, than expected to remember a lot of facts. There are exceptions; for example when no-one knows the rule, or when the rule is incorrect, or the task is simple and the speed of response is crucial.

By measuring my weight on different days I might learn a second rule: that it is increasing with time at a given rate in pounds per month. If I assume a constant rate of increase I might visualise that in ten years' time I will be seriously obese, so can apply some correction to my diet immediately. Applying the same rule of a constant rate of weight increase, but applying it backward in time, may suggest a nonsensical birth weight, perhaps even a negative weight, so when we learn simple rules we should also try to learn about the limits of their applicability.

We rarely learn a new concept in a single learning session. Difficult ideas can take many exposures, perhaps being presented with the idea in different ways before it "clicks" and we "get it". This is a reason why the teacher needs to repeat things. The paradox is that the moment that you understand something (the moment when "the penny drops"), it suddenly flips from feeling impossible, to having lost all insight into why it had seemed so difficult a moment ago. Good teachers remember the difficulty and so have patience.

Personally, I was never particularly proficient at holding lots of details in my mind - a bit of a disadvantage for a career in science you may think. In addition, I grew up with a distrust of facts dispensed by authorities and always wanted to understand the reasoning behind them, to know if they made sense. From my 'teens and right through university, whenever I was taught some new concept I initially felt that I was falling behind my fellow students. While they were happy to accept a method that they were being taught at face value, I still struggled to fully understand it. However, when I finally "got it", I frequently found that I had a deeper insight than many of them. So despite having many occasions when I felt distinctly dumb, I became comparatively skilled at exploring concepts.

Metaphors frequently provided me with a rich path towards understanding. We do not need to develop every insight from first principles, and it would be a very inefficient use of our time to do so. Our minds hold a range of models that can be applied right across the vast territory of our experience and knowledge. Sometimes we recognise the similarity in behaviour between something that we are seeking to understand, and something that we are familiar with in a completely different field. This is why a broad education is important; one never knows where one's next insight will come from. For example, if I was an automotive engineer and wanted to understand the rate at which the days lengthen immediately after the shortest day of the year, I might notice that the behaviour is similar to the velocity of a piston on a crankshaft. I would then realize that the day length would change most rapidly at the spring and autumn equinoxes.

Many of the techniques that aim to improve innovation skills such as TRIZ,[322] exploit the interchange of conceptual ideas between widely different fields, even at the very basic level. For example, the method might ask the question: "Can you solve this problem by turning it on its head?" Even though the problem one is trying to solve might be electronic, software, pharmaceutical or mechanical, an innovative solution can sometimes be found through the process of trying to interpret the idea of "turning it on its head" in these different domains (which is not always easy).

I have always been fascinated by the experience of suddenly feeling that I understand something, an Ah-ha or Eureka moment, for although it feels like a revelation, it reveals little or nothing about its own process. There is a huge difference between merely knowing the information, and possessing real insight. The first state is one in which I can only see the problem as a silhouette, a flat two dimensional representation that only has value in that particular situation. I associate this state with a dull ache in my head, and the feeling that I can't "get a handle on it". This kind of knowledge always makes me feel nervous, especially if I am required to communicate it to others, as I know that a simple childish question coming from a different angle will reveal that I really haven't a clue.

The second state is one of confidence and even pleasure (which may be short lived!). It feels as if my mind has created a multidimensional model, one that includes all the dimensions of the problem including time, and that I can mentally "rotate" this model and find a match between the silhouette it casts and what I see before me (which after all is only 2D in the optical sense). I feel confident that I have acquired a valuable tool, and grasped it firmly.

When my conscious mind is tightly focused on a problem, I am usually blind to any parallel experiences in completely different fields. However, it seems that my subconscious mind may be busy exploring its vast collection of conceptual models, seeking one that has similar qualities, for when my attention is distracted an interesting metaphor sometimes pops into my mind. Suitable distractions might be ironing a shirt, going for a walk or just a good night's sleep. My conscious mind must then decide whether it is a useful model or not. If it is, then I am rewarded with a burst of adrenalin and endorphins, and even a sense of euphoria.

So when we are being creative with ideas and gain a new insight by recognising a useful pattern, we experience a burst of well-being. Being creative is pleasurable in itself in whatever field. Perhaps we have evolved a mechanism that rewards us for crafting each new predictive skill. After all, developmental steps such as flint tools, fire and planting crops have been crucial to the survival of our DNA.

Understanding what is taught

"Any fool can know. The point is to understand."
- Albert Einstein

There is an important difference between learning and understanding; the acquisition of information does not necessarily lead to its use in effective conceptual ideas. Howard Gardner, who has written about the different kinds of human intelligence, says that "most students don't really understand most of what they've been taught?"[323] They have learned the data, but not integrated it into an effective mental predictor that subsequently enables them to use that information across the wider field of their experience.

In the world of physics, learning all the facts is not enough, for progress in ideas is only possible if students learn the concepts as these are powerful predictive tools. The Nobel Laureate Richard Feynman described his brief experience teaching in a particular South American University, where Physics was not taught conceptually, but instead as a liturgy or creed.[324] Students learned to accurately recite the various physical Laws without comprehending their deep meaning; "I finally figured out that the students had memorized everything, but they didn't know what anything meant", "So, you see, they could pass the examinations, and learn all this stuff, and not know anything at all, except what they had memorized". The format simply tested their ability to accurately recall sections of text, so despite being "educated" they graduated unable to usefully contribute to the world of physics, except perhaps to teach more students in the same way. This is an extreme case, where a scientific subject is taught as if it is a creed (the doctrinal statements being extracted from the recommended physics text book, written by a member of the faculty staff of course).

There are also those who have acquired a deep analytical knowledge of their subject, yet lack a broader conceptual insight. Many years ago I interviewed prospective employees for jobs as electronic engineers within our research laboratory. These were fresh graduates from the top UK Universities where they had studied many examples of quite complex electronic circuits. We only interviewed the best candidates, but I was looking for enthusiastic people who understood what they had been taught.

I presented each of them with a diagram of probably the simplest circuit they had ever seen in their degree course. It consisted of just three elements; a source of electric current, a capacitor and a switch.[325] All three were connected together in parallel, so there were only two connections in the entire circuit, it really couldn't get simpler than that. Then I would ask: "Starting with the switch closed, tell me what happens to the voltage across this circuit when I open the switch?"

Typically, ten percent of the candidates looked at me as if I was a complete idiot for asking, and immediately gave me the correct answer (the voltage rises from zero, increasing linearly with time). A capacitor is like a water tank, and electrical current is like water flow, so the level (the voltage) rises steadily with time. The other eighty percent were puzzled, as they had never been given such a simple example during their extensive (and expensive) education. Most insisted that "the voltage would rise exponentially", though could not decide what exactly that meant in this particular case. Some told me that I had "forgotten to include the resistor" in the circuit.

You see, they had been shown a worked example many times before in their course work which was similar but included a resistor. Connecting a resistor in parallel with the other three components would indeed have led to the voltage rising at an exponentially decreasing rate towards a steady level. (Using the water analogy, the resistor would be like a leak in the water tank).

Their failure to grasp the conceptual nature of such a basic aspect of electronics was a concern, but their reaction to being asked an unusual question was also revealing. One angrily accused me "why are you asking me something I don't know?", as if it was my fault he could not answer. I was not trying to embarrass the interviewees, merely to find out if they had a conceptual understanding of the topic in which they had acquired a detailed expertise, as evidenced by their degree certificate. The competent ones had less of a problem describing how more complicated circuits would behave, but I was surprised how few of them had grasped the conceptual nature of their chosen area of study.

When I told one of their university professors about my experience with his students, he simply refused to believe it. It was inconceivable to him, that they could have learned so much, yet still not "get it". His students' strength lay in their ability to deal with complex analytical problems, not necessarily in reducing these to conceptual insights. In time I gave up asking this simple question during the interviews, it just caused too much embarrassment, for all concerned.

So to summarise, the process of education would appear to have already been well optimised in terms of the teaching of simple information, in that it is primarily based around language with its inherent constraints. However, when it comes to ideas and concepts, these are acquired more slowly. A good teacher uses language to express a single idea in a succession of different ways, and eventually the penny drops for the pupil; the idea takes hold. If only there was a way to quickly implant ideas, to transplant conceptual models into another person's mind. Perhaps conceptual ideas are always going to be slow to absorb?

My own experience of education has left me with a failure to understand the nature of how I come to understand something. If I think something is clever, it means I do not fully understand it yet. Once I understand something, I cannot see what had been the problem. Study is obviously the key part, but there is something else less tangible. It feels as if I must stand patiently beside these external insights, anoint myself with associated information, and await the moment of realization, when insight mysteriously appears within my own mind, and I feel blessed.

How much of reality can we know?

Before moving on, let us briefly explore how our learning bottleneck might limit just how much we, as an individual, can possibly know about the reality we are surrounded by. The total objective information content of a human mind will be limited by the learning rate multiplied by the learning time; in other words the information rate multiplied by the total time that information flows in. What I mean by objective information, is the information arising from external reality, as opposed to anything that arises from within our mind through introspection.

Let us initially assume that our total learning time is 30 years. This could be the result of 8 hours a day every day for a 90 year lifespan. Those thirty years comprise 946,080,000 learning seconds. If we assume that we can learn at 20 bits/per second maximum when full attention is given, that would suggest a total of around 19 Gigabits, or 2.4 Gigabytes, significantly less than can be recorded on a single DVD.

But even this is grossly optimistic, as there is a very significant proportion of our time when we are not learning at the maximum rate, (or even not at all), for example when we are reflecting on what we already know, or simply performing a skilled action such as driving on our journey home. Just how much of that journey do we actually remember? As we saw with the record performances of memory athletes, learning performance falls off significantly with increased task difficulty. You may remember how difficult it is to study continuously for several hours, you need breaks, or your mind wanders.

If we devoted all our intellect to observing our world, we would have no time to construct and refine our internal models, and it is these predictive models which allow us to function so effectively with such a limited sensory information bandwidth. The fraction of time we are learning probably falls significantly with age, as our ability and enthusiasm to learn something new is reduced, or as the saying goes: "You can't teach old dogs new tricks".

As we gain the wisdom of age we capitalise on the increased value of what we already know, observing less and introspecting more. We have so much invested in our internal model of the world, our idea of how it is, that we may prefer not dig too deep among the foundations in case the whole edifice should be threatened. So one's entire life's experience of reality is based on information that could easily fit on a DVD, and an iPod could contain the totality of a whole family's experience.

It may seem too little information, but remember the fractal images I showed earlier, which revealed that great complexity can be created using a few simple rules. Could we imagine recording our life's sensory experiences so efficiently? If someone's learning was achieved almost entirely through reading text, then yes in principle. But in most realistic situations we do not know where our attention is located.

Consider our sense of sight, we may know that we only learn at 20 bits per second maximum, but what part of the image are we learning from? The best we could achieve would be to record the image that fell upon the retina, with the limited resolution that we know the retina provides us with. We learned that the information capacity of the eye itself is almost a million times greater, around 6 Megabits per second, so we would need many hundreds of thousands of DVDs at that rate. However, let us not forget the achievements of those who have no sight at all. The fact that they can be as knowledgeable as sighted people, suggests that a single DVD might be representative of our total learned information capacity after all.

Technology

Mankind has developed by using technology to gain advantage, whether by flint tools, bronze swords, steel guns, ploughshares, tractors, cars or planes. Until recently, most of our new technologies were mechanical devices, aimed at improving the speed and efficiency of growing our food, travelling, and increasing our military power. But this has now changed. Today, the majority of new technologies are based on electronics and information, and are capable of providing us with very large amounts of information.

Before progressing further, it will be valuable to consider some basic properties of our communication networks today. It is common practice to describe network capacity in bits per second as "speed", but this is a really misnomer as differences in the actual velocity are not what constrains the bit rate. Wireless information travels through the air at essentially the same speed as the speed of light (in vacuum). Similarly, information travels along cables at around two thirds of the speed of light, whether it is carried as electrical signals along copper conductors, or optical signals along optical fibre (the light is slowed in glass by the ratio of the refractive index). Hence all information that is communicated, either electronically or optically, spans the intermediate distance at speeds approaching the speed of light.

For short distances, the transmission delay may be dominated by other factors, such as the time taken to perform some electronic processing. This typically occurs at various pieces of equipment at either end of the system, and at intermediate branching locations. Communication via an information network is rather like road communication via a motorway network with a well maintained speed limit. If we want to maximise the rate at which we can communicate goods, we must use vehicles with greater carrying capacity (or more vehicles on multi-lane roads simultaneously) and avoid bottlenecks. So henceforth, when I use the term "speed" when talking about information, I mean information rates in bits per second, not velocity.

While simple dial-up technology offers speeds of 56 kbits/second, current broadband technology provides usable speeds ranging from a fraction of a Megabit per second, right up to many hundreds of Megabits per second, depending on the technology available (copper wire, wireless, optical fibre) and the distance over which the signals must travel. You will note that these bit rates are far greater than our observations of the maximum information rate that a human being can absorb, which it appears is a few tens of bits per second at most. Does this matter? Well not necessarily: If information is cheap to transport, there is little incentive to deliver it efficiently, especially if it makes the information easier to deal with at the far end.

Where our attention lies

Let's now explore whether our awareness of these bottlenecks might enable us to optimise some of those technologies in the immediate future, especially in the context of sound and vision. The bottleneck tells us that we can only absorb a small amount of information, but we can only exploit this knowledge if we know precisely where our attention lies. When our memory champions are competing, all their attention is focused on the memory task that they are presented with, so there is no doubt about what they are learning. However, in daily life, we can choose to focus our senses on many different aspects of the experiences we are exposed to. When we listen to words, we might focus almost entirely on the meaning of the words, as we would do when checking the winning lottery numbers. At the other extreme we could be listening to a poem or song, following the tune, the rhythm, or the emotional expression of the voice, and hardly notice the words at all. We can hear the same song a thousand times and still get the lyrics wrong.

With vision, there is a far greater range of possible places that we can focus our attention. We explore the scene before us, by shifting our gaze around the scene, in patterns that are generally unique to each individual. A woman drives by, in an open topped car, and we look; but how and where we look, will be determined by our personal interests. Do we look first at the woman, her clothes, or the car, its registration plate, its colour or make? Our attention may not be entirely located around our centre of gaze either. When I am sat at the wheel of my car at the traffic lights, my gaze may be focused ahead, but my attention might be on the colour of the traffic light in my peripheral vision.

In the next section I explore where knowledge of the learning and recognition bottlenecks can be exploited, and where it cannot. In order to do this, I will need to explain some of the basic principles behind our phone system.

A brief history of the phone

Alexander Graham Bell is famed for having invented the telephone in 1876 (and also for successfully patenting it), though over the previous thirty years others had developed much of the technology.[326] Indeed, it is now recognised that the Italian Antonio Meucci had invented the telephone before Bell, reportedly to connect his second-floor bedroom to his basement laboratory and thus communicate with his wife who was an invalid.[327]

For the next century the basic technology of the telephone stayed the same. A microphone converts the sound pressure waves that are emitted by the person speaking, into a fluctuating electrical voltage that is a simple replica of the fluctuating sound pressure. This electrical signal is conducted over telephone wires and routed via the exchange to the appropriate telephone receiver, where the electrical voltage drives an electromagnet that deflects a diaphragm to generate a pressure wave that is a replica of the original pressure wave at the microphone. This sequence is the basic mechanism behind the land-line telephone.

With the invention of transistors, digital electronics were introduced to an ever greater extent. The initial use was within the telephone exchanges, which by that time used electro-mechanical devices to steer the electrical signals to the appropriate recipients (originally, human operators swapped plugs to switch connections). Later, digital electronics were incorporated into telephone handsets to increase their functionality. The really big step was when the analogue electrical signals were converted to digital form, just ones and zeros. Completely acceptable phone quality was achieved by converting the analogue speech signal into digital form at 64 kilobits per second.[328]

This digitising of the signal provided two major benefits: The first was that these digital signals could be carried over vast distances without any detectable loss of quality whatsoever, provided that the signal was boosted regularly. For people used to the noise and interference on long distance phone conversations, both the quality of the sound and the depth of the silences were quite amazing. The second benefit was that now the signal was in digital form, it was very easy to interleave vast numbers of simultaneous phone conversations onto a single much higher bit rate connection. So for example, a thousand simultaneous phone conversations between two cities did not require a cable with a thousand wires, merely a single connection capable of carrying 64 Megabits per second (1000 x 64 kilobit/s). This principle, called "digital multiplexing", is used throughout all today's communication networks.

The development of optical fibre communications gave huge information carrying capability to the cables linking our cities. A single hair-thin fibre made of glass, could transport many millions of phone conversations simultaneously, so there was little need to consider more efficient ways of encoding the speech content of phone calls. However, the development of mobile phones changed this, and suddenly focused attention on ways of compressing speech information, ways to communicate the same phone message, but at a lower information rate. Now that we are aware of the bottleneck, we know that there is a theoretical limit to which normal speech might be compressed, of around 20 bits per second.

Compression and delays

It had been possible to make phone calls over radio for some time, but the technology was cumbersome and had limited range. Transmitted radio wave energy dissipates in two dimensions at once, as it spreads out in all directions (e.g. up and down and left & right). So the power falls off as the square of distance. A factor of ten increase in distance, would need a hundred times more power to be transmitted. If one wanted to make a single hop wireless phone-call across the globe, it would require an aerial of huge proportions, plus a huge power-hungry transmitter, so would not be mobile in any sense whatsoever. For example, when Marconi first transmitted simple Morse signals across the Atlantic in 1902, he needed 25 kilowatts of power and an aerial 200 feet high and 200 feet diameter.

The breakthrough in mobile phone technology came with the idea of splitting the territory into a large number of comparatively smaller cells, each provided with its own transmitter/receiver mast (hence the term "cell-phone"). The signals are carried between adjacent cells, either by cables or microwave links, to form a network of cells (a "cellular network"). So for a "mobile" phone call over long distance, only the very first and last parts of the connection need be communicated by radio waves, just the connections between each of the two handsets and their respective neighbouring masts. Because cell-phone networks in different cities across the globe could easily be interconnected together through long transcontinental and transoceanic cables, the mobile phone user experiences the illusion that they are making a single-hop radio connection across huge distance.

Early mobile phones were big power-hungry "bricks". If mobile phone networks were to become practical and convenient, the handsets had to be made more energy efficient. It takes energy to transport information. More information requires greater power to transmit it over a given distance, and a mobile phone that needs more power must either have a bigger heavier battery, or is disadvantaged by a shorter battery life. In addition, low efficiency means shorter range, so more mobile phone masts are needed. Suddenly, it became important to know just how low an information rate one could use and still achieve acceptably clear phone communication.

Research into the science of speech intelligibility resulted in techniques for electronically compressing speech data. These potentially allow a dramatic reduction in the information rate required to communicate speech. In principle, huge reductions can be achieved using enough computing power. However, there are two factors that limit how much compression is useful in a mobile phone: First the computation process involved in compressing and decompressing the signal (before and after transmission respectively) consumes significant battery power, so there is no point in saving transmitter power if the additional computing electronics within the handset consumes more than is saved.

The second factor is more fundamental: Compression of the speech signal and its subsequent decompression take time to perform, and greater compression intrinsically results in longer processing delays. In a two-way conversation, additional delays are an unnatural experience. In an ideal constructive two-way conversation, each participant takes their turn in speaking, and listening to the other participant. There is a brief silent period during when the conversation switches from one party to another. Hence, a conversation generally consists of alternating speech segments and silent periods. When face-to-face, both participants share a common reality of the conversation: one speech segment is separated from another by pauses that are identically perceived by both participants. Using the briefest pauses and other clues enables useful conversations where the words almost overlap. However, when there are delays greater than 160-200 milliseconds in what is heard, they seriously interfere with the spontaneity and perceived intimacy of the communication, as the listener waits for the response. It may not be immediately obvious, but pauses in speech convey meaning, intended or not.

Satellites cause delays. Before our world was linked by a web of optical fibre networks, intercontinental and transoceanic calls would frequently be carried via synchronous or geostationary satellites.[329] In order for these satellites to remain in a stationary position in the sky above the same point on the Earth's surface, they must make a complete orbit just once every twenty four hours in order to precisely track the rotation of the earth. This is a very slow orbital rate compared with most satellites and is only achieved by placing satellites at a considerable distance from the Earth, around 35,786 kilometres.

A phone conversation there and back via one such satellite is subject to a delay of more than a quarter of a second each way, and calls from one side of the globe to the other required two such hops at least, over a total distance of 4 x 35,786 km = 143,144 km, giving a delay of more than half a second each way, so taking a full second for the round trip. Someone saying "Darling, do you love me?" to their distant partner on the other side of the world might misconstrue their lovers delayed response as a newly found reticence!

Today you are unlikely to experience such delays on the phone yourself for reasons I will explain shortly. However, you will probably be familiar with the consequence of this delay when watching video news reports from various news "hot-spots" around the world. Satellite communications is the only solution when communicating from places where conventional land-line access is unavailable or unreliable. You will probably have noticed that when the man in the studio asks the roving reporter a question, they do not react for a moment or so because the signal containing the question has not reached them yet. It makes the roving reporter seem a little dumb sometimes, so they often adopt a strategy of nodding their head while waiting for the next question. We the viewers may think that the nod indicates that the reporter is listening to the question, but actually they are still waiting to hear it.

The broadcaster could introduce a delay into the communication that we experience from the man in the studio, and this would halve the delay we experience for the roving reporter, but would make the man in the studio seem equally dumb. The studio probably feels that we will make more allowances for a dusty reporter in the field (especially when seen over a poor quality, low resolution image), than we would for the neat High Definition newsreader in the studio.

Today, disturbing delays on long distance calls are a rarity. Fibre cables are now the preferred means of carrying almost all intercontinental phone communications, primarily due to the very low cost, but also the low transmission delay when travelling over the much shorter direct path across Earth's surface. For example, the two-way delay in crossing the Atlantic via optical fibre cable is just 60 milliseconds. However, mobile phone systems require signal compression, and this is now the dominant delay in most mobile phone conversations.

Any conversation that is subject to large delays requires a more formal disciplined way of speaking. No mobile phone user would want such long delays, so mobile phones constrain the degree of compression to keep the delay within an acceptable value. Typical GSM mobile phones manage to compress the speech down to 13 kilobit/s, while still maintaining much of the individuality of the speaker's voice.

Military voice communication systems can operate with information rates as low as 2.4 kilobits per second by sacrificing more of the speaker's voice qualities. There may indeed be strategic advantages in concealing the speaker's identity. Such systems are still intelligible, though sound somewhat like the famous physicist Stephen Hawking. Incidentally, computer synthesised speech has improved significantly since Stephen first started using his synthesised voice. He could certainly get a better quality "voice" using today's technology, but the sound of his voice has become too much of a personal trademark for him to want to upgrade now![330]

But what if the delay is not a significant concern, such as in a one way communication where time synchronisation is not required, like listening to a pre-recorded talk? Just how much can an audio signal be compressed without losing key information? Of course it depends on what we consider as information: obviously the message itself, but what about the identifiable character of the voice, the pitch, the intonation. Speech synthesis systems such as Stephen Hawking's voice system, or ebook text-to-speech facilities, are seldom troubled by the signal processing delay (latency) associated with high levels of compression.

If the message is really only the text, and long delays are acceptable, then in principle the message could be compressed down to the narrow width of the learning bottleneck, around 20 bits per second without losing any information. This could be achieved by using software to convert speech to text, followed by software to compress the text based on Shannon's insights into language redundancy, and of course reverse the process at the receiving end.

Next I explore how our bottleneck impacts acoustic experiences beyond mere words.

When words are not enough

When we use a phone, our primary interest is in the message, we generally do not care that we are listening with only one ear, to a monaural audio communication of limited quality. High fidelity is not a requirement, we would only complain if poor sound quality impaired our ability to understand what was being said, or to recognise the speaker. However, when we listen to a well narrated play, or to music, the situation is completely different since we hunger for acoustic realism, for the sense of an acoustic scene spread out before us faithfully replicating the experience of being there.

Despite the richness of the experience of listening to a concert, and the complexity of modern surround sound systems, we possess just two audio sensors, our two ears. These allow us to determine the approximate bearing of sources of sounds from left to right, and when we hear a sound that interests us, we can orientate our head to help us locate and "focus" on the sound. Similarly, our pinnas (the external bits of our ears) modify the spectrum of the sound that reaches our ear-drums depending on its elevation and whether the sound source lies behind us. So although we only possess two acoustic sensors, within our mind we are able to build a more detailed spatial representation of the acoustic scene that lies around us.

In the earliest days of stereo recording, the stereo effect was so novel that it was common to arrange for one instrument to be heard solely through one speaker on one side, and a vocalist to be heard solely through the opposite speaker on the other side. It was convenient for the recording studio, as only a single microphone was needed if the two parts of the performance were recorded separately and subsequently combined. This produced a completely artificial effect, but one quite novel compared with previous experience of monaural sound, so it was initially very impressive to the first-time owner of a new stereo system such as myself.

Sound engineers experimented with what they called "Dummy Head" recordings, in which a pair of tiny microphones were placed one in each ear of a replica human head. When such recordings are listened to on headphones the effect is very realistic, except that the sounds recorded are only appropriate to a single fixed orientation of a listeners head. It is not possible to turn one's head towards the virtual instrument and experience what would be heard in a live situation, i.e. change the balance of the sounds heard in both ears such that the sound still appears to originate from the same location. Modern recordings of live musical performances are made by synthetically constructing a stereophonic sound scene from multiple recordings using a large number of individual microphones, each placed close to the individual performers or instruments. Later a skilled sound engineer "mixes" these to produce an effective sound stage suitable for multi-speaker sound systems.

We cannot predict where a listener's attention will be focused when they listen to high quality sound. When an experienced instrument player listens to a full orchestra they may choose to focus intensely on the sound of their own kind of instrument, as that is where their discriminatory skills will excel. We have no way of knowing this internal state of mind, so although we know that the learning bottleneck indicates that we cannot take in more than 20 bits per second, we cannot optimise how the information is encoded or transmitted to take advantage of it. However, we do know something about the limited capability of the ears as sensors. Ditchburn's earlier estimate of the information capacity of the human ear is about 10,000 bits per second, and this implies an ultimate theoretical limit for the compression of Hi Fidelity sound, with no detectable impairment.[331]

Limited Vision

I started my journey by considering the requirements for a HiFi visual display, as I described in the introduction. Now that we understand so much more about how we actually see, let's explore whether we can take advantage of the bottleneck to simplify things. What interests us may lie anywhere within the scene in front of us, and with our sense of vision we can make use of knowledge of our point of gaze. Remember that our eyes can only resolve fine detail around the very centre of our vision, so we know that any spatially detailed information we take in, must be coming from the small region around the centre of our gaze.

When we view a high resolution display screen, we are actually only able to see high resolution over the tiny part of the screen that we happen to be focusing on at that moment; the rest of the screen is experienced by our eye as a blurred low resolution image. This may sound implausible, but when I was researching possible uses of eye tracking, I devised an experiment that allowed me to demonstrate this. I wrote a program that modified the display on my computer screen such that the image was blurred everywhere except within a small central region around where my eyes were focused. My eye tracking spectacles provided the necessary signal to steer this small high resolution window around the screen, tracking where I was looking.

I was able to demonstrate the effect most effectively by filling the screen with text and reading it without difficulty, despite that fact that most of the screen was blurred to the extent that the text was totally unreadable. Text is especially sensitive to being blurred. For most other things we look at, the information that we take in, reduces gradually with increased blurring, but with text, almost all the information lies in the detail, and when the detail is lost we have nothing. This is why the task of reading is the one most in need of good eyesight or corrective spectacles.

A conventional 2D image, such as a computer screen or a painting, is a device for broadcasting an essentially identical image to multiple viewers. Each point within the image radiates light energy in a wide range of directions, so be seen by as many eyes that have a view of the image. A real 3-dimensional object broadcasts different mainly 2-dimensional images to different viewers, depending on their position relative to the object. But if a synthesised image is only to be viewed by one individual, the image details could in principle be tailored to suit just one pair of eyes.

I speculated that one might provide the effect of a high resolution image transmission system, but with a much lower information rate (and using less light energy) if the viewer's point of gaze information were transmitted back to the transmitting terminal. This could enable the transmission process to concentrate more visual detail specifically within that central region of the viewer's eye. What if we had a display that tracked the retina, and whose pixels were precisely matched to the varying ability of the retina to resolve detail as it decreases away from the centre of our gaze? Then in principle we could provide the experience of a perfect image provided we matched or exceeded the raw information capacity of the human eye, which Ditchburn's estimated to be 6 Megabits per second.

Such technology is within the capabilities of today's eye tracking technology, but it is currently cumbersome and expensive. More significantly, point of gaze tracking systems would be required for each additional viewer, as multiple viewers are likely to be gazing at different parts of the picture. The idea was a non-starter, partly for this reason, but mainly because developments in fibre optic transmission had made the transmission of conventional video so cheap to implement.

The ultimate low capacity videophone

We have seen how the sound of a phone conversation between two individuals is more amenable to compression because our attention is focused almost entirely on the textual message, (which we now know has considerable redundant content). Similar clever tricks are also possible within the technology of videophone conversations. We might expect that adding video to a two way speech conversation would greatly increase the information rate required. However, when we analyse our point of gaze during such interactions, we find that our eyes spend almost all of the time focusing on the corners of the mouth and the eyes, moving between them, tracing out a triangle, or indeed not paying attention to the face at all in order to concentrate on the voice.

So vision does not add a lot of valuable information to a two-way conversation; there is even evidence that it is easier to spot people who are lying when only the sound is available.[332] However, when an image of the other participant is available, our eyes may seek out visible clues to the emotional response of the individual, which are dominantly the eyes and mouth. In addition, when the audible speech is difficult to comprehend some degree of additional lip-reading can resolve ambiguities. So an ideal videophone system would provide greatest visual clarity around these parts of the face.

This process has been taken to the extreme in research towards a potentially very low information capacity view-phone system. The system animates a locally synthesised model of the speaker's mouth, instead of continually transmitting a dynamic image of it.[333] The details of the model of the mouth are transmitted at the start of the communication, for example as a simple "wire frame" model representing a range of possible mouth expressions (A wire frame model is a visual presentation of a three dimensional or physical object used in 3D computer graphics).

At the distant receiver, this computer generated model of the speakers mouth is then animated, rather like a very sophisticated ventriloquist's dummy, using a relatively small amount of additional information from the distant speaker. The rest of the speakers face can be transmitted at a lower frame rate and lower resolution. Though this approach is very speculative, it could enable the image within a view-phone system to be transmitted using as little as one kilobit per second of additional data. (It is also a step towards making realistic telepresence robots, where the speaker's mouth movements are transmitted to a remote location where they animate a physical model of the speaker's mouth). However, if the viewer's attention were to move away from the mouth to the face in general, they would see an unnaturally static and passive face and eyes, (typical of individuals who have used too much botox). The experience might be disturbing, for we are highly sensitive to any unnatural facial behaviour.

What about Data?

What does the bottleneck tell us about the transmission of data? We used to think that faster data rates would always be of increasing value when communicating with people, but the limited rate of our learning bottleneck tells us that there is a diminishing benefit of faster information rates, especially for non-visual and inter-personal information. Although much of our entertainment is provided in the form of video, whether through TV or Internet video, most of our learning still comes via text, and we have already seen how text is quite an efficient channel for communicating information, especially when in digital form.

Evidence for this lies in the surprising success of communication methods that are very limited in their information capacity, such as SMS texting. While the phone companies were envisaging a lucrative data-rich future, with customers demanding lots of voice calls and video, they suddenly found that the demand for simple SMS texting was increasing at a startling rate. In 2010 it was the most widely used data application in the world, with 6.1 trillion SMS text messages being sent.[334]

When compared with the transmission of speech, the size of an SMS text message is trivially small, just 1120 bits maximum, yet many of today's phone users prefer to communicate via a text message, rather than speak human to human. After all, if time is important, an SMS text message is very succinct.

Even with our high speed Internet, low speeds are sufficient to meet many demands. Twitter, the popular social networking web application, constrains the information per "tweeted" message to just 140 characters, yet 120 billion of them are now sent each year. Such brief messages appear quite cryptic when viewed by unfamiliar users such as myself, as they force the user to think how to compress the message and be more efficient in encoding language. The availability of an error free digital channel makes the redundancy of normal language less valuable.

If these forms of communication become dominant in our society it may change the way we communicate in general, but there is a risk that we may lose the skills of intimate vocal communication, and perhaps also of writing anything of significant size or depth. Roughly half the "tweeted" messages are "pointless babble" or valuable "social grooming" depending on your point of view, but this shows that there is a need within our society to maintain our relationships by exchanging little pieces of information, to chat, to gossip.

Who would have imagined a decade ago that a network of such limited information capacity would be so successful?

The Internet

The total international Internet bandwidth has increased seven-fold over the last five years, reaching 76,000 Gigabits per second by 2011. This equates to 34,000 bits per second for each Internet user worldwide.[335] This is more than a thousand times the human learning bottleneck, so it is evident that we are increasingly able to provide vast quantities of information to everyone. It is as if we are given almost instant access to the greatest library in the world, and in a real sense we have, in the guise of the World Wide Web. Not so long ago, it took considerable effort to research any one topic. Now we are spoilt for choice, there are so many web pages with opinions on any single topic, so now the challenge is sorting and sifting between them.

The ease of making our own opinions available to the world means that in addition to all the valuable content, there are now plenty of poorly thought-out ideas floating around in cyberspace. The fact that we have a voice can give us the illusion that we have authority, and untested opinions propagate freely. Ideas that are attractive can draw together a whole community of supporters, even when contrary to the evidence. Prime examples are: The 9/11 conspiracy theories, claims that President Obama is not a US citizen, or that Fluoridation of water supplies is a communist plot.

There is of course a flip-side to this, in that speculative ideas that might previously been ignored can now be aired and explored. In the fields of science offbeat ideas can be tested and then accepted, or rejected if found wanting, all leading to a deeper consensus knowledge. In other areas of our lives, such as the arts, opinions rule. There is no movement towards global consensus as there is with science, but instead the tendency towards widely separated islands of what is of special interest, and what is "cool".

In this chapter I have explored the implications for education and for technology. Perhaps it is no surprise to find that the process of education is already well optimised around the bottleneck. However, it does reinforce the greater value of efficiently communicating ideas, rather than simply presenting students with an excess of information and subsequently testing them on it.

A simple calculation of the maximum information that one person can ever absorb in their lifetime, leads to remarkably small numbers of bits when compared the data we now store on our home computers, emphasising the adage that "it's not what you've got, it's what you do with it that counts".

We also looked at how the bottleneck relates to our communication technology, both historically and today. Insight into our bottleneck makes it much easier to explain the unexpected success of low information rate services such as SMS texting and Tweets.

Now in Part Three I risk exploring what the bottleneck means for you and me personally.

Part 3

The Subjective Implications

Chapter Eight

Now it gets personal

"We all see with memory. Even if we look together we can't see the same things. We're all alone"
- David Hockney, artist [336]

We are all alone

We have learned how our experience of the present, is almost entirely a prediction based on our history. Now we must confront the fact that it is not based on the world's history, but our own personal life experience. Probably most of us are already uncomfortable with the idea that our experience of reality is not an immediate truth, but a simulation. Now I will reveal how our simulated reality is unique to each and every one of us. This is where it "gets personal". Some of the ideas can be unsettling, as they call into question much of what has seemed solid ground.

The idea that we can share an experience is an illusion, as our unique internal historical model of reality dominates our moment by moment perception of now. This means that almost everything we experience is subjective, but because we can agree on many aspects of our shared history we experience the illusion of objective reality. As infants, we learn to sign up to this consensus reality since that is what makes us social and civilised beings, as I discovered soon after my mother told me the facts of life.

As a participant in this consensus reality, I can make three key assumptions:

1/. There is a reality out there. (Admittedly, this is an act of faith on my part, but without it, mental illness beckons.)

2/. Each of us runs a unique simulation of it within our mind, based on our limited experience of what is out there. (Information absorbed directly through our senses first-hand, and second-hand through what we have been told, read, or seen on TV)

3/. Most of what we experience in the present moment is based on our unique history-based internal simulation.

So the Now experience contains only about $1/1000,000,000,000$ of Now. The rest is history, our own personal history. (Based on the ratio between the information rate of our learning bottleneck, and the earlier estimates of the information rate corresponding to the experience of visual perception.)

Your "Youniverse"

When you or I consider the universe, we are referring to our personal idea of what is out there. For the purpose of this book, I shall call it your "youniverse", to distinguish it from the actual universe that we assume exists out there. But just as the words "youniverse" and "universe" sound identical in English, none of us can know the difference between our own "youniverse" and the universe itself.

To help clarify the difference between them, consider the differing levels of detail in each. It is easy to imagine that objects in space are increasingly fuzzy at greater distances because this is what we generally observe. However, the universe probably exhibits interesting detail throughout its entirety: Recent space probes to Saturn have revealed the surprising complexity of its rings and we are now discovering that many distant stars also possess planetary systems.

In comparison, one's youniverse is a very distorted place; it is person-centric, the amount of detail being entirely dependent on what one has observed and learned during one's life. It is built entirely from what we personally know, not what is. For example, I will know more about my own body, my own clothes, my own car, my own journey to work, my own hobbies, my own friends, my own job, than I do about anything else or anyone else. A professional astronomer may know quite a lot about a particular galaxy of interest, yet know less about the Moon than many enthusiastic amateur astronomers. For the rest of us though, almost all our knowledge is about things on this planet, with negligible knowledge about the rest of the universe.

"In an infinite universe, the one thing sentient life cannot afford to have is a sense of proportion."

- Douglas Adams[337]

If we were to construct a scale model of the universe in our living room, nothing that we are familiar with would be large enough to be visible, because the universe is so vast and we are so small in comparison. Yet if we constructed a model of our youniverse, in which the amount that we know about things, (hence the complexity of our mental model), were used to scale their relative sizes, the room would be crammed full of familiar things, as that is the way our mind is filled.

For most of us, the familiar place where we live and work would probably occupy almost as much of our youniverse as the rest of the world put together. For a world expert on the disease Malaria, it might also contain a hugely detailed mosquito that occupied more of the space than their own family. So when we consider the relative knowledge we each possess about different things, there are vast differences in the depth of our information. For some matters, we have knowledge of our ignorance, for example, I know almost nothing about the malaria disease. For other topics such as politics, our confidence in our own opinion is largely unrelated to the level of detail in our knowledge.

There are as many different youniverses, as there are people on the planet. Each of us inhabits a youniverse that is unique to our self alone, and is the only one that makes sense to us. No other individual will have had exactly the same experiences from exactly the same viewpoint. True, there will be many common features within our youniverses: For example, names such as Adolf Hitler, Albert Einstein and Elvis Presley can be found in most of them, but often with different attributed meanings.

Despite the differences between our youniverses, we find ways of interacting with others that avoid too much conflict. Consider these three statements:

1/. M********* United is the world's greatest football team.
2/. Men have set foot on the Moon.[338]
3/. This "Kilogram weight" weighs 1000 grams.[339]

I know and accept that the first statement is only likely to be true in a few people's youniverses. The second I assume is true in most people's youniverses, and can be tested by asking other people's opinion, while the third can be tested rigorously through repeatable scientific experiments.[340]

The fact that this last one can be argued to have some testable objective truth paradoxically makes us less passionate about it.

Alone in your private youniverse

Some ideas are very seductive, such as believing that my own nationality, religion, colour, sex or football team is the best. However, ideas that make us feel uncomfortable are much more difficult to accept, ideas such as: We are insignificant in the universe. There may be no point to life. I may have no free will.

While we can be shown the evidence for ideas such as these, it is often easier to accept a comfortable untruth than a scenario that threatens to leave us feeling alone in our personal universe. This is the problem posed by multiple youniverses. What happens to all those people in my life that I currently feel close to, if I realize that my only experience of them is through my own mental simulation of them? Surely I have lost a very important part of my life and am isolated, perhaps feeling alone? If I truly were the last human alive on this planet, I might not want to live.

The reality is that we do interact with others, and by and large we establish a rapport and agreement on what the world is made of. We happily accept that the visual world continues to exist when we close our eyes. So in our daily lives we live as if it is all "out there", and that a single objective reality is plain to be seen and experienced by anyone. However, for the purposes of this book and the implications of the bottleneck, I would like you to remember that the truth is different. The "mind's eye" has no optics, no lens and no screen. We can only imagine the world that we find ourselves in, it is something that we must dream up.

The "Many Worlds" theories

You may find this talk of many different youniverses confusing, but a remarkably similar idea already exists within the world of physics, and it may be useful to explore this area a little. The "many-worlds" theory is an alternative interpretation of quantum theory first proposed in 1957 by physicist Hugh Everett, as a way of making sense of some of the bizarre implications of the theory.[341] [342]

The world of physics used to be a very reasonable place, at least it was until the development of ideas of quantum theory which is now the bedrock of so much of today's technology. Without it we would have no transistors, lasers, optical communications, or mobile phones, so the theory is thoroughly validated by experimental evidence. Yet some aspects (of the widely accepted Copenhagen interpretation[343] of quantum theory) are deeply unsettling to most scientists, for quantum theory implies that the actual state of something may only become physically real at the moment when it is observed or measured, not beforehand. Until that point, some knowledge is fundamentally hidden.

Physicist Erwin Schrödinger was sufficiently disturbed by these implications that in 1935 he devised a "devilish" thought experiment to confront his colleagues with the mind-blowing consequences of the new theory if proven.[344] He described an experiment in which a cat, now known famously as "Schrödinger's Cat", is placed in a sealed box with a mechanism that kills the cat with cyanide gas if triggered by the detection of a radioactive particle from a radioactive source, all contained within the box. After leaving the box sealed and the cat unobserved for sufficient length of time that there is 50% chance that a detected particle has triggered the cat's death, we might choose to open the box and would expect to find the cat either dead or alive with equal probability.[345]

So far so good, but quantum theory tells us that until the box is opened and the cat's condition observed, the cat exists simultaneously in a superposition of two states, one dead the other alive. In other words, the death of the cat (if that is the result) only becomes a physical reality from the moment it is observed. Schrödinger never proposed that the experiment should be performed, but by choosing to describe his thought experiment using a soft furry cat he forced his colleagues to confront the more bizarre implications of quantum theory in relation to our everyday world. As famous physicist Neils Bohr is quoted as saying: "Anyone who is not shocked by quantum theory has not understood it"![346]

The many-worlds theory was introduced as a way of avoiding this paradox of physical reality being caused by the observer. In this theory, whenever there are alternative possibilities[347] "the world" divides into separate worlds, in each of which one or the other of these possibilities are solid truths, not woolly probabilities. For example, when I reach a fork in the road, my single world splits into two worlds. In one world I take the left fork and in the other I take the right hand one. I continue to experience my journey in just one of these worlds, yet the many-worlds theory suggests that the other world continues to exist equally somehow, somewhere, yet completely inaccessible to me.

Prior to this idea, reality had been viewed as a single unfolding history. The many-worlds idea views reality as a many-branched tree, where every possible outcome is realized by the repeated splitting of reality into successively more universes. While I who finally observe one experimental outcome occupy this universe, my twin who was absolutely identical up until that moment, now occupies a different universe, parallel but diverging, based on the opposite outcome. In one of these universes the cat lives, in the other it is dead and both these scenarios existed long before I opened the box.

The idea has been developed in various forms, but most scientists would still prefer to believe that there is only one universe, the one that we are in. However, the many-worlds theory provides ready explanations for several of the otherwise inexplicable aspects of our universe. For physicists the theory implies that almost all possible alternative histories and futures are real, each representing an actual universe, though some universes may have no future.[348] [349]

These worlds are essentially completely separate, and encompass all possibilities, since every possible outcome of every event defines or exists in its own "history" or "world". Put more simply, the theory suggests that there are a very large and possibly infinite number of universes, and everything that could possibly have happened in our past, but did not, has indeed occurred in some other universe or universes.

The idea may seem absolutely crazy, and is irritatingly difficult to disprove, (as we can only observe our own universe). However, it is attractive to physicists who have struggled to come up with better explanations for some of the weird things that they observe. For example, one strange property of the universe we find ourselves in, is that there is no obvious scientific reason why certain universal fundamental physical constants of our world, should be finely tuned to just the precise values that have enabled life, and the probability of this being by chance ought to be almost negligible.

It is suggested that if any of these fundamental constants were slightly bigger or smaller, the universe would be unlikely to lead to the establishment and development of matter, astronomical structures (stars, planets, and galaxies), the diversity of chemical elements, or to life as it is presently understood. The many-worlds theory neatly solves the probability problem, by saying that there are an almost infinite number of universes. We naturally find ourselves in the one with just the right parameters for life.

So if what we choose to look for, does indeed influence the successive splitting of our universe, then what we think and how we think will in some way determine the nature of the particular universe that we subsequently find ourselves in. Hence, if a new universe is created every time a decision is made to look for a particular logical hypothesis, then we may inevitably end up in a universe that is surprisingly well explained by the patterns of mathematics.

More could be less

The idea of a near infinite number of physical universes, feels very irrational, and wasteful, especially when we are used to ideas of conservation of mass, energy etc., so it is difficult for us to conceive of so much of everything. However, there is one very interesting idea that dramatically changes all that. It is based on the fact that an entire ensemble is often much simpler than one of its members. For example the minimum information content of a number, is the information required to define the shortest computer program that will produce that number as its output.

So the following number may appear long and complicated to describe: 1.41421356237309504880168872420969...., but it is simply the square root of 2, or $2^{1/2}$, expressed to a large number of decimal places.[350]

If a rule totally describes something complex, then the information content of that something is no more than the information content of the rule. If we apply this idea to the multiverse, it suggests that we need less information to describe all possible universes, than we need to describe just one specific universe. The universe we see could only be described using a huge amount of precise detailed information, but all possible universes could be defined by running a simple iterated program, that repeatedly steps through all possibilities.[351]

An excellent example of this approach is the beautiful image from part of the Mandelbrot set that we saw earlier in Chapter 4 (figure 18). If you remember, it was generated by successively repeating a very simple equation, and the same equation generates an infinitely complex image that extends to infinity in all directions.[352] Furthermore, slight differences in the starting conditions leads to completely different patterns.

So, surprisingly, provided that we include all possibilities, all possible universes with all possible physical constants, the amount of information required to describe the entire situation is relatively modest, and indeed probably much less than we currently need to describe the single complex universe we find ourselves in. So we have no need to reject the many-worlds theory because of its wastefulness.

We used to have a physics that made sense wherever the universe is observed from, indeed we would describe it as if we had access to an external Gods-eye-view of it, though that is clearly a nonsense as we are inside it. More recently, the question of what happens to information falling into a Black Hole has shown that for physics to make sense, we must restrict its description of the universe to what a single observer can see.[353] [354] So even in the world of physics we have lost our objective idea of the universe.

The purpose of this brief diversion into the world of physics has simply been to introduce two ideas: The key role played by the observer of reality, even within the solid field of physics, and the idea of many coexisting worlds. I am not suggesting that these physics concepts provide a physical basis for what follows, just that these ideas are not just confined to the world of psychology.

If like me, you find all this head-numbingly difficult to comprehend, just console yourself by knowing that most physicists find the idea of a near infinite number of *physical* universes, just as difficult to grapple with as most of us find the idea of multiple *psychological* youniverses. Soon I will show how this idea of personal youniverses can also help resolve imponderables, especially in the arena of personal communication, but first let's delve a little deeper into some of the things that this idea of multiple physical universes throws up.

We have been considering two kinds of multiple universes, so we need to clarify the differences: The ideas in this book focus on multiple *personal* psychological universes, (youniverses), each of us inhabiting our own, separately. In contrast, the idea of multiple universes within physics is that although multiple physical universes exist, all the people who we are interacting with at this moment share just one of those possible universes with us.

If life were simple, this would completely clarify the differences, but there is a version of the many-worlds theory in which the physical splitting between universes is determined by the act of observation. This "many-minds" interpretation of quantum mechanics, first introduced in 1970 by H. Dieter Zeh, extends the many-worlds interpretation by proposing that the distinction between worlds should be made at the level of the mind of an individual observer.[355] The key role of the observer implied by quantum physics suggests that the number of universes may be limited by the number of universes a single observer can distinguish. So bizarrely, the information capacity of the human brain may limit the number of universes in the multiverse.[356] The reason that I have described these strange physical theories is that it raises the spectre that each of our psychological youniverses might also be different physical universes. This is a heavy philosophical area, best explored by brighter minds than mine, so time to move on.

Narratives

"Life is a tale told by an idiot
- full of sound and fury, signifying nothing."

- William Shakespeare[357]

When I was a child my parents used a euphemism when they wanted to say that I was lying. They would accuse me of "telling stories", I presume with the assumption that a story is a piece of fiction. Similarly, a "tall story" was a euphemism for a lie; perhaps the metaphor implied an unstable narrative with a weak foundation. I was hurt when my parents used this phrase to accuse me of deception while I described a surprising personal experience, but I now realize that our entire lives are built on stories.

While we live in the moment, our learning bottleneck means that most moments of experience are lost forever. However, the remembering self is a storyteller, and what we keep from experience is a story, a narrative that makes sense of our lives. We can have experiences that in themselves do not make sense, but we need the stories that we construct around our experiences to make sense when remembered, for making sense of things is what we humans do. Most of the time we are unaware of this process, although we may occasionally notice that our own internal storyteller is practicing how we will describe an experience to someone else.

Our consciousness constructs a narrative with hindsight. Many things may have happened "but I need a story" as the newspaper editor might say. Here is an analogy: A teenager's parents return from a quiet weekend away to discover that their home has been trashed in their absence. When they ask their teenage daughter what happened, she endeavours to construct a single intelligible narrative from her weekend of difficult to remember chaos, a story just sufficient to satisfy her parents, a continuous tale despite her extensive periods of unconsciousness and sleep over the past two days. Our subconscious mind is like that teenager; it unashamedly creates a story that is just sufficient to satisfy our conscious mind. Our bottleneck limits how much of the sequence of events we actually absorb, but our mind joins the dots, creatively fills in the spaces, rather like our blind spot that you learned about in Chapter Two.

Stories shared are the roots of our culture, for good or ill. Some stories only make sense within a particular community, whether a nation, a religion, a cult, a family, or even a pseudoscience, and their lack of more general acceptance is tolerated by outsiders, providing they don't cause problems.

In contrast, the narratives of science achieve consensus by excluding subjective and cultural experiences, enabling them to be shared globally. They are the stories of only those aspects of experience that we all can more or less agree upon, and agreement is generally achieved through experiments. However, at the cutting edge of new scientific ideas multiple conflicting stories can coexist, all as yet unproven theories. We have no observations yet that confirm speculative theories of dark matter and dark energy, and we are yet to detect gravitational waves, despite Einstein predicting them, and physicists spending vast resources on experiments to detect them.

Once we step outside the world of science, our observations and memories are converted into quite personal stories. For example, research by Nobel Prize winner Daniel Kahneman has revealed how our "experiencing selves" and our "remembering selves" perceive happiness differently. He says: "We don't choose between experiences, we choose between memories of experiences. Even when we think about the future, we don't think of our future normally as experiences. We think of our future as anticipated memories".[358]

One of the first people to measure and appreciate just how imperfect our memory can be, was British psychologist Frederic Bartlett.[359] He narrated a Native American folk tale: "The War of the Ghosts", to a group subjects who were asked to recall it on several occasions up to a year later. The narrative made sense superficially, but contained various illogical aspects and several discreet non-sequiturs.[360]

When his participants were asked to retell the story, they had great difficulty to do so accurately, even after they had heard the same story several times. Where details of the story did not fit with the participants' understanding of it, they were omitted in the retelling, or transformed into things that made more sense to each participant in the context of their own cultural norms and expectations. From his studies Bartlett concluded that our memories are simply an imaginative construction or reconstruction that closely relates to our past experience and our present attitude. Indeed, when you have related a series of events to a friend, you may have found yourself filtering out the bits that do not make sense to you, knowing that it will make the tale more credible and less confusing to them.

From his experiments he developed a theory of reproduction of memories: When a story is verbally communicated from one person to another, the listener's brain processes the content rather than the actual wording. They digest the material, extracting and absorbing the characteristics which appear important in the context of this particular listener's unique background and attitude at that moment. They then organise these characteristics into a rational and coherent arrangement before being able to produce their reconstruction of the story. So you can see, what comes out can simultaneously be both much more, and much less than what goes in.

Memories are malleable; they grow and evolve when given attention. We may think that remembering is a "read-only" process, one which leaves the original source intact, but research now suggests that reminding a person of something, makes that recollection temporarily revert to an insecure state in which it can be modified, even erased. In other words a memory is rewritten each time it is accessed.[361] This is similar to some early forms of computer storage in which the data could not be read without destroying the data, so it had to be rewritten each time any data was accessed.

So on every successive occasion that we remember something, we memorise it afresh, largely forgetting the original memory. If we have reflected on the memory, we will have rewritten the past incorporating aspects of that reflection. This process is generally beneficial to us: "The brain isn't interested in having a perfect set of memories about the past. Instead, memory comes with a natural updating mechanism, which is how we make sure that the information taking up valuable space inside our head is still useful. That might make our memories less accurate, but it probably also makes them more relevant to the future".[362]

I have retained only two detailed memories from my infancy, the first when I was standing in a white cot crying for attention, and in the second I was seated in a play-pen watching my father sitting upright in his bed while playing the violin. I am sure I only remember these now, because I have remembered them occasionally and repeatedly over the intervening years. I can even remember an occasion when I was about five or six years old, being asked what was the earliest thing I could remember, and proudly recalling these two events. Though they now both seem clear and detailed, I have no way of knowing just how much of their content was truly from my original experiences.

Factual memories tend to fade with time if not recalled, but emotional memories are more persistent. This property has been exploited by those who possess remarkable memories for faces, by associating each with an emotional context.[363] Unfortunately, this also means that traumatic events are more difficult to forget. Experiments have shown that this memory re-consolidation process can be interrupted by administering a particular drug at the time a memory is being recalled. This prevents the memory being rewritten, and so effectively erases the memory.[364] [365] The method offers hope to those suffering from post-traumatic stress disorder, to help them overcome the disabling effects of traumatic memories.[366]

The substituted memory often provides a narrative that makes more sense to us than the actual past, it is tidier and the anomalies are removed. Sometimes we will have acquired greater insights into the original situation during the intervening time, so the substituted memory may be a more "correct" interpretation of the original experience. Other times the memory will be modified by acquired prejudices, and deviate further from the truth. If you have ever discussed shared childhood experiences with siblings, but many years after the events, you will appreciate this point.

False memories

Elizabeth Loftus conducted extensive research that showed how easily we can implant false memories in people, simply by asking them about a fictional incident set in their past that was never part of their experience. When questioned again on successive later dates, they became increasingly convinced that they had indeed experienced the incident, (such as being lost in a shopping centre as a child).[367] This has clear implications for the questioning of crime suspects and witnesses.

In psychological therapies patients are often asked to imagine a situation. However, the act of imagination simply makes the event seem more familiar, and that familiarity can easily be mistakenly related to childhood memories rather than to the act of imagination. The effect is cumulative in that the more times participants imagined an unperformed action, the more likely they were to falsely remember having performed it.

In her book: "The Myth of Repressed Memory: False Memories and Allegations of Sexual Abuse", she warns that "therapists and lawyers have created an industry based on treating and litigating the cases of people who suddenly claim to have "recovered" memories of everything from child abuse to murder".[368] It is understandable that she has been criticised by some therapists, lawyers, and individuals who believe that peoples' recovered memories are true, as indeed they might well be. However, she has not said that every case of recovered memory is false, merely highlighted how easy it is for us to acquire false memories when questioned in an inappropriate manner, and that extra care must be taken by all parties concerned when damaging claims are made. This process may also explain many of the alien abduction stories that people have recalled under hypnosis. It is worth remembering just how remarkably detailed were the experiences that people had during the hypnotic regressions I described in Chapter Three.

Although we are happy to stay within our own idea of reality, on occasion it is valuable to enter into another's story to improve communication. When I was very young I shared a bedroom with my older sister. One night she awoke from a nightmare, terrified and distraught, which of course woke both me and my parents. Mother came and tried to console her, unsuccessfully at first. My poor sister was babbling about a blue bag of sugar which made no sense to me at all. My mother then turned to me and said: "Richard, could you go downstairs to the kitchen and fetch the blue bag of sugar?"

I was immediately confused, it was one thing for my sister to be ranting crazy stuff, as she had just woken from a nightmare, but surely my mother knew it was nonsense? Reluctantly I went down to the kitchen but failed to find what they both seemed to want. I felt quite frightened, for I seemed to be in a different reality to both of them. Was it me who was confused or them? As I returned upstairs to tell mother that I had failed to find what she had asked for, I suddenly realized that she had briefly entered my sister's mental world as a way of calming her, and it had worked. Her nightmare was over, as was mine.

My mother knew exactly what she was doing when she entered my sister's hallucination, she did not believe it was true yet was able to participate in it. However, this is not always so. We all confabulate (Confabulation is the replacement of a gap in a person's memory by a falsification that they believe to be true); it is conspicuous when we see it in the sick and traumatised, yet we all do it.[369]

I had a widowed aunt who lived alone some distance away. She began to suffer from dementia resulting from Alzheimer's disease, though none of us realized it at the time. My daughter was passing nearby and called in to see her. All seemed fine until my aunt mentioned about the people who came into the house in the middle of the night. My daughter was sufficiently alarmed by this that she phoned to tell me. My aunt seemed quite plausible which made the story particularly disturbing; however, when she continued to describe how Tony Blair (the UK prime minister at the time) came at night to discuss policy with her, it immediately became clear that my aunt was confabulating. It would be easy for me to say that she was confused, but she was quite clear about the situation, it was we who were confused by it! This was how we discovered that her mental health had deteriorated and that she needed help. When we are told a tale, our trust is like a piece of elastic, stretch it too far and suddenly it breaks completely.

We create stories that make sense of things that are otherwise incomprehensible. It is quite common for stroke victims with paralysed limbs and even blindness, to deny that there is anything wrong with them, at least for a few days, insisting that they are physically able. These people, who otherwise are mentally unimpaired, nevertheless confabulate elaborate stories to explain away their problem.[370] It is evident that they are not lying, they are telling it as it truly appears to them. Furthermore, when they come to terms with their paralysis they often deny their earlier confabulation. They have forgotten their previous story and it now makes no sense to them either.

Although we appear to share our internal models with each other through language, our internal models are really very personal. Take the idea of

"England": The word will mean very different things to each of us depending on our geography, circumstances, history and politics. We may agree on both the spelling and the map coordinates, but for the most part, our internal models will differ greatly from person to person. Being born in England, I associate it with home, but for most of the world's population it has other meanings, some positive, some negative. The word "England" may evoke different emotional responses depending on contexts, such as football, colonialism or war. Yet provided those involved in any dialogue are able to recognise and understand the context, they can communicate effectively. Sometimes though, we choose not to understand our fellows.

It is often difficult to see one's own culture objectively. When I first graduated from college, I spent the summer working in Virginia, USA, where I stayed in a boarding house for miscellaneous "foreigners" (as we were known). I was given a room to share with an equally young and naive Irishman from Dublin. I had never been to Ireland, and he never to England. I had been brought up as a Protestant and he as a Catholic. He had never got to know a Protestant before, and I knew almost nothing of Catholicism.

We got on fine, but whenever we touched on the subject of our shared history, it was apparent that each was completely ignorant of the others' story, especially the history of Anglo-Irish relations. Though a few of the revelations that emerged could be integrated into our own stories without too much difficulty, the majority were facts totally at odds with each other's story. It was as if we had each learned from a different movie filmed on the same location. As we talked, I realized how just much we invest in our own story, and how difficult it is to comprehend another's position when the communities have been separated culturally, despite their physical proximity. I realized that our history is not so much a truth, but is just "his-story". It is a narrative that makes sense of our own direct experiences when they are added to the stories passed down to us by our ancestors.

"History is written by the victors"[371]

When I was taught history at school, I was led to believe that I was being given the facts, the truth. However, I now appreciate that the victors of social struggle have generally used their political dominance to suppress their defeated adversary's version of historical events in favour of their own.[372] In some sense this is a Darwinian survival of the fittest storyteller. Before recorded history, genocide would be the ultimate weapon, extinguishing not just a race but also their remembered story. In the Anglo-Irish conflict there have been no winners, so both sides get to retain (and refine) their stories.

Recent totalitarian regimes have successfully manipulated historical narratives for their own ends, by promoting more elegant stories than those emerging from men in muddy trenches. As French philosopher Paul Ricoeur said:

> "We carry on several histories simultaneously, in times whose periods, crises, and pauses do not coincide. We enchain, abandon, and resume several histories, much as a chess player who plays several games at once, renewing now this one, now ... another".[373]

Famous people leave us with a multitude of different stories about themselves and their lives, some heroic, some monstrous, others sympathetic to the personal reasons behind each. Real people are so complex that we cannot hope to capture them in a single narrative, but each additional narrative can give us greater insight.

As a scientist, I am interested in the history of scientific discoveries and breakthroughs, and the heroes responsible for them. When we have been personally involved in some activity that becomes successful, we each have different stories, invariably ones that place greater emphasis on our own area of expertise and experience. As time goes by, a single public story begins to emerge, often one in which the heroes are those who have been the best publicists.

Great scientists are often shy people, satisfied with the respect of their peers rather than with public fame. Technical success often depends on the successful promotion of existing ideas. As time goes on, stories are told, books are written, and a single coherent story tends to emerge, one that in time becomes the accepted "history", the "truth", of who invented the telephone for example.[374] Society wants heroes, idealised role models to unite society and feature in movies. The real complex "warts and all" characters are often of less immediate interest to the media and the public.

Our History Revision

Many of us have had an experience which has forced us to reassess and revise our own history. When my wife was in her mid-50's, quite by chance she suddenly discovered that the man who had been her "father", was not her real father. He was a friend who had married her mother when my wife was just four years old and had subsequently adopted her (she was brought up by her Grandparents for the first few years of her life).

Suddenly it gave her insight into many things that had perplexed her: As a child, she had struggled to understand why her father showed less interest in her than in other children. She probably felt that she did not deserve his affection for some reason. Armed with this single piece of new information, she could now reconstruct the story of her childhood, such that it had fewer puzzling inconsistencies. It was a huge "AhHa!" moment for her, and an emotional one too, though she naturally felt frustrated and sad that no one had told her before, but at least now her life's story "made more sense".

When we have built our story brick by brick over decades then suddenly discover that there is a deep crack in the foundations, we have choices. We can painfully retrace our steps back to that fracture, and then rewrite the story step by step. This can be very difficult as it challenges us to abandon so much of what we cherish from our past: Who are we? What really has been our relationship to others? Or we can paper over the cracks and turn a blind eye to the paradoxes and inconsistencies in our lives. For most of our lives, this seems the easiest way forward. It is only when the crushing burden of painful contradictions becomes too much, that we consider a major reconstruction of our story. Such changes can be very uncomfortable to make when they affect us emotionally. Those who have devoted their lives to their career often experience something of this when they suddenly retire, or are made redundant and laid off from their jobs.

Science also has stories, and the breakthroughs in science come in a similar way, but the world of science restricts itself to those things which we can collectively agree upon so can easily let go of the past. Once the science story has been rewritten to incorporate the new collective thinking, scientists are quick to forget all the previous years of "ignorance" and enjoy the benefits brought by the new insight. As the world of hard science largely ignores any emotional reality, it is not usually held back by emotional arguments. However, it is worth remembering that both in science and in personal relationships, at any given moment in time we believe we have almost the complete picture, while hindsight repeatedly reveals this not to have been the case in the past.

Errors in transmission

Stories mutate over the years through various mechanisms: the outcome of deliberate propaganda, or just the result of our unconscious quest for meaning, however, sometimes stories evolve simply due to errors in their reproduction. Before the invention of writing, all historical knowledge was handed down verbally, generation to generation, through stories told to be remembered, and passed on. Given our new understanding of the potential for serious errors in remembering, it is reasonable to question just how accurately this process could be over hundreds of years. Perhaps errors could be minimised if knowledge of special importance, such as the "word of God", was passed on by rote, rather than by comprehension and interpretation.

The write stuff

With the invention of writing, the information within written texts could be reproduced with few errors. Furthermore because the process of reproduction no longer required the transcribed material to be understood, errors could be reduced by using transcribers who had a good knowledge of reading and writing, but without requiring extensive knowledge of the subject matter. The remaining errors were those that arose when translating texts between languages, from Greek to Hebrew to English for example, or from Old English to modern English. The invention of the printing press reduced errors even further as printed copies provided faithful facsimiles without the intervention of human scribes.

There are many paths through the forest

The invention of electronic documents with click-able hyperlinks has enabled us to jump within and between documents. It was initially anticipated that this would open up an exciting new way for novels to be written, one which would enable the reader to choose their own path through extended stories when read on a computer or an eBook. Writers could then create multidimensional texts in which each reader experienced a different story, possibly favouring the reader's tastes or interests. Such a book could be re-read, each time the reader could discover new content as a different path was followed.

This approach has been very successful for electronic versions of encyclopaedias, manuals and user guides, where only the most diligent reader would read the paper version linearly from start to finish. However, although the flexible format is commercially successful in computer adventure games, it does not seem to have influenced the way that eBook novels are written. The creator of a computer adventure game wants to provide excitement through giving lots of choices to the player, enabling the game to be enjoyed an unlimited number of times. The novelist on the other hand, has a specific agenda to portray the consequences of choices made by their characters.

It also seems that we prefer the novelist to lead us on a journey, not to ask us to make choices along the way. We have seen how memory champions use the journey method as the most effective technique for memorising information, and I speculated that a linear story may have been of evolutionary value in finding one's way home. Perhaps we have evolved to prefer a linear narrative, as it makes more sense of the dimension of time, suggesting cause and effect, an ordered and predictable universe. With a flexible click-able hyperlink format, we might feel that we were missing out on those sections of the text that would inevitably be bypassed; after all, we would be upset if we discovered that a chapter was missing from a conventional book. In contrast, when we play a computer based adventure game we have chosen an experience based around multiple decisions, where we are creating our own journey.

Many novels interweave a second subsidiary story within a single linear text. Often this other story is merely hinted at until near the end, when the reader experiences the delight of finally recognising the connection between these apparently unrelated details, and achieves a new understanding of the story. The preferred structure is still one that can be understood as a linear narrative, if only with hindsight. In general, we do want to finish a story with an understanding of it, and get pleasure if we feel we have been smart enough to have solved a bit of puzzle on the way.

Memories come and go

The narratives that we construct from our experiences are stored in our memory, written somehow into our neurons and their connections. So as we learn, more and more of our brain's cells are organised in a way that is useful to us. Without the bottleneck, the world that we experience would be equally detailed throughout our life, but we now know that we gradually create the place we inhabit, our youniverse, through what we learn. At birth our youniverse contains almost no detail, but as we absorb experiences the amount of detail gradually increases as we build an increasingly complex model of what is out there. Time's arrow appears to move forward as gradually more and more of our brain cells are co-opted to build an increasingly complex and more realistic model youniverse.

We learn fastest when we are young, so that is when our youniverse undergoes the most rapid period of inflation, (just as we currently believe the physical universe did after its birth in the big bang). Our learning rate then slows with age, as we rely increasingly on the knowledge that we already hold. If we are unfortunate enough to develop senile dementia in older age, our youniverse begins to shrink again, time's arrow reverses as we revert to more childlike ways.

Many of you will have relatives or friends who suffer from dementia, often the result of Alzheimer's disease. For these people the narrative of their lives is gradually disintegrating, as if the words, the sentences and pages from their life's book are being lost or mislaid. The symptoms may long go undiagnosed, as the sufferer may appear in relatively good condition and still cope effectively as long as they are in their familiar surroundings. They often function much better when dealing with the past than with the novelty of the day. My ageing aunt, who I mentioned earlier, could talk intelligently and at great length about her family-history investigations, yet would panic when faced with the possibility of a visit by members of the family or some other new situation. It would seem that she found it difficult to update her narrative.

For such people, a change of environment can be catastrophic, causing them to lose their balance psychologically. Often dementia is only identified when the individual has had a minor accident and had to be hospitalised. Then suddenly, almost everything they are surrounded by is novel, and they just cannot cope. For all of us, if we have an internal model that fits reasonably well with what we experience, then we can absorb the difference. The problem for people who are gradually losing their memory is that their existing models of what lies before them are gradually disintegrating. For those of us with healthy brains, experiences repeated over time increase our familiarity and confidence, while for them, successive experiences become increasingly alien and more difficult to understand.

Alzheimer's and dementia often seriously impair short-term memory but have less impact on long-term memory. Sufferers may not be able to recognise themselves in the mirror, but can recognise photos of themselves in their youth. Hospitals and care organisations have found that many dementia patients can be calmed by showing them a variety of objects dating from their early days such as their childhood. One way that carers do this is by exploring the contents of "memory boxes" with groups of patients. These are full of memory-evoking items such as old money, stamps, bus tickets, kitchen utensils, photographs, and magazines which are used to encourage reminiscence and conversations with relatives and staff. Sifting through the contents can help calm their anxiety, trigger warm emotions and improve the quality of their lives.

"You're History![375]"

When the body that hosts our model of the world finally dies, our imagined world collapses to zero, but what happens to all our knowledge? When we die the particular narrative that runs within our own consciousness dies with us. However, the very molecules from which our bodies are build are not destroyed in death, but recycled into dust, to soil, and eventually into further living things. The same is true of our narratives. Though our own story-teller falls silent in death, many fragments of our narrative are likely to remain, to be recycled within the narratives of others. When we participate in society we cross fertilise our narratives with others, exchange ideas, often forgetting where they came from. Studies have shown that some of the chapters of our own life story are actually experiences borrowed from our closest family members.[376]

Famous people live on through favourable autobiographies and unfavourable biographies, all distorting the complex details of real lives lived to make credible narratives, each to appeal to readers with different prejudices. Nowhere is this more evident than in politics, where anyone that has made their mark upon the world is destined to be remembered as a thousand different personalities, all bearing the same name. There is great diversity in the reputations of individuals such as Stalin, Mao Tse-tung, Winston Churchill, Che Guevara and Margaret Thatcher.

For the rest of us, fragments of our stories are retained by our family members and by others whose paths we have crossed throughout our lives. If you have tried to unearth your family history you will have probably discovered multiple (and often bizarre) stories that do not fit with what you had been told. One of my Grandfathers had the surname of Skinner. I was told that the family, who came from Yorkshire in the UK, had changed their name to Skinner a few generations back to avoid a conflict with another business name. Recently I was contacted by a distant relation who had been told a rather different origin of the name; that one of our ancestors had "married a Red Indian" (a skinner) in America and brought his son back to England to carry on the family name.

It seems that the more glamorous the story, the better it propagates forward in time. If the latter story were to be true, I might have some Native American blood in me. I wonder if that could qualify my offspring for a US College grant! The artist Salvador Dalí said: "The difference between false memories and true ones is the same as for jewels: it is always the false ones that look the most real, the most brilliant",[377] and no one was more familiar with the hinterland between truth and illusion, than Dali.

No-one gets out of here alive

How does a predictive mind cope with the idea of its own death? Most of our predictions are based on the idea of us being a witness or observer, yet when our power is switched off (our brain dies) our witness ceases to exist. Our whole ethos is that we continually build insight through experience, improving our ability to predict our future, yet we are incapable of learning anything objective about what might follow from the moment of our own death.

Our inability to predict what happens after death presents us with an unusually difficult problem. When we are young, our own mortality is easy to ignore, and many of us find it easier to live our lives in complete denial of that reality, considering it a morbid thought. It is easy for us to celebrate each birth and mourn each death, blind to the paradox that the former ultimately and inevitably sentences us to the latter.

An alternative is to either invent or inherit a story that makes us feel better, such as we "go to a better place". The common thread in these stories is the expectation that it will be like a gentleman's club, reserved for the select few, the chosen ones, a sort of chill-out place with no mention of housework or who does the cooking and cleaning. Most of these stories include some kind of disclaimer: that if the One in charge of the overall universe is not entirely satisfied with our behaviour while we are alive, we will be excluded from the club and punished when we die, and perhaps recycled into a lower quality life-form too.

It is possible that one of these stories is true, but I am not relying on it. The very large number of different stories on offer, makes it difficult to choose which to believe, so I personally treat it the same way as I do the national lottery: As the chances of winning seem tiny compared with the chances of losing, I have decided not to participate. However, it is quite possible that while I am dying I will experience exactly what I expect to experience. If I have built an imagined youniverse in which those who have "sinned" go to "hell", then I might well die in fear, unless of course I am smug enough to believe that I have qualified for the other club. So fearing death itself while living, may increase our anxiety while dying, so perhaps is to be avoided.

Interacting with others

Shared stories

Each of us creates personal stories to make sense of our lives and these stories may be profoundly different from those of others we encounter on life's journey. However, every time we share an experience with someone, it is likely that our stories will include some common ground. We might expect our shared memories to be very similar, yet are often surprised how different our memories are when recalled years later.

The extent to which our memories of a shared experience correlate with each other will depend on several things: Firstly; what we each absorb will be determined by where our interest and attention lies, and that will largely be directed by our individual previous experiences. So at a very basic level, our senses may be focused on very different aspects of the experience and be blind to the rest.

Next, while my own sensations contribute to my experience, so too do those of anyone else that I am interacting with at the time, so we share the experience through a shared narrative. For example, if two of us watch a football match and exchange comments and reflections on the match, both during the game and during the shared journey home, our experiences will be modified to make them more similar. My fellow spectator might point out to me why my initial judgement of a foul by a player was wrong, and I adjust my memory appropriately. Similarly, things that I had observed will get incorporated into my colleague's memory of the match.

When later we go our separate ways, we further refine our stories and may continue to do so over the years. While sitting at home that evening reflecting on the match, I might modify what I remember based on my recollections of what had happened in previous matches. A week later I might discuss the game with another supporter who was spectating from the other side of the pitch, or a supporter of the opposing team. Each time the story of my experience can get modified a little further, or reinforced from a biased perspective. There is no way back to that moment of observation, and even if there were, we see largely what we expect to see, and want to see.

It is much more fun sharing an experience with someone who shares one's own tastes. We generally choose to spectate among fellow supporters, rather than with the opposition, unless we are just looking for a fight! Similarly, it's no fun taking someone to a concert of your favourite music if it is music they dislike. One of the key things we seek in a relationship are shared beliefs, stories, fashions, and affection, to reinforce the idea that we have got it right. On occasion, we may choose to explore differences in views, to consciously improve the quality and depth of what we accept as true, but this can feel like sailing into the wind. Some relish an argument and enjoy strong debate as a competitive sport, but most of the time we prefer others to agree with us, or at least to appear to do so.

Identical twins, who share almost all their childhood experiences, will develop quite similar narratives. This is likely to be reinforced by those outsiders who cannot differentiate between them, and interact with them as if they are the same person. When they are in close contact and the relationship strong, they will inevitably possess a shared youniverse in addition to their own, so it is not surprising that separation can be particularly stressful for them.

Taking people personally

If you were the only human being on the planet, you would only need to consider your own youniverse. But we are not alone, we relate to parents, children, friends and strangers. Even alone on a desert island we cannot escape the knowledge that we are born of parents, so there is always the idea of other people in some part of our youniverse. In our minds we hold predictive models, not just of things that are out there, but of people too. However, our idea of other people is very different from our idea of other things, because we take people personally.

The difference may be clearer if you try a little thought experiment: The next time that you are out in some public place with people around you, try to imagine that although they look like people, they are really just robots, designed to learn, so programmed by whatever information they have acquired through their sensors. Despite looking exactly like humans, imagine they have no will, no consciousness; they are simply acting in response to their programming.

This idea probably feels awkward, as we are very reluctant to concede that something that looks exactly like a human should not be held responsible for its actions. If it had been programmed by someone, then I might say that the programmer is responsible, but what if the robot had simply been programmed to learn from what it was able to experience? It is easy to blame a human for a behaviour that we don't like, because we endow our simulations of people with a sense of responsibility.

You could try the same experiment with people you know, family or partners, imagining them being robots too, but I am tempted to warn: "don't try this at home". It is easy to offend people by treating them as mere robots; we may appear arrogant and insensitive.

We can gain insight into how we take people personally by imagining the drowning of a close friend who is a sailor. Consider the difference between our emotional response to learning that they had been washed overboard by a freak wave, or alternatively had been pushed overboard by a fellow crew mate, yet both with the same outcome. Unless we decide to take "acts of God" personally, we find it far easier to feel blame and anger towards another human being, than to a wave. If instead, the sailor's accident had been caused by a dog belonging to another crew mate, we might experience an intermediate emotional response (e.g. "He should have controlled the dog, it was his responsibility").

It is easy to feel righteous indignation towards the acts of other humans, but we rarely experience such strong emotions towards objects or machines. In the classic BBC TV series: Faulty Towers, John Cleese plays the irate hotel manager (Basil Fawlty) who finally and completely loses his temper with his car when it refuses to start. He gets out, gives the car a verbal warning, counts to three, gives it one more chance (as if it might then decide to start all by itself!), and then says. "Right! I warned you. You've had this coming to you!" He then grabs a nearby branch of a tree, and starts beating the car mercilessly with it. He acts as if the car is a badly misbehaving adolescent, quite ridiculous behaviour to most of us, but that is what makes the sketch so hilarious. It is notable that when we imbue objects with human characteristics and personality (anthropomorphism), we do so more often with affection than hatred: "I love that car".

When we fail to see eye-to-eye with someone, we convince ourselves that while we ourselves are completely rational, those who we are in conflict with are simply being unreasonable and acting illogically. This asymmetry has a value to us, for in order for us to understand everyone we ever interacted with we would require a vast amount of information, and as we have seen the bottleneck precludes this. But if we had no bottleneck we would have access to so much more information about other people during the experience. This would overcome the limitations of our simplified models of each other, but multi-person interactions would become as complex as a chess computer program.

So we save our more detailed predictive reasoning for those few people that we are closest to. For all the rest we rely on crude approximations based on our personal history, and triggered by a few sensed features: hair colour, skin colour, accent etc. We do of course carry one reference model for what is appropriate behaviour, and that is our idea of ourselves. By ignoring the likely disparity between our own history, and that of others, we can engage in a wonderfully self-satisfying sense of blame ("*I* wouldn't behave like that").

It is all too easy for us to get caught up in this game, so when I am struggling to communicate with someone who appears to be acting unreasonably, I sometimes explore the idea that people are automatons, programmed by their experience. I try to step back and remind myself: This person lives in a world created almost entirely from their prior experiences, which are probably very different to my own. Though I think they are being unreasonable, they almost certainly make their judgements entirely from a position of reason within their own youniverse. Indeed, I have no logical reason to believe that they are any less reasonable than me, and it is likely that our simulated universes differ sufficiently that I should not assume that they are identical. I may have already made some completely invalid judgements based on my assumption that we have shared, and lived in the same youniverse.

For example, I might imagine that all reasonable people think the same as I do. For this to be absolutely true, it would require their models of reality, to have an identical logical structure to my own. The models within each mind have been determined by each individual's unique experience. As no two minds have shared access to (or control of), the same viewing position, everyone's internal models will be different, hence the phrase "a different point of view". Different minds may make similar predictive statements under many circumstances (The apple will fall downward. It is safe to cross the road), yet still differ significantly in others (The driver in the blue car caused the accident. The soccer goal was offside).

When we reach the age of three or four, most of us develop what is known as the "Theory of Mind", the ability to understand our own thoughts (beliefs, intents, desires, pretending, knowledge, etc.), and to understand that others have beliefs, desires, and intentions that are different from our own.[378] This enables us to interact socially in ways that take into account how we expect others to behave and react. Not everyone develops a complete theory of mind, and there is evidence that it is impaired in people diagnosed with autism or Asperger's syndrome.[379]

Some have gone so far as to say that such people cannot understand other people in this way, while the rest of us do. However, I would express it differently; in that those with autism or Asperger's syndrome know only too well that they struggle to understand others, recognising the complexity of the problem, while the rest of us wrongly assume that we are able to understand everyone else!

I say that, because when I was a young man, I naively thought that everyone thought the way that I did, and that what was important to me was equally important to all others. I believed that I could understand others simply by understanding myself, and so predict their needs, how I should interact with them, and their reactions.

For much of the time, this predictive model worked well for me, but there were occasions when it failed me completely. Being confused by this, I soon developed a modified predictive model: that some people were wilfully illogical and unreasonable. (Incidentally, this strategy has been deliberately used by many despots to keep their enemies confused). This new model made me feel better about the difficult interactions that I had with people, as now I had an explanation, but it was not effective at predicting people's behaviour. To add to my confusion, my geeky logical mind considered people's emotions to be some kind of unwanted aberration so not really valid, despite the fact that emotions affected much of my daily life!

Then one day, it suddenly dawned on me that many people had very different needs and values to those of my own. After years of dealing with "unreasonable" people, I began to learn about the complexity and differences in people's personalities. I soon discovered that many of my assumptions about other people had been completely wrong, that people had very different priorities to my own, so I learned to listen and check my assumptions a little more.

I now realize that everyone acts reasonably, but only within their own reasoning process at that moment. The dictator, the terrorist, my children and my wife, all act within their own reason, however disturbing it might be for us to admit it. When the psychotic man listens to voices that tell him to act, his sense of reason makes him act in ways that are reasonable to him, but may be totally unreasonable to we who observe his psychosis, and his acts.

When I judge another person to be unreasonable, I may think that I am describing one of *their* deficiencies, in truth I am revealing one of my own; my inability (or unwillingness) to come up with an effective predictive model for their behaviour. My model of them is somehow inadequate. Of course I may not want to acknowledge their reasoning behind their actions; for fear that it might weaken the case for my own intransigence and lead to compromise. We rarely like to deal with unreasonable people because we feel unsafe and ill equipped to predict outcomes. On the other hand, when I describe someone as being "reasonable", it simply means that I have been able to use reason to predict their behaviour, and so provide a good match with what I observe. It is easy to feel comfortable with reasonable people.

Although other people's logic can be difficult to deduce, predicting their emotions can be impossible, especially when it's the opposite sex, or between parents and children. Previously I described how so much of "seeing is actually our experiencing an idea of what a received image represents. Nowhere is this more evident than with the human face. You may be surprised to learn that normal intelligent people find it very difficult to actually see a face as an image, rather than what that face represents. Close your eyes and try to visualise the face of someone close to you. More often than not we find ourselves having to remember a picture or photograph, rather than remembering a direct visual experience. Try drawing or painting their face from memory, it can be remarkably difficult compared with remembered images of inanimate things.

For most of us, as soon as we see a person, we immediately substitute an idea of that person in our mind's eye. It is usually more urgent for us to interpret their emotional state towards us, than to count the freckles, or notice the wife's new haircut. Portrait artists must learn how to suppress this substitution, and art students may find it easier to copy an image of a face that is inverted, as the substitution then no longer occurs (faces are very difficult to recognise when inverted). Chimpanzees can recognise faces either way up, presumably, they have gained experience while hanging upside down.

So we interpret a 2D image of a face, as a 3D object, a head, and as the head of someone who has emotions. You can demonstrate this very effectively, by folding a picture of a face. Try it with a face from a magazine or newspaper. It just requires three straight folds in the paper to make the picture have a three dimensional property as follows: First, fold the paper back along a line that passes midway between the eyes and through the chin. Next, fold the paper forward along a line that passes through the centre of the left eye and the left corner of the mouth, and repeat this process for the right-hand side. Now you should have a picture with three folds, such that the centre line including the mouth and nose, projects out of the picture somewhat. The following figure should make it clearer.

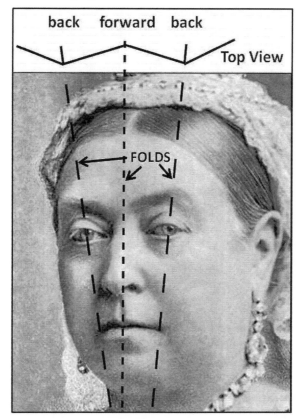

Figure 29: Fold any image of a face along the centres of the eyes and corners of the mouth, as shown. Now you can change the emotion expressed, simply by tilting the image forward and back.

Hold the picture directly in front of you, and tilt it towards you. If you have folded it as instructed, the face should "smile". Tilting it back causes it to frown, and you will be able to find a neutral expression somewhere between the two. This works for pictures small or large, and even when the face is viewed at an angle. The most important part, are the folds around the mouth, as this is where our mind derives a prediction of the face's emotional state. It is a nice party trick done with faces on banknotes, and an interesting experiment tried with photos of relatives, especially the one who refuses to smile! Now while viewing the tilted image, try to suppress your emotional interpretation of the expression and try to see it as it is: the original 2D image with 3 folds across it. It is surprisingly difficult, and a somewhat reminiscent of the previous experience of trying to see the Necker cube image as just a flat set of lines.

Where is the spirit?

If we inhabit a universe within our mind, and it is populated entirely by the thoughts, sensations and experiences of our lifetime, then we are the very creator of our universe, of all that we survey. If this is true, then where does it leave religion and spirituality? Let me declare from the start that I personally fall into the "don't know" category. As a scientist I find that it is possible to explain the vast majority of my life's experiences. However, as an open minded scientist I must accept that any certainty in this area would require an act of faith, and as a human being I have experienced several things that completely confound the scientist in me.

A fundamental drive for Homo sapiens is to seek explanations for our experiences, and when our basic needs are satisfied we seek the meaning of life itself. As we cannot know the universe, we can only speculate. The astrophysical description of the universe leads us to the conclusion that we are incredibly tiny, insignificant and impotent in the overall scale of things, yet our egos drive us towards a description that gives us significantly greater prominence in the overall picture, one that gives meaning to our lives.

I have little patience with those who misuse religious creeds to justify acts of prejudice and bigotry, people who profit from dividing man against man encouraging fear and hatred between communities. But I am sympathetic towards those who have a spiritual approach to life which transcends individual religions, a belief that we are all connected.

As a scientist, I can find no repeatable evidence for a spiritual reality that would convince most scientists, yet I personally choose to live my life as if it has a purpose, and that we are all connected. I am attracted to ideas that have the potential to unite us in resolving some of the issues that threaten to extinguish our species, such as war and climate change. There is little evidence so far that we can resolve these problems using science and logical reasoning alone, on the contrary they appear to have been significant contributors.

Throughout this chapter I have shown that the universe you find yourself is unique to yourself, your own personal youniverse. Our youniverse is described by stories which we create to replace experiences, stories that make continuous sense of what we have sensed both now and in the past, stories that we subsequently modify throughout our lives. There are a multitude of stories out there, and some stories become accepted "truths" within society.

Although in some sense we are each alone in our youniverse, our youniverse contains simulations of other people (including a simulation of our own self), so we do not feel alone, and these simulations are as good as it gets. We project responsibility onto the people in our simulations, but rarely onto inanimate things. Our frustrations with unreasonable people are just evidence that our simulations of them are inadequate to predict their behaviour. If we are to relate to others, it is important that we can deduce their emotional relationship to ourselves, which we infer by reading faces and other clues. However, we have seen that our idea of a person readily interferes with our ability to see them as they really are.

In the next chapter, I explore the extent to which we are either a victim within the narrative we find ourselves in, or writers of our own story.

Chapter Nine

Creating the world we inhabit

An old Cherokee told his grandson that a battle goes on inside each us. "The battle is between two 'wolves.'

One 'wolf' is Evil. It has anger, envy, jealousy, sorrow, regret, greed, arrogance, self-pity, guilt, resentment, inferiority, lies, false pride, superiority, and ego.

The other 'wolf' is Good. It has joy, peace, love, hope, serenity, humility, kindness, benevolence, empathy, generosity, truth, compassion and faith."

The grandson thought about it for a minute and then asked his grandfather: "Which wolf wins?"

The old Cherokee simply replied, "The one you feed."

We are what we Eat

"If you are what you eat, you are what you see and hear."
- E.A. Bucchianeri[380]

Both body and mind are slowly built through the years. It is often said that "we are what we eat" and it is evidently true that from our birth onward, we are built entirely from material we have ingested throughout our lives. When archaeologists examine the bones of ancient humans, they can determine the composition of the diet that they lived on, simply by measuring the distribution of elements within the bony material. For example, when bones purporting to be those of the English King Richard III were recently discovered, analysis of their composition revealed that they were from someone who ate a high-protein diet, rich in meat and fish, and this was characteristic of someone who lived a privileged life in the 15th century. The bones were subsequently confirmed to be those of the king by matching the DNA with that of a descendant.

Our digestive system retains that which is necessary for a healthy body, while the majority of what we take in passes through us and back into the environment. It is worth noting that a short-term change in diet has little effect on the overall proportions of the materials from which our bodies are built, and that the balance of our diet is of greatest importance in our earliest years, for it is the very foundation of our adult bodies. Deficiencies and toxins in childhood can be especially damaging, leading to permanent impairments and handicaps in adulthood.

What is true for our bodies is equally true for our minds. From the moment of our birth (and maybe a little earlier), we slowly build a model of the external world within our mind. We build our youniverse, piece by piece, from whatever we retain from our experiences.

We can think of our predicting mind as a subconscious mechanism which makes a best estimate guess based on our experience. It then presents this guess to our consciousness with all the confidence of a slick salesman. The message we receive is: "This is the way it is", not: "This is my best guess". So the world we create for ourselves and then inhabit, our youniverse, is constructed from the raw materials of our personal experience. This would suggest that the qualities of our youniverse will be determined by what we have spent most of our time experiencing, so for example a normal healthy childhood environment will help build a healthy adult youniverse.

Food for thought

However, as any chef or architect will tell you, it is possible to create many different things from the same raw materials. Using these analogies, would suggest that both the quality and variety of the raw materials is important. A wider variety of raw materials greatly increases the range of possible outcomes, whether creating a meal, a house or a youniverse. So a narrow range of personal experiences will limit the range of possibilities within our youniverse. The quality of the raw materials will also limit the possible outcomes.

The chef adds value through his conscious creative skills, but our mind adds value to the information that we have ingested through the process of introspection, both consciously and unconsciously. The more we think about what we have sensed, the greater the value we can extract, because the variety of things that we can predict is increased.

Before language was invented, all our experience originated from our own senses, and hence was dominated by our immediate surroundings. Much of what we learn today comes from other people, through books, videos and word of mouth. Some of this information originally came from other people's senses, and this is how we have all built our growing knowledge of the world, building a shared reality.

But what is the role of fiction? For thousands of years humans have enjoyed stories, initially as spoken by story tellers, but today devoured through novels and movies. We have a special hunger for fictional books and films that involve people and relationships. Recent research has shown that reading literary fiction improves people's understanding of other people in real life situations. Reading literature about people apparently helps us to read people. It probably enables us to rehearse real life scenarios.[381]

The effect was not seen in those who read popular fiction or non-fiction books instead. Why the distinction between the types of fiction? (I am ignoring any suggestion of literary snobbishness). Popular fiction stories tend to be tidy, leaving little unexplained by the story end, whereas literary fiction leaves the reader to work out the intricacies, sets conundrums, puzzles ambiguities that are not resolved in the stories themselves. Popular fiction should entertain during the reading. The characters and situations should not demand too much mental effort to absorb the complexities. Good literature may be less entertaining, but more absorbing and thought provoking, stimulating the reader's mind to develop more sophisticated models of the complexities of the world and other people's behaviour.

Popular novels are easily forgotten after reading, but a great movie or piece of literature can push us to revisit the ideas many years after we have first experienced it. I notice this distinction when I have been to see a movie and someone asks me if it was any good. I have to differentiate between my immediate enjoyment while watching it, and its value with hindsight some days or weeks later. I find some movies very exciting and entertaining at the time of viewing, yet they hardly trigger a memorable thought in the following days. Other movies plant the seeds of ideas deep in my mind which continue to thrive, resurfacing later to trigger satisfying discussions with others.

Commercial factors today tend to demand media that provides instant gratification, so the majority of novels and films don't prompt much subsequent thought. It is fashionable to protect our young children from things that might disturb them. Traditional folk tales and fables often contained darkness and mystery.[382] But now many of these stories have now been sanitised by Disney and Hollywood to provide tidy endings, leaving nothing that might later tax a young mind. It may be no coincidence that teenagers now demand vampire and horror themes in their movies and books.

In your dreams

"One night I dreamed I was a butterfly ... I was conscious only of my happiness as a butterfly, unaware that I was Chou. Soon I awakened, and there I was, veritably myself again. Now I do not know whether I was then a man dreaming I was a butterfly, or whether I am now a butterfly, dreaming I am a man"

- Chuang Chou

We all experience fiction directly in our dreams. Occasionally someone tells me that they never dream, and then the following day they come and tell me that to their amazement they had a dream last night. It seems that many of us forget our dreams as soon as we awake, yet our minds spend some time exploring unusual experiences while we sleep.

How do we know the difference between our dreams and reality? We rarely confuse the two, though occasionally an intense emotion felt within a dream intrudes when we are awake. Sometimes I have carried a dreamed memory of an event into my awakened state without realising that it was a dream. It was only half way through the following day that I realised just how incongruous the experience was, and I filed it back into the fiction section of my memory where it belonged.

It seems that in our youniverse we are able to keep a clear distinction between "real" experiences, and fictional experiences that we have gained through movies, books, and dreams. None of these fictional experiences are experienced through our bodies to any significant extent; they are experienced in our mind, yet not sensed, so are "non-sense". Perhaps this is how we know to keep the distinction. It is worth noting that we cannot train a physical reflex by reading a book, that connection between mind and body seems to be disabled while we absorb information in these ways.

Reading a violent novel may raise our adrenalin, but does not generally produce muscular responses; and most people manage to stay in their seats while watching an action movie. But what if we provide a sufficiently immersive experience in the way that Virtual Reality systems and simulators aim to do? We use simulators to successfully train pilots to fly, train soldiers to fight, and train police when not to shoot, so clearly there are situations where fictional experiences modify the reality we subsequently experience in our youniverse.

To make these systems work we must minimise the parts of the experience that conflict with the virtual one that the simulator is trying to create. Visually, it helps to either fill the field of view or obscure everything except the simulator screen. If the subject is wearing a head-mounted display, then it is important to stabilise their field of view in space, if only to stop nausea. High screen resolution helps; yet it is not always important as most of our eye's field of view has low resolution.

If the majority of our senses tell us the same story, then our mind believes it, so can integrate the experience into our idea of reality, our youniverse. Then our body believes it too, it "makes sense". Virtual Reality is being used to train people in roles that involve risks to someone or something, people such as surgeons, soldiers, and safety workers in hazardous environments like mines and oil refineries. In chapter six, I showed that we can only learn a skill by making mistakes and learning how to increasingly minimise them. Virtual Reality systems provide a unique tool to enable skills to be learned, but with zero actual hazard. So although an extensive diet of fictional movies and novels may not change our youniverse significantly, Virtual Reality experiences evidently have the power to do so.

It's all in the game

So where do video computer games fit in this picture? Visual realism is rapidly improving through larger and higher-resolution screens, 3D, and more realistic computer generated imagery. Physically; we now have motion sensors (Wii and Kinect) that encourage a high level of physical involvement, in addition to dedicated game controllers. Consumer demand is pushing the development of computer games towards ever greater realism, (indeed they have been the main driver in the development of faster and higher resolution video for PCs).

There will come a point where the quality of the immersive experience is sufficiently high, that it will feel real when taking part. Then it will directly contribute to our youniverse. This is unlikely to cause problems provided that the majority of our time is spent experiencing physical reality. Computer games are designed to be addictive and a few people spend a very significant proportion of their waking hours immersed in these virtual worlds rather than the external physical world. They feel more at home in a youniverse created by a game designer, than the one where they eat and sleep.

If our youniverse becomes shaped by what we experience, especially during our earlier formative years, and a particular "unreal" experience occupies a greater part of our waking experiencing life, then that unreality will tend to become our reality. A child exposed solely to the experience of video games based on action and violence, with no experience of the "real world" would grow up inhabiting a reality composed only of what it had experienced. It is likely that it would expect action, crashes, threats and violence to be a continual part of everyday life, and probably have no insight into the pleasures of stillness or more harmonious relationships. Fortunately, most children have plenty of other experiences on which to ground their developing youniverse.

If the vast majority of someone's emotional experiences come from virtual worlds, might they become dysfunctional in the real world? Are they more likely to be lonely and lacking the emotional skills to form mature human relationships? Perhaps they will just become more skilled at functioning and building relationships within those virtual worlds.

I am not suggesting that computer games are bad for us, just that most things in excess can cause us harm. If a disproportionate fraction of our life experience is in contradiction to the physical world which our bodies must inhabit, then we will be less able to predict the real world than our peers, and therefore perhaps less able to find happiness and fulfilment in the real world. Of course it might be possible to find happiness and fulfilment in a virtual world, but at some point the human body needs to feed and excrete. It would require a support system or a doting parent to care for these functions 24 hours a day, while Johnny lives out a fulfilled heroic life in a virtual world through his avatar.

Mind-altering drugs also offer an alternative experience of reality. For a few people, recreational drugs such as alcohol and cocaine are highly toxic, in that they have a disproportionate effect on their lives. They tend to blur the otherwise clear distinction between what is experienced in dreams and what is experienced in everyday life. For the majority of people, soft drugs can be used recreationally without much harm, and if we are only under their influence for a small proportion of our life, then the youniverse we create for ourselves will still have a foundation of sobriety. But if we start at a young age and are under the influence of some mind altering chemical for a large proportion of the time, we may become paranoid. Our experience is likely to shape the world we subsequently inhabit, making it more difficult to modify it towards a shared functioning reality.

To build a healthy youniverse, we need a balanced diet across a wide range of experiences. If we are to function as physical human beings in a shared objective world based on physical reality, then we need our youniverse to share many common features with those of others. This is how we find a consensus reality, where we can function as social civilised members of the human race.

A brief look under the bonnet

In this book I have chosen to focus on our actual measured performance as intelligent learning beings, the black-box approach. I have not described details of our brain's internal architecture and structure, as plenty of excellent books cover this already.[383] [384] [385] [386] However, I will briefly describe a couple of interesting internal details.

The human brain is very different from our computers. In our modern technological world we use computer simulation programs to provide answers to hypothetical problems, such as future climate change, or how the air will flow around a car or a plane that we are designing. The programs are configured through software, and run on computer hardware that remains physically unchanged while programs are run. (There may be an occasional upgrade in memory hardware when it is switched off).

Our brain is never switched off during a normal life, yet from conception it grows in size and capability, and is physically reconfigured in response to what we sense and experience. Though our simulation of our youniverse is mostly contained within the "software" of our grey matter, there are some aspects of our developing youniverse that have a more physical presence within our brain.

Within our visual cortex, there are groups of neurons that respond to particular structure in the image we see, For example, there are stripes of neurons corresponding to different orientations of visual structure within a viewed image. Some stripes of neurons respond to vertical lines and others to horizontal ones. Animals that are raised while young, without exposure to any horizontal structure (e.g. lines) in their visual environment fail to physically develop stripes of cells representing horizontal structure within their brain.[387] [388]

When the brain has developed to maturity this structure is fixed. The absent stripes of neurons do not develop when the subjects are subsequently exposed to normal images. As a result, they are unable to see any visual structure in that orientation, ever; they can never recover the ability to resolve what it missed during its brain's development. So here is evidence of a brain developing its physical architecture in response to its sensory experience.

Something similar occurs with the human condition of a "lazy eye", where both eyes do not track together (preventing perception of depth through stereo vision). If the condition is untreated in childhood while the brain is developing, normal stereo vision cannot subsequently be restored. So our developing brain evolves in response to experience, and missed perceptual experiences in early years can ultimately limit our ability to experience some things in the future.

The second example concerns the remarkable case of "The Jennifer Aniston Neurons". Today's brain imaging technology, though valuable in revealing which regions of the brain are active during particular activities, has insufficient spatial resolution to measure the activity of individual neurons. Recently however, it has become possible to monitor a few individual neurons within the brains of fully conscious human subjects, using electrodes.

The opportunity to do so arises during a preparatory stage in the treatment of patients suffering from intractable epileptic seizures. Many such seizures are caused by just a tiny region of defective brain tissue. If the location can be precisely identified, it may subsequently be removed by surgery without significantly harming the rest of the brain. Because seizures are sporadic, it is necessary to implant electrodes within the brain and record the signals on the sparse occasions when a seizure does occur, so that the precise location can be deduced. This information can then be used to direct the subsequent surgery. After the electrodes are implanted, patients are monitored continuously over several days until a sufficient number of seizures have been recorded to enable decisions to be made on subsequent surgery.

A single probe implants an array of separate electrodes into a region of the brain tissue, and by use of clever signal processing, it has been possible to independently monitor the electrical signals from several individual neurons, for example within the hippocampus. This has provided a unique opportunity to study the responses of these neurons when patients are exposed to a range of experiences, such as images and sounds.

In the initial experiments hundreds of images were presented to the patients, covering a wide range of subjects, such as well-known people and places, while monitoring the responses of their brain cells. It revealed that neurons in the human medial temporal lobe respond in a remarkably selective and abstract manner to particular persons or objects, for example: Jennifer Aniston, Luke Skywalker or the Tower of Pisa. These neurons have been named "Jennifer Aniston neurons" or, more recently, "concept cells".[389] They provide strong evidence that our longer term memory processes are based around concepts rather than details.

For example, one subject produced a strong signal from one particular neuron whenever they were shown and consciously recognised an image of the actress Jennifer Aniston. However, it did not matter what orientation or context was represented by the image; the neuron gave the same strong response. Furthermore it also responded to the name "Jennifer Aniston", when presented as an image of written text or as spoken words. Each neuron typically fired to only one concept; the "Jennifer Aniston" neuron would fire to different pictures of the actress but not to other celebrities.[390]

However, later it was also found to respond to an image of Lisa Kudrow, one of Jennifer's co-stars in the TV series "Friends" that made them both famous. More intriguing is that there was no response when the image presented was that of Jennifer together with actor Brad Pitt, her husband at the time. It is important to appreciate that there was negligible response when the subject was shown the majority of images, so the neuron's response was highly selective by concept, yet remarkably insensitive to context. It is all strong evidence that long-term memories are stored as abstractions, and that our thoughts throughout our life define the function of at least some of the physical neurons within our brain. We would expect that someone obsessed with Jennifer Aniston would have quite different wiring of their neurons, when compared with someone obsessed with football.

The idea that we fill our brain with things we like and that give us pleasure is an attractive one. However, we sometimes spend significant time dwelling on things that we don't like, and these thoughts also become embedded within our physical brain. If we hold a resentment against another person, then every time we dwell on it we reinforce the representation of our idea of that person within our own mind. Paradoxically, we build an enduring physical monument to them from our precious brain cells, so they become a part of our body that we carry with us always. The more we hate something, the more of our precious neurons will be devoted to our idea of it.

So every human skull contains an intricately constructed model that represents everything its owner imagines exists out there. Like the ship in a bottle, the fabric of our model within is finely detailed, but in no way can it reflect the totality of what exists out there, just as there is no way that a real ship could ever pass through the neck of a bottle. But unlike the three dimensional model in the bottle, the one in our skull incorporates the additional dimension of time, in stories that weave together the pieces of our experience and so make our youniverse.

Our past has steered us to this place

Every experience we have adds to the solidity and complexity of our youniverse, the place within our mind where we live out our lives. Experiences that are repeated are incorporated into predictive rules within our mind, and these enable us to function and plan, both in space and in time. However, it would be wrong to think that our youniverse has simply been created from the sum of all our steadily absorbed experiences to date, and that their sequence in time makes no difference. For just as our early years are the most crucial in nourishing our growing bodies, our early experiences have a strong influence on our ability to accurately sense and absorb what is "out there".

We might expect that experiences that are repeated through our life will have resulted in a more accurate model of that experience within our youniverse. However, it may not always be so, for our developing internal model steers where we subsequently direct the attention of our senses. For example, intense emotional experiences early in our life can limit and shape all further experiences. Fear of flying, snakes, women, aggression, commitment or emotional intimacy, could each have led us to avoid further experiences which might otherwise have provided a more balanced view. So our past experiences may have significantly steered our present thinking. The philosopher Joseph Campbell wrote how our early programming subconsciously affects so many of our future life decisions:

> "The experiences and illuminations of childhood and early youth become in later life the types, standards and patterns of all subsequent knowledge and experience, or as it were, the categories according to which all later things are classified - not always consciously, however. And so it is that in our childhood years the foundation is laid of our later view of the world, and with that, our perception of its superficiality or depth: it will be in later years unfolded and fulfilled, not essentially changed".[391]

Some of my own early programming only became apparent to me quite recently. My mother died at just 39 years of age when I was just 10 years old. Eighteen years later when my Grandmother died, a little voice in the back of my mind told me that I could safely continue to ignore my own mortality for another couple of generations. However, later that same year my otherwise fit father had a sudden heart attack and dropped dead at the age of 57.

It was a big shock to me. In that one year, I changed from being a reasonably confident youth of 28 years, to feeling that I was a lone adult man naked under the stars. I had suddenly learned that I couldn't rely on the continuity of life, or at least couldn't rely on average mortality statistics. While most of my peers continued to act as if they would live forever, I became all too aware of my own mortality. What I did not realize, was that I had subconsciously taken on the belief that I would die before I reached 60.

My father had died without ever enjoying retirement, and I started to avoid making any long term plans. I have now come to realize how much this unconscious programming has influenced my life decisions, and just how ridiculous some of these now seem. For example, I recently noticed that I had only been renewing my Internet domain name for a couple of years at a time, thinking that to pay for more years would probably be a waste of the quite trivial sum of money involved.[392] Though my thought process might seem morbid to you, it never did to me, as it was the only thinking I had. However, it did have a positive influence on much of my subsequent life, as I endeavoured to avoid leaving things unsaid and undone, so if I should die unexpectedly it would not be with regrets.

How do we feel about this place we find ourselves in?

While we can agree on objective facts about some things around us, we also hold very different opinions about many others. On topics such as: other people, gender, colour, race, nationality, age, taste in music, fashion, football team, we may hold strong views; good or bad, or just not be interested.

There are, however, two extremes, where we feel either positively or negatively towards most things. Most of us would consider extreme optimism or extreme pessimism to be unrealistic attitudes perhaps even symptoms of depression, bipolar disorder or a drug induced euphoric state. But given that we have built the world we inhabit from our thoughts, it is useful to explore how our positive and negative attitudes determine the world we experience, our youniverse, for the world we experience is dominated by what we focus upon.

Some years ago I spent an interesting week with a group of people who were searching for life's meaning. We were based in an old mansion in the Peak District of England, surrounded by beautiful hills. We had a free afternoon and with my encouragement the whole group decided to go for a walk to the top of the nearby hill[393]. It was a beautiful summer's day, and as we climbed that grassy hill we were surrounded by the scent of wild flowers and the sound of skylarks singing overhead.

I had spent my childhood roaming these hills, and being familiar with the location I knew that once we reached the hill's summit we would be greeted by an incredible vista on the far side. In my excitement I hurried ahead a little and was finally rewarded with the sight of the purple heather of the Dark Peak's hills stretching out to the North, all in stark contrast to the iridescent green of the grassy view to the South[394] and the hill we had just climbed. I stood there, my spine tingling with the excitement of it all, waiting for my colleagues to arrive and to be equally enthralled by the view that I had promised them.

What was taking them so long? I retraced my steps and found them huddled in a group a hundred yards back, facing back the way we had come. Their attention had been drawn to the tall chimney of the local cement works in the far distance, and they were pointing and moaning about it being a terrible blot on the landscape. They were all agreed; it was a crime, shouldn't be allowed and completely spoilt the area. Now agreed, it was within the boundary of the Peak District National Park, but it was there long before the idea of a park was suggested, and furthermore it provided valuable employment for the local people. But the group were all agreed, it had ruined their afternoon walk.

I of course was still in rapture of the beauty that without doubt lay all around us, so in my irritating scientist way I asked them to estimate precisely what fraction of the total view was spoilt by this "blot on the landscape". It turned out to be less than a millionth (when expressed as a solid angle). For those who needed something to moan about in order to feel good about themselves this was bit of a setback, nevertheless I managed to get them to turn around and complete the last bit of the climb. They soon forgot all about the cement works when they saw the view beyond, and had still forgotten it when we later retraced our steps back down the hill.

If you want to estimate where you stand on the optimism-pessimism scale, ask yourself a few questions about the present, such as: do you love more people than you hate? do you like more people than you dislike, do you like more music than you dislike, and if so by how much? What about the anticipated future, do you expect things to get better or worse?

If we lack self-confidence, then defining ourselves by what we dislike is an attractive strategy. We can then identify all the people who we think are worse than ourselves, whether they are celebrities who we have never met, or the people next door. We can easily make absolute statements of what music is "crap", and what dress style indicates that the wearer is to be despised.

All this may help us to bond with, and feel part of our little "gang" or tribe, and if we are particularly isolated in our idea of ourselves this might be a tribe of just one, ourself. I can feel special, a celebrity in my own personal fantasy, where the things that I do and think are of great significance in the world. I am special because everything else is not. I can feel good without actually doing anything. Reality TV programmes are popular because they feed our need to see people behaving worse than we can imagine doing ourselves.

This way of thinking is a very effective counter to the observation that we are a completely insignificant part of space and time within the universe. However, it does have one major disadvantage: The world I inhabit, my youniverse, is mostly unpleasant. My gang and I are a tiny island of light in a vast ocean of darkness, so my expectations of the world beyond are low. This place can sometimes be fragile too. If some life event ever leads me to question my unrealistically inflated idea of my own importance, I may become depressed, and then absolutely everything feels negative. Helping hands reaching out to me from more optimistic worlds may seem no help. But let's not forget the key advantage; that I can feel significant in my personal universe.

In contrast, it feels good to be optimistic for it make life's journey more pleasant, and most of us prefer the company of optimistic people. But there is a downside to optimism, the great potential for disappointment, failed dreams and hopes dashed. Compulsive pessimists on the other hand, are rarely disappointed, having anticipated the worst, things generally turn out better than they expect.

Healthy individuals occupy the entire spectrum from optimism to pessimism. While optimists are good at spotting possibilities, pessimists are better at recognising potential hazards. Only an optimist would set sail across an ocean in search of undiscovered continents. However, as a passenger, I would prefer that the airline pilot only decides to fly if he feels it is safe to do so, because an unrealistically optimistic pilot might take unreasonable risks.

Fear and paranoia

What is less healthy for both our mind and our body is when we live with anxiety or fear. These can interfere with our ability to predict reality, from the limited information we take in through our bottleneck. It becomes paranoia when they cause significant delusions. Although only a few unhappy people are consistently paranoid, we all have the occasional moments of paranoia, and here are a couple of examples of my own:

I was crossing the street, when an attractive woman coming the other way beamed me a nice smile. For a fraction of a second I thought: "that's nice", but before I could smile back I found myself thinking "maybe my buttons are done up wrongly, or my zipper is undone, or I have some other untidy feature that has attracted her ridicule". So my response was not a smile but a look of anxiety which she probably thought was unfriendly. My own insecurity had steered my thoughts in a negative direction.

A continuous threat can lead to paranoia. My teenage years were at the height of the cold war, and I grew up very conscious of the imminent threat of nuclear war. While at boarding school, I read much about the effects of nuclear weapons, first-strikes and Mutually Assured Destruction (MAD), I even built my own Geiger counter. I guess I thought that if I understood the situation I could somehow reduce the risk.

One dark winter evening, not long after the Cuban missile crisis, I was eating dinner with the rest of the school in the huge dining room, when suddenly all the lights went out and everyone started to stamp their feet. For just a few brief seconds, my confused mind imagined that nuclear war had kicked off and I was quite frightened. A moment later the lights came back on and the pupil next to me reminded me that it was Halloween. Someone had just been messing with the lights.

I was intrigued that the simple sensation of the lights going out, had flipped me into a completely inappropriate prediction of what was going on because of my anxiety about the cold war. It was a case of momentary paranoia; no harm had been done and my subsequent experience had immediately corrected my prediction error. More severe cases of paranoia persist even in the face of contrary evidence, so can have a marked antisocial effect on people's behaviour.

In all areas of our life we seek to "explain" our experiences in order to feel safe as we move into our future. In science this safety usually comes from a rigorous analytical understanding of how to build a bridge or how a nuclear reactor works, whereas in personal relationships our safety comes from accurately predicting other people's emotional response to our actions. When we imagine the future we are simulating the future based on our experiences from our past, so strong experiences such as a death, a rape, a Chernobyl, a Hiroshima, can have a huge influence on what we envisage. If we are fortunate, we will have only experienced these through TV, film or literature, i.e. through someone else's simulation, that of the film director or the writer.

My own fear of nuclear war came not from exposure to radiation, but solely from my exposure to other people's stories, TV, books, radio. Despite our insecurities, the world has become a safer place, at least for those of us in developed countries, for example our life expectancy has greatly increased. Yet it seems that the absence of real threats such as disease and poverty, has led to a hunger for entertainment that portrays scary fictional scenarios such as crime and emergency medicine. We now entertain ourselves with portrayals of our own society that are far more negative and crisis-filled than average lives. There is no market for good news, which paradoxically is good news in itself. For in the past, the greatest demand for upbeat movies and entertainment has been in the darkest days of war. Who needs a horror film, when real horror is available?

Fear is a great motivator. Politicians and advertisers know this all too well, so often encourage a disproportionate sense of fear towards various threats. For example, we are far more concerned with the relatively small numbers of people who die in acts of terrorism, than with the vast numbers of deaths attributed to road accidents, smoking and alcohol. So our governments find it far easier to elicit votes and taxes through our fear of a few terrorists, than from the threat to our entire civilisation by climate change.

We are born as social creatures; most of us have at least one parent to form a community with. We can participate in several overlapping social communities: our family, our friends, our gang, work colleagues, sports club, school, town, city, nation, continent, each of greater size, including humanity itself. Though we can imagine being a part of something bigger, perhaps even "all that there is", in our daily lives most of us give strongest allegiance to smaller groups. Worldwide problems such as pandemic diseases and global warming require global cooperation, and this can be difficult to achieve when nations and individuals are preoccupied by competition between each other.

It is fashionable to be focused on our self or our family, striving for ourselves rather than the greater good, however, historically progress has come almost entirely when there has been some external threat, for this is when people have shared ideas and skills, and resources such as food and comradeship. The London blitz during the Second World War created close community bonds between those being bombed out of their homes. However, when the threat is still just a potential one, when we are still living the good life but in fear of its demise, then we may think small, even buy a gun. Our paranoia might make us prepare for the breakdown of civilisation: move to the countryside, build a fortified family sized shelter, stocked with arms, ammunition and enough food for a year, expecting the worst at any time. This is not a good direction for civilisation, but one that makes sense to those caught in a climate of fear and with little sense of the greater community. We need to remember that big problems can only be solved by big communities.

We can manage our own paranoia as it seems entirely reasonable to us at the time, but encountering someone else who is being paranoid can be very disturbing because we cannot predict their reactions and responses. For example, if I smile at someone on the street and they respond aggressively with: "who are you looking at?!" I have no insight into their reasoning, no adequate model for their behaviour. I don't know if it will be safer to ignore them and walk on, or to engage them in conversation.

When I see some apparently negative characteristic in humanity that has persisted, I ask myself: could there have been an evolutionary benefit from it? Those people prepared for Armageddon may seem paranoid to the rest of us, but only because life goes on, for now. Perhaps paranoia among a small fraction of the population has been essential to the survival of Homo sapiens through flood and famine throughout our long history. I imagine that the biblical figure of Noah would have seemed very paranoid to his friends while he was building his ark, at least until the rain got really heavy.

I carved myself a set of animated puppets

"Imagine all those people"

- John Lennon[395]

At this stage it is worth remembering that within our minds we carry models of all the people in our lives. For the people that we know well, our models are complex, based on the many real experiences we have shared, with added ideas that we have developed about them through our own introspection. For those with whom we are less familiar our models may be much simpler, and may even be derived from someone else's model of them, passed on to us as an opinion via a friend or the media.

When we are away from the people that they represent our models of them still persist in our mind, close by, merely a thought away. And when we do think of them, we may well engage in a hypothetical dialogue with our model of them. We imagine what they will say, how they will respond, what opinions they might express. However, what we forget is that we are having a dialogue with a simulation in our own head. It is only as accurate as the idea we have of the person. Our introspection serves only to reinforce the limited information that we have about them, so tends to give the illusion that we know the person better.

For example, if there is someone who we believe has been critical of us in the past, our representation of them in our youniverse is likely to be criticising us whenever we give it some attention, even in our dreams. The real individual is probably thinking about other things, but we only have access to our limited model of them which we alone have created. It is conceivable that the real person died some time ago, yet we can still hear our model of them criticising us.

So we populate our minds with all these characters, and animate them with our own thoughts and insecurities, like puppets. It is no wonder that we are often confused when we relate to other people, for we inevitably have relationships with fictitious characters that are based more on our history, than on the present moment. We have relationships with our ideas of people, not the people themselves.

If you have been in conflict with someone, then you may well have found yourself rehearsing what you would say to them, and what you think they would say in return, and how you would then respond etc. etc., having a complete dialogue with them, even an argument, losing sight of the fact that you are standing completely alone in the shower!

This is what we humans do; we try to predict the future based on our past, so rehearsing a dialogue with one of our own internal characters, is our way of trying to optimise the future outcome for ourselves. The challenge is to stay open to the present experience, whether it is having a shower, or engaging with someone for real. When we interact with people, it is all too easy to be communicating with our personal caricature of someone, and to not hear or see them.

Where do puppets go when they die?

If our experience of someone is dominated by our mental model of them, this casts a new perspective on the experience of bereavement. Consider the difference between the experience of missing someone close to us when they are merely physically absent, or when we know that they have died. In both cases we have a detailed model of them in our mind's eye, one that we have built over time and through our shared experience. This familiar model does not die with the death of the individual, and may even survive essentially unchanged until we ourselves die. Whether a person is absent through death or through distance, we can still hold a conversation with them within our mind.

The clear difference is the finality of our relationship. When there is no hope of future interactions to be enjoyed, it is a cause for grief. We change the binary characteristic of their puppet-like model in our mind from living to dead. Sometimes there is uncertainty, for example when a soldier is reported missing in action. Then until the ambiguity is resolved both possibilities co-exist; we hope for their life and fear for their death.[396]

We have the power to re-imagine our puppet. We have our memories, and we can choose which memories we revisit and so reinforce. We may recall our memories of their difficult last days or years, or instead remember those qualities and events worthy of celebration. Either way we can mould our future recollections of one who has died. If remembering is too painful, then not remembering will in time result in less to be remembered. The unremembered fade into history, assisted by our own loss of memory with age.

We have yet to mention one other key character that is modelled in our mind; our idea of ourselves. How we define ourselves within our simulation is crucial, it is where we fit in our imagined world. It is often hard to remember that we are no-one else's opinion of ourselves. Of course it's possible, and even quite likely, that no one else sees us the way we see ourselves despite our attempts to project a particular image. After all, to them *we* are just another simulated person in *their* own personal youniverse. They need to make sense of us in the context of all their other ideas and assumptions. However much we might try to act benignly; there will always be someone who chooses to see us as bad, if only to make them feel good. Such people may be open to changing their opinions, but most aren't interested. I explore this further in the next chapter.

Taking the wheel from this point on

"The world of the happy
is quite different from the world of the unhappy"
- Ludwig Wittgenstein[397]

We ourselves are not responsible for all that we encounter on our journey through life, but we are surprisingly responsible for what we feel and experience as we respond to life's events. All of us can identify things that we would like to change in our lives, both emotional and physical. It is easy to imagine that others influence our thoughts and steer our emotions, but in truth it is we ourselves who do the thinking and feeling. If we accept this responsibility we can realize the power it gives us, the power to dramatically change the quality of our lives. You may have encountered such rhetoric before in various self-help books, but here it is based on a more scientific argument.

Our early experiences may have had the greatest influence, but all our experiences and thoughts continue to modify the kind of youniverse that we find ourselves in, for what we sense and think throughout our life builds the very fabric of the world that we alone inhabit. This suggests that we should exercise more care with what we think, for our thoughts will continue to change the character of the world we experience, our future youniverse, steering our course this way or that.

We may feel that external forces and events have guided us to where we are now, but our future life will be played out in our personal youniverse whose details have yet to be finalised. So the idea of our personal youniverse has powerful implications, for if the thoughts that we think can change our youniverse, let us recognise the fact, take more control of our thoughts and start to change our future.

Let us first explore how we might influence our future emotional youniverse. Our emotional state, though considered a mere aberration by many scientists, affects almost everything that we do and experience. If we are unhappy, we may lay the blame on the world in which we find ourselves and on the ideas that we are subjected to. But as adults, we are not force-fed with ideas, we feed ourselves. No-one else makes us think negatively (though some acquaintances may encourage us in that direction!). It makes no sense for us to blame journalism if we buy the tabloid newspaper. It is we who choose what material we read and watch, and what company we keep.

Most of us say that we would be happier if we had more money, and it is obvious that not everyone can be "rich", if by "rich" we mean greater personal power or financial wealth *relative to others*. While there is evidence that unhappiness correlates to some degree with having less than average wealth, clearly that is not the whole story.[398]

Throughout history, many humans have gone short of basic physiological needs such as food and shelter, to the extent that their very lives were threatened. For them, and for many living in the developing world today, these unmet needs represent an absolute form of poverty. A man dying of starvation is little comforted by the knowledge of his neighbour's similar condition. For the fundamentally poor, their daily struggle is with the physical aspects of existence, such as hunger, shelter, pain, disease, life expectancy, abuse, war.

Though many humans suffer from absolute poverty, a limited few experience something akin to the other extreme of absolute wealth, such that they can have and do almost anything they desire, and for them all things lose their relative value.

Abraham Maslow suggested that we have a hierarchy of needs.[399] From the lowest level, these are: Physiological, then Safety, Belongingness and Love, Esteem, and the uppermost: Self-Actualization and Self-Transcendence. He used these terms to describe the pattern that human motivations generally progress through given the opportunity and motivation.[400] He suggested that we are only motivated to achieve the higher levels, when we have attended to the lower ones, so a starving man will risk eating unsafe food for example.

For the majority of us living in the west, our basic needs are easily met, so our experience of poverty and wealth is dominated by the *differences* between our lives and those of others, friends, neighbours, or with people we see in magazines and on TV. If we are fortunate to be free from real poverty we can still feel impoverished by focusing our mind's attention on the difference between what we might have been come to expect, and what we think we have. We might expect to be loved, to be famous, to have a flat-screen TV, fashionable clothes, a new car, the latest trainers or iPhone, or be able to play our drums in the apartment without the neighbours complaining.

Our materialist culture surrounds us with the idea that we should be deeply dissatisfied if we have less than our fellows. It panders to our personal insecurities, and the economics of consumerism requires it. This strategy guarantees that a major proportion of the population can easily feel dissatisfied with their lot. But it is evident from the lives and deaths of people who have great financial wealth, lottery winners and celebrities, that no amount of wealth, success or status is sufficient to *guarantee* happiness. However, if "rich" is defined in terms of happiness, personal fulfilment, or the feeling of being blessed by life, then in principle there is no fundamental limit to the proportion of the population who might be happy with their life.

I used to be an overly objective scientist, applying scientific logic to areas of life for which it was inappropriate. Although I had never thought about the logic of happiness, somewhere in the back of my mind I naively assumed that there was a "law of conservation of happiness". This law implied that in the world as a whole, the total sum of happiness plus unhappiness is constant. The implication of this idea is that, if some people are to be happy and fulfilled or both, then others must be unhappy and unfulfilled to maintain the balance.

My upbringing taught me that sacrifice and service to others was good, and this law fitted well with this belief. Many years ago when I was going through some difficult times, a good friend said to me "Everyone has the right to be happy". Inside my head I could hear myself saying "Shhh! That's dangerous talk, if everyone thought this way, society would fall apart". Fortunately, my thinking has changed, and I no longer believe that my own happiness has to be at the expense of another's.

There are many self-help books that promote the idea that we can transform our lives for the better by visualising success and happiness.[401] The idea is often presented in almost mystical terms, with prayer-like affirmations. However, if we now accept that our life is an unconscious simulation of reality, constructed entirely from our experiences and thoughts, then we can see that such aphorisms, however glib, can also be seen as a reprogramming of our mind, a redirecting of our aims, or even an antidote to an earlier mental program that is now obsolete.

So a positive state of mind, tempered with sufficient realism, can create a more benign youniverse for ourselves. An effective cure for mild depression is to review at the end of each day, whatever positive things have happened during that day. In other words, remembering happy events in our lives constructs a more pleasant world than remembering painful ones.

However, our momentum steers us along the direction that we have already been travelling. It is easy to reuse our old assumptions without checking if they remain valid, or if they ever were. To change direction, we must first recognise which way we are already going. While most of us cling to the idea that we have free will, much of what we do, think and feel is predictable behaviour, for we are creatures of habit. It takes effort to change course, to change the general direction in which our youniverse is travelling. We quite literally need to change our minds.

It is more difficult when we are surrounded by others travelling in a particular direction. If we have sought to make ourselves attractive to others through our appearance, through our fashionable tastes, then we have tied our youniverse to our idea of other people's tastes, restricting its movements. Similarly, celebrity only exists in the minds of fans. But those who can say: "I am no-one else's opinion of who I am", are free to change their youniverse.

The solution is to take control of our perceptual diet, take responsibility for how we choose to interpret what our senses are exposed to. Does the advertisement for the latest trainers, iPad, car etc. make us feel poorer? Do we live with the idea that we are how others see us? Or do we have the courage to be OK about ourselves independently of how we are perceived? Would we dare to wear designer clothing and let absolutely everyone else believe that it is a cheap Chinese copy? That would suggest a self-confident person, (or perhaps someone who is embarrassed by their wealth).

We can steer ourselves towards positive or negative youniverses. For example, if we look for threats, rejection, or to be judged negatively by others, we will increase the chances of encountering such experiences and reinforce those aspects within our youniverse. In contrast, if we look for the positive aspects of those around us, we may well find ourselves in a world with more pleasant people. So perhaps we steer ourselves towards worlds that are heavenly or hellish, depending on what we choose to do, with what we experience.

Changing our physical reality

We have seen that we have the power to change our mental experience of the world, but we can also modify our actual physical performance. The idea we hold of ourselves in our youniverse includes beliefs of the limits in our physical ability. These beliefs are then manifested in our bodies. For example, I used to believe that I needed a full eight hours sleep at night or my health would suffer.[402] Sure enough, if I slept for quarter of an hour less, I would feel really tired the following day.

Then I had experiences that made me realize that the very precise nature of the apparent physical limit was in my mind, and that I could tolerate some nights with very little sleep provided I had a reasonable amount of sleep on average. Similarly, the majority of us have a clear idea of our absolute minimum food requirements in our normal life, its quantity and frequency, yet are able to fast for many days.

The mental limits to our physical performance probably exist to protect our bodies, in the same way that the "rev limiter" in a car stops us from damaging the engine by over revving it.[403] There is a difference between our mental idea of our limit, and the point at which serious physical damage occurs to our body, a margin, just as the rev limiter in my car would be offset somewhat below the speed at which the engine would destroy itself. In competitive sports, this margin makes the difference between a good performer and a champion.

Many sports people and top athletes mentally rehearse their anticipated physical performance beforehand. For example, competitors in the high jump visualise themselves clearing the bar at a height that they have yet to clear, and have never cleared. This imagined performance helps to counter the learned experience of what is impossible for them. After all, they will have had far more experiences of failing jumps at heights close to their personal best, than of succeeding. Top competitors know that what they believe influences what is possible for them. Whether we believe we can, or we believe that we can't, both are more likely to come true.

Mental rehearsal is also a way of bypassing the learning bottleneck, for the greater our familiarity with a repetitive task, the more the limited learning capability of our mind can focus just on the tiny differences between each repetition, to optimise the task's execution. For example, most Formula One drivers rehearse driving round the circuit, while sitting in the cockpit of their stationary car waiting to go out and drive their qualifying lap. Their starting position on the grid is determined by the shortest time that they can drive this one lap, and it is not unusual for race starting positions to be decided by mere hundredths of a second in their total lap time. So they sit in the car, close their eyes and imagine driving every part of a complete lap, every turn of the wheel, even imagining the g-forces on their body that they are about to experience. They are adding to their experience, without the actual experience. Their limited learning bottleneck is then devoted to sensing and responding to the tiny differences in the grip of the tyres experienced on each real lap.

Just as the idea of multiple youniverses suggests that we can modify the future of the psychological world we inhabit, some of the many-worlds theories in physics suggest that in doing so, we may actually be modifying the physical world we find ourselves moving into. Now that is a mind-blowing thought. I wonder if that thought has just modified my future, and that of the physical world I inhabit…

When Worlds collide

When our youniverse encounters another person's youniverse, there will be differences. If we have a dialogue about things of a purely physical nature with someone, there will be plenty of room for agreement. Two physicists can jointly participate in an experiment, such as weighing something, and achieve complete agreement. But most experiences contain a large subjective element.

Sometimes when we realize the extent of miscommunication between ourselves and someone else, it feels as if the one we are trying to communicate with is living on another planet. The book "Men Are from Mars, Women Are from Venus" presents a simple picture, implying that men and women at least understand others of their own sex, but we all know that serious misunderstandings can arise between any of us.[404]

The most serious misunderstandings arise when the message contains zero information, i.e. there is no message, yet we interpret the absence of information to imply meaning. Predicting something from zero information is like dividing by zero; it results in infinite possibilities. The fact that my old friend Dave hasn't communicated with me for ten years could mean many things: He died? Or he lost my contact details when his PC died? Or he took offence at something I said (or did not say)? Or he listened to tales from my "ex"? (If I'm feeling paranoid). The smaller the amount of actual information exchanged, the greater the diversity of imagined realities, making it more likely that I respond inappropriately (like removing Dave from my Christmas card list). Zero information is just zero information as I try to keep reminding myself.

Our idea of the world has a major influence on how we interpret new information, especially where the quantity of information is small. I want to finish this chapter by illustrating how a shared lack of communication between two people, can lead to them drifting off into very different youniverses, even though they may be physically close to each other. Or expressed in the language of physics; the "quantum fluctuations" in the zero information of a silence, can cause a splitting of universes! What follows is a brief fictional tale in the lives of two people, as an example of the Many Worlds theory in relationships between men and women:

Dave and Jane have been going out together on and off for nearly a year, and although they have never spoken of it, each feels that this could be the one, the person to spend the rest of their lives with. They feel so in-tune with each other that they are convinced that they can read each other's thoughts.

One day they go for a long walk round the big lake, it is a place they both love, she for its wildlife and Dave for its excellent fishing. As they round a bend in the path they catch sight of a family group by the water's edge; mother minding a baby and father busy fishing. Jane whispers quietly to Dave: "Ah, That's nice" as Dave nods in total agreement.

Jane thinks: "How wonderful it would be to have a baby with Dave and spend long summer afternoons together as a family".

And Dave is thinking: "Wow! That's the latest carbon-fibre fishing rod he's using. I dream of being able to afford one like that someday".

The encounter reminds Jane that she had forgotten to share some exciting news with Dave; it had arrived in her mail that morning. "Dave", she says excitedly, "We've been invited to John and Sue's wedding, isn't that great?"

Dave says nothing, but his body betrays a silent groan.

He thinks: "Oh No! Not another wedding, there's bound to be someone asking why I'm still single. And knowing John, he's bound to insist on a long and bawdy stag-do, and I'm going to have to get dressed up in some ridiculous and embarrassing costume."

Jane is surprised by Dave's reaction, or rather the lack of it. She loves weddings and had assumed that Dave did too. She wonders: "He must have heard what I said, so why no response? Is he feeling pressured in our relationship I wonder?"

Then, hoping to elicit some tiny sign of enthusiasm, she quickly adds: "it's on the sixteenth of June next year", at which point Dave brings his hands to his head with a now audible "Oh No!"

And Jane is thinking: Wow! I had no idea that Dave was so anti-marriage". And then she remembers that Dave always had a soft spot for Sue. "Perhaps that's it! Perhaps he has been harbouring ambitions to get together with Sue. Maybe he has fancied her more than me all along. I seem to remember that he was always the one trying to arrange for us to go out as a foursome."

And Dave is thinking: "That damn fool, what was john thinking of? Surely he can't have forgotten that June 16th is the first day of the fishing season. Every year on that day the two of us go fishing together, it's special. We've always done it. Sue must have put him up to it just to show who's the boss now, I never did like her". "Women!" he mutters angrily, and Jane flinches.

They walk on in awkward silence, choosing to take the shorter path back to the car, Dave brooding over the fact that he will never again share those precious moments with his fishing buddy, while Jane sees all her future plans disintegrate. How can she go to Sue's wedding, knowing what she knows now?

As Dave drives Jane back to her home, he tries to work out why she is so quiet. He guesses that she feels foolish for not realising earlier, just how inappropriate that date would be for any kind of social event.

Now, back in the safety of his own home, he distracts himself from the memory of betrayal by his fishing buddy, by watching a rerun of a programme on extreme fishing while searching on eBay for cheap offers of second hand fishing tackle just like the kit he'd admired back at the lakeside.

By now Jane has called her closest friends and told them that it's all over between Dave and her and why, before slowly crying herself to sleep. Over the next few months her friends support her by relentlessly analysing and reanalysing what had happened and what it all meant.

Meanwhile Dave now goes fishing, alone, and just occasionally finds himself staring at the water, wondering what the hell happened that day.[405]

Throughout this chapter I have described the many ways that what we think can influence the world we find ourselves in. Thinking in a particular way sets us on a particular course, one which is not always easy to correct. On the other hand, here is a strong logical argument for the benefits of "positive thinking", or at least to notice how much our thoughts can change the world we find ourselves experiencing. Though this book is not a self-help book, this chapter may provide some insights into how to refurnish your youniverse to make it more fulfilling.

Next I explore what insights we might gain into the thorny subject of prejudice by considering it from the logical perspective of information. You will see that prediction and prejudice are remarkably similar processes.

Chapter Ten

The Science of Prejudice

"Without the aid of prejudice and custom, I should not be able to find my way across the room; nor know how to conduct myself in any circumstances, nor what to feel in any relation of life"
- William Hazlitt - (1778-1830)[406]

The bottleneck tells us that we are unable to absorb more than a tiny fraction of the available information in the present moment, but within that moment we are already familiar with the majority of what our senses are telling us, through our memories of similar experiences in the past. We have already distilled our history into a set of rules, and these usually predict something very similar to what we are sensing. This allows us to focus our attention on the relatively small difference between what we expect and what we sense, and this enables us to maximise the value of our limited learning capacity.

The fundamental quality that distinguishes humans from other species is the huge role that experience-based prediction plays in our daily lives. Whenever we make judgements, we are far more reliant on information from our past than on information perceived in the present moment. This means that with the exception of our crude reflexes, all our judgements are dominated by what we have previously learned. We integrate everything that we are learning with what we have already learned. The little information that is truly new to us has to compete with the vastness of all our past, and where they do not concur, our past is more often the winner.

In the memory contests described earlier, competitors are required to memorise a sequence of random numbers. Their previous experience is of absolutely no help to them in predicting the next numbers as they are completely random. This is an extremely unusual situation for anyone. In almost every situation we encounter, we are able to quickly come up with ideas, predictions of what we are experiencing based on what we already know of our situation, without having to wait for the entire experience itself. We have considerable expectations.

This can be illustrated by considering these three totally different responses to an identical hypothetical stimulation of my senses:

- I feel something touch the back of my arm. I immediately realize it is my lover gently tenderly reminding me that we must go soon, and I turn to smile at her.

- I feel something touch the back of my arm. I immediately leap off my seat while swatting my arm, "Those damn biting insects, I knew we shouldn't have camped next to the river!"

- I feel something touch the back of my arm. I immediately blab the code-word that my torturer had been threatening to extract from me using his red hot branding iron, only to discover that he had merely touched me with the cold key to my cell door. He laughs.

Each of these completely different responses was initiated by sensing exactly the same thing: My skin sensed pressure, and sent a simple nerve signal to my brain indicating this simple fact alone, but no other information. However, for each of these situations my mind had different expectations, and responded in context.

In the first case, my mind was primed to expect the sensation to be caused by my lover and my expectation was confirmed. In both the second and third cases my prior attention had primed my reflexes, causing completely different "knee-jerk" reactions from my body, even before my brain caught up. While in the third case, my expectation was manipulated by someone else. For all three cases, the input information from the moment "now" is identical; the differences in the immediate experience are entirely due to my different expectations from the past, my prejudices.

In this chapter, I reveal how this process of experience-based prediction is the intrinsic mechanism behind all prejudice, whether negative or positive. Most of our prejudices are benign and serve us well, but a few are deeply flawed distortions of reality, such as the naive positive prejudice of hero-worship, or the harmful negative prejudice of racism. It is often said that education overcomes prejudice, but under closer examination it would appear that all of our learning builds a lifetime of prejudices. Education merely replaces crude prejudices with ones that are more detailed, more accurate, and therefore ones that are hopefully more useful and less harmful.

"There is no prejudice so strong as that which arises from
a fancied exemption from all prejudice"
- William Hazlitt[407]

Prejudice is a behaviour more easily observed in others. For many years I held two strong prejudices: I believed that all prejudices were bad, and that nice people like me did not hold them. Having gained more insight into my own mental processes, I now realize that they are a key part of our everyday life, and not intrinsically bad.

The harm within prejudice occurs when we are ignorant of its profound influence within ourselves, and so unable to understand its cause in others. I hope that by exploring this process further, we can help defeat an enemy that lurks somewhere within all our minds, negative prejudice. To do this, we will see what insights can be gained by considering the process of prejudice in terms information and our bottleneck-constrained learning, rather than the more usual sense of moral judgement.

Prejudiced words

The word "prejudice" is derived from pre and judge, a pre-judgement.[408] The first two definitions of the word in the American Heritage Dictionary of the English Language are:[409]

"An adverse judgement or opinion formed beforehand or without knowledge or examination of the facts."

"A preconceived preference or idea."

The first and most commonly understood meaning is that a prejudice is intrinsically a negative thing, and this definition is particularly useful when we feel self-righteous. We are also likely to be familiar with the negative side of a positive prejudice, for example when someone who is supposed to be acting impartially, favours their own family or friends. Either way, from our own perspective, such prejudice is bad, and easily involves us emotionally.

However, if we want to gain insight into the science behind prejudice, it is more helpful to explore the second of these definitions, a completely neutral definition of the word, meaning: to prejudge, to decide before all the detail is available, to make an early decision, to take a position before all the facts are in.

There are two components to "pre"-"judice": The timing and the judgement. Let's first consider the timing: A prejudice always requires some knowledge of the facts, even if it is only the subject under consideration. One cannot hold a prejudice until one has learned something, something that predisposes us towards a judgement such as a person's nationality. But how much knowledge must someone acquire before their judgement is considered completely free of prejudice? Can someone who has acquired all the information still be prejudiced? What might "all the information" mean? And when is it too soon to make a judgement?

The second part of prejudice is the judgement itself. The purpose of a judgement is often to enable an action, perhaps an urgent action, such as avoiding a collision, illustrating that prejudiced actions can be positive and negative. A judgement is a simplification, there is less information after the judgement than before, and we may forget the details discarded in the process of judgement. In some judgements a complex opinion is reduced to one single bit of information, a decision such as: guilty/not guilty, left/right, good/bad, or to pass the other ship on the port/starboard side. In the extreme case of the death penalty, the judgement no longer retains the complexity of why the crime was committed by subsequently destroying a key witness.

Of course in common use, we tend to use "prejudice" as a derogatory term to describe the behaviour of other people with whom we disagree. The purely negative interpretation of the word relies on the assumption that we personally know what is good and bad in an absolute sense. And it is worth noting that our discomfort with accepting a less negative definition is evidence itself that what we have learned in the past influences how we receive new information.

It would be convenient for us to imagine that all reasonable minded people can agree on what constitutes a prejudice and what does not, but in the real world this is highly subjective. We often encounter those who seem both knowledgeable and intelligent, yet are suddenly shocked when they express a prejudice about something on which we hold a completely different point of view. Consider the difference between faith and prejudice, both imply trusting a belief without all the supporting evidence, yet one is generally considered benign and the other is not.

Our internal predictive model generates subjective opinions that we personally may consider as objective truths. We use words such as "prejudice", "objective", "opinionated" as if they have some absolute significance, that we are holders of true knowledge. But they are all simply expressions of the extent to which we concur with each other. When I say that someone is being "objective", it simply means that they have expressed an opinion that I agree with. Let's be frank, I would never say it if I disagreed with them.

You might argue that someone is also being "objective" when they can back up their opinion with evidence, but this only applies when I accept their interpretation of the evidence. An opinion shared by many does not become a fact, but consensus gives us the confidence to ignore the distinction. If a group of us agree to limit the range and extent of what is observed or discussed by using a constrained formal language such as science, then within that context it will be as if we are being objective.

As physicist Niels Bohr put it: "Physics is to be regarded not so much as the study of something a priori given, but rather as the development of methods of ordering and surveying human experience. In this respect our task must be to account for such experience in a manner independent of individual subjective judgement and therefore objective in the sense that it can be unambiguously communicated in ordinary human language."[410] It has been said that "science has enjoyed an extraordinary success because it has such a limited and narrow realm in which to focus its efforts, namely, the physical universe".[411]

"Common Sense" is just such an agreement. It is something that we can all agree upon, perhaps repeatedly sensed by ourselves and concurring with what we have learned from those around us as part of our culture.[412] Common sense and objectivity are ideas that only survive intact when confined to the dry land of reason. If we are to stay with the illusion of objectivity we must steer well clear of vast areas of rich experience such as love and other emotions, areas that encompass so much of what we consider important in our personal lives. Our feelings towards our own family, our taste in music, food, clothes or our favourite sports teams, are certainly not shared by everyone.

When we say "sports team or musical band "X" are brilliant/rubbish" we might deceive ourselves that we are making a statement about what they are, forgetting that we are speaking only of our personal taste. In reality we are just expressing our subjective opinion on how they perform, and on how that affects us emotionally. It is merely a statement about how we feel in relation to them. Our belief in our objectivity is like the belief in Father Christmas for the child that knows the truth about Santa: We collude in the illusion because it continues to bring us valuable gifts. An objective world is much more comfortable to inhabit, especially when based on our own beliefs.

If I say someone else is "prejudiced" or "opinionated", I am stating no more than that I disagree with their subjective opinion (or maybe that I just don't like them). Equally I might be accused of being opinionated whenever I try to communicate my "objective" opinion to someone with a differing idea of things. The uncomfortable truth is that we are all prejudiced and opinionated, since it is fundamental to how we humans function, though some reveal their opinions readily while others conceal their own.

Varieties of prejudice

We think of prejudice in terms of personal attitudes, but a prejudice is a prediction based on limited information. It is vital to remember that prediction is the most valuable skill we humans possess. Although we have few outstanding *physical* qualities compared with other creatures, our species has been able to achieve mastery across our planet through the use of our brain as a predictive tool. We each make unconscious predictions as a means of perceiving and exploring the detailed world we are in, despite the limitations of our senses and of our learning bottleneck. We navigate our way through the present (and towards the future), using what we have learned from the past. We find it almost impossible to live entirely in the moment, because we continually plan and judge what should be our course of action in the future without any knowledge of the future, and we create cohesive yet largely fictional stories of our past, based on mere fragments of information.

Fully conscious prejudices

As we are unaware of these unconscious processes, it may be difficult to appreciate how much of our perception is determined by prejudice, but we can gain some insight by first considering some of our more conscious prejudices. For example, we consciously make predictions through the rules of science. We make observations and then convert them into insights and rules that enable us to extend into new areas, ones in which we as yet have no detailed knowledge.

Consider the science behind Apollo program that took men to the Moon: Throughout history, men had observed the effect of gravity and other forces on an object of a given mass and struggled to understand them. When Sir Isaac Newton conceived his elegant physical laws of motion he did not do so spontaneously. His skill was to compress a myriad of observations made by himself and by others into the most compact form possible, into generally applicable rules that enable us to predict what will happen, for example when we attempt to hurl an object into space.[413] [414]

Although many aspects of the Apollo program were incredibly complex, Newton's laws of motion, despite being formulated as early as 1687, were sufficient to describe the dynamics of the trajectory of the 1969 Moon mission. The fact that the launched capsule could reach its precise destination a quarter of a million miles away with only the tiniest of mid-course correction, is testament to mankind's use of predictive science, the journey being made almost entirely by dead reckoning from the initial launch conditions, the mass, the required thrust and direction. The scientists had prejudged the required rocket thrust and direction during the launch phase, in order for the capsule to coast the next quarter of a million miles to the Moon.

This was possible despite our lack of experience of the space it would traverse because empty space contains no significant surprises, there is little of any consequence between the Earth and the Moon. Only when they reached the Moon's surface did they encounter things that they could not predict, such as the depth of the dust on the surface.

Compare that with the task of navigating a sailing boat across an ocean to a specific destination. There are many unpredictable influences along the journey, such as the wind strength and direction, that make it essential to take frequent measurements of one's position and apply many successive course corrections. In the journey to the Moon there was little to be learned along the way that would help with navigation. The initial predictions based on centuries old theories were sufficient, while on the sea journey, almost continual learning is required.

The extent to which our predictions are sufficient to determine an outcome is likely to be determined by the simplicity of the actual situation, as revealed by these two examples. The Lunar space programme was an incredible achievement, but perhaps made us over-confident in our ability to solve problems on Earth, for there is nothing on our planet that is as simple as space.

As a scientist working in a research laboratory, I was occasionally required to be a bit of a detective. An experiment or system being tested gave a puzzling result that did not fit with what was expected, with what our current understanding predicted would occur. We were naturally prejudiced by our past experiences and sometimes this made it hard to spot something completely new to us, especially when we had become emotionally attached to what we had already learned and what had served us so well till now. We would devise all sorts of excuses for the result until the evidence for a new phenomenon became so overwhelmingly conspicuous that we were forced to modify our existing ideas. In this sense a good researcher needs some of the skills of a detective to try to predict an explanation based on past experience, yet always to be open to the possibility of the completely unexpected.

Mostly unconscious prejudices

We also hold many prejudices which we are unconscious of most of the time, yet are readily brought to our conscious mind by giving them our attention. One example of a valuable prejudice is that I should drive on the left hand side of the road. Although this is the law in the UK, once we have learned to drive it soon becomes second nature rather than a continually conscious awareness of the letter of the law.

Whenever I see a car coming towards me in the distance, I do not immediately ask myself which side I should expect it to pass me by. Instead, I rely on my long standing prejudice that we will all keep to the left side of the road (as I live and drive in the UK), and I can drive for hours without ever consciously remembering it. Without this prejudice, my attention would be distracted by this question with each and every car that came in the opposite direction, and make driving on busy roads almost impossible. So when I leave the UK to drive in Europe or the USA, it is essential for me to keep reminding myself of my prejudice, and remember to override it and drive on the same side of the road as the local drivers.

When I graduated, I spent the summer being driven around the States by a friend who had recently emigrated. Although he had been driving in the States for two years, I was rather unnerved to see that he had a small note stuck to the centre of his steering wheel to remind him to "Drive on the Right". You see, he knew that old prejudices can reappear when you least expect. Having driven on the left in the UK for decades, he was worried that this habit might surface inappropriately. He was a teacher, and knew that two years of education or experience is insufficient to completely annihilate decades of prejudice.

However, I was soon to learn just how easy it is to pick up an unconscious prejudice. Over that long summer, I had travelled many thousands of miles in cars and buses that drove on the right hand side of the North American roads, but only ever as a passenger, so I hadn't consciously been too concerned with which side of the road we were driving on. A month after I returned to the UK, I rode my motorbike across country to visit another friend. When I set off to return, it was a beautifully quiet summer evening, not a car on the road. All was well with the world.

I had been riding along for about fifteen minutes, when suddenly I noticed a car approaching in the distance, driving on the wrong side of the road. I surmised that it was some idiotic youths larking about, just trying to scare me, but as the car continued to head directly towards me I became increasingly concerned. At the last minute I had to veer off into the ditch to avoid being hit by the car. I swung round, fist in the air shouting "bloody idiot" at the car's occupants. But instead of the grinning youths I expected, I saw a family group, all staring open-mouthed with shocked expressions. Suddenly the penny dropped; it was I who was on the wrong side of the road!

Fortunately, on that day the only casualty was my pride. I had survived months of crossing streets in the USA by keeping vigilant. Now back in familiar territory I had relaxed, and a little bit of subconscious programming rose to the surface and almost killed me. I had discovered how unconsciously learned prejudices can be dangerous, and how they can influence our behaviour when we least expect it. I sometimes wonder what that shocked family told their friends when they got home, their tale probably involved an "idiotic youth".

Completely unconscious prejudices

We also hold prejudices that we are almost completely unconscious of, yet nevertheless influence our actions. Many of these relate to our ideas about other people. Remember how we create and animate a puppet-like model in our mind for each person we encounter? Well, this is where our opinionated prejudices lurk, both good and bad. Although they normally lie hidden, with effort it is possible observe our own prejudiced mind at work. As I have done so over the years, I have become increasingly amazed at the tricks my own mind plays on me.

My next-door neighbour had a dysfunctional relative come to stay for a couple of weeks, a visit which subsequently stretched to a couple of years. Not only did she give him a fair amount of grief, but when he left the house she played her music at maximum volume, even to the point of seriously damaging his sound system. Whenever I heard loud music coming through our adjoining wall it usually signified the start of a very unpleasant few hours, so I was predisposed to expect a bad experience. Eventually the offending family member moved out and peace returned.

About six months later, I was working at my computer when suddenly I heard what appeared to be very loud music coming through the wall from next door. Immediately my heart dropped. I guessed that the problem had returned and braced myself for the inevitable disturbance. However, after a few minutes I suddenly realized that the sound was not a loud sound heard through the adjoining wall, but instead it was a barely audible sound from the little speakers of my own PC (which had spontaneously decided to play some music from a web page). I burst out laughing at my own acquired paranoia and marvelled how my assessment of "loud" had been so distorted by my idea of the sound's origin. I am fascinated by my slowness to unlearn a prejudice, and wonder where else in my life I am equally out of contact with current reality.

Many of us would be happy to live by the ocean, with the continual sound of the waves breaking upon the shore, but we might be very upset if back in our city apartment we heard exactly the same sound coming from next door's HiFi system, relentlessly day and night. These are clear examples of the subjective nature of the intensity of things we sense. Our preconceived idea of the cause can have a huge effect on our experience, especially if we think that people are involved, for then we can take it personally, thinking: "I wouldn't behave like that".

Mad Driver

I will now risk revealing the extent of my own prejudices, with examples of some of the things that go on in my mind while I'm driving my car. When we are in our vehicles our view of our fellow drivers is usually obscured and brief, yet as we generally have a clear view of their vehicle and its motion, our mind is free to make prejudiced guesses about the actual driver based on what little we do see (at least my own mind does).

Driving along the motorway I occasionally notice a vehicle weaving erratically outside its designated lane. My very first thought is that the driver is drunk or on drugs, and I assume it's a male. If the weaving abruptly stops and normal lane discipline is resumed, I then revise my prejudice and guess that the driver was sober, but trying to change a cassette, or sending a text message on their mobile phone.

Sometimes it is possible to get a clearer view of the possible cause, as we pass by in the adjacent lane. On one occasion the erratic driver turned out to be a woman swivelling in her seat, screaming at her misbehaving children in the back. On another occasion, the driver of an erratically driven truck was attempting to apply butter to a cracker on his knee, a scenario that my years of experience failed to predict!

I also have a wealth of prejudices about drivers based solely on the appearance of the car they are driving, its type, colour and condition. Who would you expect to be driving a tiny new bright pink Nissan Micra saloon? My own prejudice is that it is a first car, bought for an eighteen year old girl by her father. How about the respective drivers of a bright red Ferrari, and an ancient Volkswagen camper van? I am sure you already have some ideas about them.

Throughout our lives, we invent stories that make sense of our experiences: While driving in traffic along a main road I see a vehicle apparently waiting to pull out from a side turning. It is a woman driver in a large white 4-wheel drive vehicle. I make space for her to pull out but she fails to respond, and seems completely unaware of anything outside her vehicle. I am now annoyed that I am holding up both myself and the traffic for her. I notice that she has a cigarette in one hand and a mobile phone held to her ear in the other. I immediately feel that I know her type!

But I might be wrong. After all I have only glimpsed her for a mere second or two. For all I know, she might just have heard that her child has had an accident and been rushed to hospital. Perhaps the doctor is on the phone to her, asking crucial questions about the child's medication, and she is having her first cigarette in years to calm her down. No wonder she is distracted.

All this creative drama can be going on in my head and in remarkable detail too. My predicting mind animates a little puppet to represent this person with whatever odd ideas it can conjure up from its history. And the stories that I choose reflect my own state of mind at the time, whether I am stressed and angry, or relaxed and in love with the summers day.

I am a guy who enjoys driving, so as you can see this is a fruitful area for my prejudices to explore, and one in which I have by now revealed my foolishness. For you it may be very different, however, there will be areas of your life where you too imagine detailed stories that make sense of what you see and hear. Perhaps you feel that you know about someone's character by seeing what car they drive, what clothes they wear, the street they live, their accent or the colour of their skin.

Fashioned in our own image

Although the primary function of a car is as a means of transport, for many it is also a fashion item whose purpose is to create an image of us in the minds of others. Let's be honest, there are many people who "wouldn't be seen dead" in a car of a particular type or age, or even colour. Many men feel that their status among others is strongly influenced by the image of the vehicle they drive. The large market for fashionable cars that are demonstrably unreliable and expensive to run, suggests that for many car owners, once the primary function is met, the most important quality is the image that their vehicle projects.

The same applies to our clothes whose primary function is warmth (and modesty), yet in affluent economies their secondary function of promoting our image through the idea of fashion, completely dwarfs that of their primary function. Both cars and clothes do have other functions, but these remain the dominant reasons for choosing them.

The concept of fashion requires us to invest in an idea of an external observer, in particular the idea of what that observer might value in how they see us. So in our mind we craft puppet characters which incorporate our idea of how these characters might judge us. Much of the pleasure derived from fashionable cars, clothes and other fruits of our material culture, come from our belief that others will identify us with a higher status cultural group. It therefore relies on the idea of the existence of a lower status community of less fashionable people. We assume that we can manipulate other people's prejudices through what they see of us.

For a few creative individuals, fashion is about breaking from the status quo, having the courage to wear what conflicts with the norms of their peers. Whereas, for those who follow fashion (my wife doesn't think I am one of those either), it is about conforming to a style, a uniform which we believe will be approved by our peers and encourage a positively prejudiced view of us as people.

We want to feel good about ourselves, and only the most secure individuals can achieve that from within themselves. So we might try to dress in a way (or choose a car) that we imagine will make other people say "you look attractive", "I like you", "I admire you" or "I respect you, because you are cool". We might target a specific audience, for example specifically those who recognise that my car or handbag is a very special one.

If we were the last person on the planet and knew that there was no-one else to impress, even the most fashion conscious of us might choose different cars and clothes, perhaps going for comfort or utility instead. There are no absolutes in fashion (apart from not wearing socks with sandals my wife assures me); it is about wanting to feel special, not average. So as the average is changed by fashion, what is deemed fashionable will always evolve with time, what is thought to be attractive, comes and goes, and returns again.

Different cultural groups follow their own distinct fashions, whether the latest elegant Paris dress designs, or baseball hats worn back to front. Today most of us can afford clothes that satisfy their primary function, so clothes that are elegant or in good condition are no longer unique signatures of success. We now have styles that imitate poverty, with faded denim jeans or holes in the knees, or try to create a cool ghetto myth with trousers hanging down to expose underpants. These different "islands" of fashion are possible because we create very different puppet-like representations in our mind of external observers from the cultural group we are seeking to impress.

Fashion is communicated almost entirely through vision, which is our most powerful sense because of its range and angular resolution. Yet our vision is also our most superficial sense, in that it is the least penetrating, revealing nothing more than the very surface of complex objects and interesting people. While many people spend precious time working on their appearance before going out, hoping that others won't "see through" their mask, much less time is spent polishing a personality, or practicing conversational skills. Many Islamic women say that wearing an all-covering burka liberates them, in that it stops them feeling judged by their appearance. Yet paradoxically, having concealed the complexity of female fashion, what remains for the observer is a blank canvas, onto which we who are kept ignorant, may project all manner of judgements.

You might feel that this discussion of fashion trivialises the idea of prejudice, but I use it to logically explain the subjective nature of our prejudices about people, and how they are based on our very limited ideas of how other people think. Our well-meaning attempts to eliminate serious negative prejudices in society may fail if we cannot understand the mechanism itself. Our history is littered with atrocities caused by prejudice of race, religion and skin-colour. Sadly it is one area where our civilisation has made negligible progress, as it continues to be the cause of much suffering in our world.

When is the right time to decide?

"Prejudice is a great time saver.
You can form opinions without having to get the facts"
- Elwyn Brooks White[415]

We are all familiar with the negative consequences of prejudiced judgements in society, yet this same human tendency has been vital for the survival and success of our species. A prejudice is an early decision, a position taken before all the facts are in. If we were ignorant of our learning bottleneck we might assume that, if willing, we could take each situation at face value, absorb all the information necessary at the time, and then make a considered judgement. But now we know that is fundamentally not possible to do so. So we have to rely on our history, to predict what is likely and to focus our attention on what is most important to learn from the moment.

Making timely decisions and judgements can be crucial, whether we are choosing when to cross the road, or trading on the stock-market. So our prejudices exploit the value of our previous experience, to minimise the delay that would result from making decisions based solely on what we sense in the present. Our prejudices save time, and can prevent us being paralysed when too much information is available to us.

Here is an example of what I mean: Imagine a couple of naive city guys who find themselves walking in the African Savannah but know nothing of the animals there. They are suddenly disturbed by a "thundering" noise which gets louder and louder and look up to see a large grey blur coming towards them. The more decisive guy acts on his prejudice that "whatever it is, I should probably get out of its way", so jumps to the side (and being decisive he has little hesitation in choosing which way to jump).

However, his strongly analytical colleague wants to know what it is before he acts. He watches intently as it gets closer, gathering yet more and more detailed information about the object: skin colour, markings, size and apparent weight, confident that when he has enough information, he will know just what to do….. "Thump", and is crushed to death. His friend, who survives entirely due to his prejudice, later learns that it was a charging Rhino. Although he was ignorant of much of the detail, his prejudice saved him.

You might say that he used his instinct instead, but where do we imagine that our instincts come from?[416] Putting aside any metaphysical ideas, instinctual behaviour must either be learned, or inherited through ones DNA. I doubt our survivor was born with all the necessary information in his DNA. It is more likely that he had learned from other experiences throughout his life. Although we all have an inborn instinctive reflex to flinch away from objects moving into our field of view, it would have been triggered too late to save him. There is plenty of evidence that our inborn instincts alone are insufficient to protect pedestrians from being attacked by speeding cars.

We reduce complexity to simplicity by the act of deciding, discarding detail, replacing a larger amount of information with a much smaller amount. Decisiveness is one of many personality traits measured when assessing people's suitability for roles, and is a strong characteristic of military leaders and of most leaders of industry and commerce. Making timely decisions is just as important as making well thought-out decisions in many of the situations that they face. Of course both are important, but a leader who cannot make a decision can lead to disaster.

Decisive people tend to be more comfortable with the idea of learning from mistakes, and may even happily share examples of their own mistakes. Some decisive people may have developed their skill in response to their own discomfort with handling complexity. They may feel the need to collapse complexity into simplicity as soon as possible. Others may be addicted in varying degrees to the risk and excitement of their actions, even to the extent of taking risks with other people's jobs or finances.

At the opposite end of the decisiveness scale are those who are detail-conscious, analytical people who are comfortable with dealing with complexity. They may be less comfortable with reducing complex situations to what they see as a crude Yes or No, fearing that strong decisiveness can lead to outright dangerous behaviour, decisions made too soon. In contrast, strongly decisive people can feel frustrated by what they see as the "paralysis by analysis" of those who are strongly detail-conscious.

Many workforces rely on teams with plenty of detail-conscious staff to actually do the job, who are led by a smaller number more-decisive people. Of course we all have both qualities within us in varying proportions but we probably know a few people who display aspects of these archetypes quite well. These traits are neither good nor bad, they are just more or less appropriate to the specific roles that people are asked to perform. Those with strengths at either end of the scale can feel painfully out of place if required to perform their opposite roles.

So how does decisiveness relate to prejudice? Well, a strong decider might be seen to be more prejudiced than a detail-conscious person. Equally, one who finds it impossible to make a decision might be thought incapable of prejudice, (though in some sense this is deciding not to make a decision yet). It is evident that a detail conscious individual absorbs more information than a decisive one before making a decision. However, which is the most appropriate behaviour will depend entirely on the situation.

This all goes to show that the appropriate timing of a judgement is what is important. The survival of our species and success of our civilisation demands decisions. It is not enough for us to simply observe and accumulate information, we must act. As Leo Tolstoy said "All that is necessary for evil to triumph is for good men to do nothing".[417]

When fifty shades of grey become a black and white affair

We have seen how prejudice involves a simplification at some point in time; it is a prediction based on our previously accumulated knowledge combined with a small amount of new information (which is intrinsically limited by our learning bottleneck). These early judgements are an essential part of our human behaviour, and the majority have a positive value. However, the darker side of prejudice emerges when we mistakenly confuse our new-found simplicity with external reality.

We must never forget that simplicity is in the mind of the perceiver. At any given moment in time, the clarity of our point of view may merely be a measure of our own ignorance. For example, a Jewish colleague who lived in Northern Ireland told me that during the "troubles", the local people often asked if he was a Protestant or a Catholic.[418] When he replied that he was neither as he was Jewish, they then pressed him to clarify whether he was a Protestant Jew or Catholic Jew. They could not understand someone in their cultural environment, who could not be defined by one of these two categories.

All prejudice is based on information, yet we rarely consider this aspect of prejudice in anything more than qualitative terms, so let's now explore how much information we attach to our opinions. When we form opinions on various issues, we make judgements to different degrees of accuracy. The accuracy may be limited by our ignorance, our laziness, or by our current estimate of the value in ascribing accuracy to a judgement. Remember that these potentially inaccurate parameters are what we use to construct our model of everyone and every thing in our youniverse.

This is important to appreciate, as the world we experience is the one we create in our mind. So this information limit is like a quantum limit applied to our experience. It is as if we create our models from Lego building bricks, the more bricks we use to build our models; the more our models will faithfully represent the real things. If we tried to build a Lego model of a real aircraft from just four Lego bricks, it would be a very poor representation, easily confused with other types of aircraft, or even mistaken for something completely different. The land of Legoland[419] only appears to be a recognisable model, because vast numbers of bricks are used to create the objects within it.

The early computer game of Pong[420] was the crudest simulation of the game of tennis that could be created on the earliest personal computers. For we who were only just discovering this new form of entertainment, this two-player game was exciting to play, yet its elementary portrayal of tennis contained only tiny elements of the real game. Early PCs were too slow and too simple to portray anything like a realistic game of tennis on the coarsely pixelated screens, yet reducing the game to its most elementary form made it one of the first successful interactive computer games. However, if a friend invited us round for a game of tennis today, we would probably be disappointed to be presented with a game of Pong.

So it is with our prejudices, a simple idea of a situation enables us to make a timely response when we have limited capabilities, but it may not provide us with an accurate prediction of reality. Pong is not tennis, and however much we might practice playing it, we would see little improvement in our real tennis game. Similarly, rehearsing our simple prejudices time after time simply reinforces them. It provides us with no clearer insights into complex realities. To do that, we must acquire more information with which to refine our prejudices.

Let's explore how much information we use to describe various things we experience. In an earlier chapter we saw how information can be conveniently described in the form of digital bits, the number of bits determining the accuracy of this information.

Most physical things are inherently complex, so can only be fully described by the use of several parameters or dimensions, and with significant precision in each. So for example, when describing the key physical attributes of another human being we might include their sex, age, height, and weight. (There are many other characteristics that we can assume are common to almost everyone, such as number of ears, arms legs, so we generally don't mention these unless they are an unusual feature, such as a missing arm or an extra finger).

In chapter one we saw how the accuracy of a measure can be quantified by the number of bits (binary digits) required to describe it. We characterise each parameter with a sufficient number of bits to tell us what we need to know:

Sex: if we assume just Male or Female, we need just one bit.

Age: 1 year accuracy in 128 years requires 7 bits ($2^7=128$).

Height: 1 centimetre accuracy in 2.5 metres requires 8 bits ($2^8=256$).

Weight:1 kilo accuracy in 128 kilos requires 7 bits ($2^7=128$).

Note how various parameters require different numbers of bits to achieve the required resolution. To specify all four of these parameters for one individual requires just 23 bits (1+7+8+7), but this is not the person, just a sufficiently crude approximation to enable us to identify the individual within a small group of people. If we needed to identify one person within the entire population of the planet, far more information would be required, and even then, information of this sort would not tell us much about them as a human being.

When we consider those we know very well, there is surprisingly little we know about them with any great accuracy: Their sex, yes, their age quite likely, but we probably don't know their height within a centimetre or their weight within a kilo. But we do hold many subjective opinions about them, for example, how attractive, how good a cook, how careful a driver, how entertaining, how smart.

Now pause for a moment and ask yourself how accurately you characterise some of these qualities. It is highly unlikely to be on a scale of more than 8 levels, which is only 3 bit accuracy (2^3). Indeed, few of our opinions are held to any better than 2 bits accuracy, giving just 4 alternatives (2^2, i.e. 2x2), for example the four options of: I hate it / I don't like it / I like it / I love it.

Amazon's web purchasing system uses a five-star rating system for reviewing how customers feel about their products. Although five point scales are probably the most common on the Internet, the ratings tend to cluster around two different numbers (e.g., 1 and 5) rather than offering a normal distribution where the ratings cluster around a single value (e.g., 3). So the average of these ratings is not always an accurate reflection of product quality, but instead is a statement of conflicting opinions.

The central three star category: "It's OK", tends only to be used when we don't have an opinion, and people with less passionate opinions are reluctant to "waste" their time submitting reviews. Typically, positive ratings outnumber negative ratings, perhaps because people are reluctant to admit they have made a bad purchasing decision.

When it comes to our opinions about other people, and issues such as politics and religion, we hold them with quite low accuracy and the subtleties tend to disappear. Our opinions about people are often reduced to little more than For or Against: we apparently are content for our social networks such as Facebook, to ascribe only one bit to "Friend", or "Like".

Choosing or voting between just two options conceals the actual strength of our opinion. This is not a problem in elections involving a large number of voters, as the averaging of a large number of Yes/No votes, provides a more accurate measure of the average opinion of the voting community, provided of course that most people vote. However, when we describe an individual's qualities using just these two extremes, the similarity between reality and how they appear in our youniverse, may well be entirely lost.

As we have already described, we create a puppet-like model of someone in our mind, based on our ideas about them. So if our idea of someone is simple, we can only expect our model of them to exhibit simple unsophisticated behaviour, and as we now know, what we experience will be dominated by what is already in our mind. But real people are always complex however attractive it may be to resort to our crude stereotypes.

Daniel Kahneman gave a moving example of this when he wrote of his experience in Nazi-occupied France, explaining in part why he entered the field of psychology: "It must have been late 1941 or early 1942. Jews were required to wear the Star of David and to obey a 6 p.m. curfew. I had gone to play with a Christian friend and had stayed too late. I turned my brown sweater inside out to walk the few blocks home. As I was walking down an empty street, I saw a German soldier approaching. He was wearing the black uniform that I had been told to fear more than others - the one worn by specially recruited SS soldiers."

"As I came closer to him, trying to walk fast, I noticed that he was looking at me intently. Then he beckoned me over, picked me up, and hugged me. I was terrified that he would notice the star inside my sweater. He was speaking to me with great emotion, in German. When he put me down, he opened his wallet, showed me a picture of a boy, and gave me some money. I went home more certain than ever that my mother was right: people were endlessly complicated and interesting".[421]

We have seen how the external world is far more complex than the structure (and storage capability) of our brain, so even if we had unlimited learning time we could never create a truly accurate internal representation of it. However, we can devise simplified models of what is out there, and as we observe and learn from subsequent experiences over time, our models become more detailed and increasingly accurate.

Consider what happens the very first time that we encounter someone from a particular foreign land or from a cultural group that is novel to us. We observe the features that are most different from what we expect and initially ascribe these as features common to all people from that country. If we just meet a few more similar people, our internal model becomes a bit more detailed, but often remains remarkably crude. We may think "they all look the same to me" because we only have one model in our mind to represent this national type. They all appear very similar until we have time to learn the differences between them.

I can still remember the very first time I met someone who was black skinned. I was an eight year old child in an all-white school in an all-white community, and the headmaster had organised a visit by a guest from Ghana. Strangely, I cannot remember if the visitor was a man or a woman, evidently their sex was not the feature that most grabbed my attention that day. What I do remember is that their skin was very black, and that they wore a long colourful traditional costume. I also remembered that they spoke with a funny accent (not "proper" like the rest of us Yorkshire boys).[422] It took many years before my idea of black people became more detailed, and in any way realistic.

If we have only ever met one person from a particular country or region, our experience of them may initially colour our idea of a whole population. When I travelled around the USA on the buses, I quickly developed views on which cities were safe and which were not. With hindsight, I realized that I had acquired positive prejudices for the places where I had made a personal connection with someone, and negative ones where I perhaps had just a single unfriendly encounter. I subsequently discovered that my prejudices bore little relationship to the day-to-day reality experienced by the people of those cities, and realized that I had judged whole cities on the tiniest of personal experiences.

The objective world of science revels in simplified models, especially in physics where simplified rules appear beautiful and are sufficient most of the time. The rest of our lives however, tend to be far more complex and subjective, and filled with dirty detail. Simplifications may help us make quick decisions, but at the cost of the subsequent blindness to so much important information.

The idea that Africa is hot and dry, or that the British people are unemotional, may seem adequate as long as we spend all our lives in Texas, and the simplified idea that the "Arabs" are one single cohesive group, may enable us to make some big decisions, even to start a war, but may leave us blind to the detailed insights necessary to win such a war.

Problems arise when we forget that the simplification is only in our mind, and not in reality. The world out there is no less complex because we "understand it", we have just developed some mental models that enable us to make quick decisions, both good and bad. This is what we must strive to remember: that our apparently clear view of the world is almost entirely built on prejudices, acquired on our own unique journey through life, and that our prejudice is just *our* prejudice, our partial-sightedness, a small but useful caricature of an incredibly vast and complex world.

Old fashioned

When we construct the puppet-like characters that populate our youniverse, we imbue them with our past prejudices. The less we know of the individuals, the more they are caricatures or stereotypes. We may even have fashioned some of these caricatures entirely from other people's prejudiced opinions. The personalities and behaviours of real people evolve over time, so when most of our personal experience of someone is from the more distant past, our caricature of them may be way out of date, and this caricature is the personality that we interact with, not the current reality of a real person.

If you are a parent of adult children, have they ever accused you of treating them like children? Do you try to advise them on subjects that they are actually quite knowledgeable about? In our private youniverse we have constructed simulations of the people in our lives from our experiences of them, and our idea of that person within our simulation will have an approximate age. I don't mean the number of years they have lived, but the maturity age we subconsciously assume when we communicate with them.

This idea that our caricature of someone carries an assumption of their maturity age is obviously a simplification, as that age differs depending on the context of our interaction: Is my daughter helping me with my new computer? Am I attempting to advise my son on a career? However, the idea of an assumed average maturity age is a way to explain miscommunication between the generations within families, why we often communicate in a style assuming a different age and maturity than the reality.

This age will not simply be a numerical average of all their ages (i.e. half their actual age), and neither will it be their current biological age, unless we are asking ourselves that specific numerical question. We might expect it to be the average of all our experience of that child. We have more contact with our child when it is a baby, and progressively less contact as it goes to school, plays with its friends, finds a partner, goes away to college, and moves away to a job. Of course, not all parent-child relationships run this course but we can make adjustments for that later.

From birth until first school age, a house parent might experience their child for the majority of the time that they are not sleeping. When the child goes to school there will then be considerable times when neither parent nor child are experiencing the other, and as the years go by this proportion of shared experience time will tend to fall. The reality is that we have vastly more experience of our young child, than when our child has matured into an adult. When my "child" is aged 40, the shared parent-child experience during the second half of that child's life might account for less than one percent of the shared parent-child experience during the first half of that child's life.

In general, we have much less knowledge about our child as an adult, and occasional visits and phone calls may do little to change this idea of the maturity of our offspring. It takes vigilance to see past our history-based internal model, and be open to the adult personality that is here now. We may even be reluctant to let go of our idea of ourselves as a parent, having lost a sense of who we are beyond that role.

Of course this works the other way too: Our grown child has little experience of relating to us parents as equal adults, so may find it difficult to think of us as peers with vulnerabilities like their own. The foundation of their relationship with parents may be adolescent rebellion, and this may well persist or resurface in their adult mind. I personally could never imagine that my late father felt towards me in the same way that I do towards my own children. Sadly, I was never able to talk to him as an equal and explore our shared experience of parenting, as he died shortly after seeing my firstborn for the one and only time.

There is a big difference in the learning capabilities of a child and a parent. A learning child's early ideas are readily replaced and superseded with new insights based on their current experiences, but it is difficult for "old dogs" to learn new tricks. So this is where we parents must be conscious of our prejudices and remember that our thirty-year-old offspring is probably vastly more capable than we might imagine. Parents who spend significant adult time with their grown children, are able to reinforce the reality of who they really are, and slowly correct the easy prejudice that they are still children or adolescents.

Old age can bring further problems of misjudged maturity. As our sight and hearing diminishes we rely more and more on our internal ideas of people that we know, and are less able to perceive who they might have become. Age related memory loss and senility tend to strip away more recent experiences, leaving a very outdated idea of those we relate to. Perhaps you are familiar with an aged relative who thinks you are still a little child.

Our prejudices about individuals are not the only ones that are likely to be out of date, for we make the same errors with our ideas of whole nationalities. Historical prejudices about nations are sustained because few of us have any personal experience of many nationalities. Previously we saw how our idea of the world is somewhat like an old school globe, an incomplete model that is likely to be out of date. Growing up during the cold war, my school atlas showed the entire area of Europe occupied by the Soviet Union in a uniform red colour, so it was easy for me to assume that all Soviet citizens were of similar mind. Today we are gaining insight into the profound differences between peoples of the fifteen former Soviet republics (Russia, Bulgaria, Romania, Latvia, Estonia, Georgia, the Ukraine etc.), gradually ascribing more information to them, information that differentiates between them.

Polarised opinions

Informed opinions vary widely from person to person. If we were able to gauge people's opinions by monitoring their change in pulse rate or blood pressure, we would expect to see a wide spread in what we measured. And so it is with carefully considered opinions; most cover a wide spectrum. But there are some things that many of us feel strongly about, for example, politics, religious belief, global warming, immigration and the use of the death penalty. Opinions on these are not uniformly distributed but tend to be polarised towards one extreme or the other. When we hold one of these positions we may sometimes wonder how any intelligent person can hold the opposing view to your own!

There are two main reasons for holding a polarised opinion: The first is a lack of detailed information, an innocent ignorance, and the second is committed prejudice, a determination to hold to an extreme despite further evidence to the contrary. If we have only acquired one single binary bit of information about something, our opinion in intrinsically polarised to one of only two options (e.g. Hero/Villain, Black/White, Conservative/Liberal, Pro/Anti-Nuclear power, Pleasant/Yuck, Guilty/Innocent).

The figure that follows shows two different kinds of distributions of opinions, one well distributed, the other quite polarised.

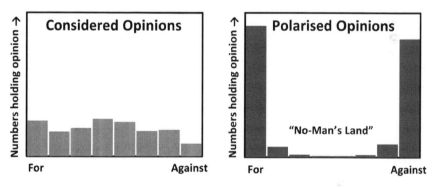

Figure 30: Informed opinions tend to be widely spread, but some opinions become polarised, with "no-man's land" between.

We are more readily influenced by people whose opinions are close to our own; we probably find them easier to trust. These two charts represent the spread in opinions expressed by a group of people when asked whether or not they agree with something. In the first chart we can see that whatever opinion an individual might hold, there will be a fair proportion of people holding fairly similar opinions. It is therefore likely that such an individual can be informed and influenced by other like-minded people. This "diffusion" process could in time enable someone to significantly change their opinion as they become more informed.

The opinions expressed in the second chart are unlikely to be changed. The majority hold one or other extreme opinion, and they find it easy to ignore any inputs from the opposing side. More importantly, the few individuals holding more moderate views are unlikely to encounter similar minded people due to their scarcity. A typical example of this situation might be opinions on the safe use of nuclear power.

If we have an open mind, any additional information that we learn will refine our opinion and give it texture and depth. But, if we have access to more information yet choose to ignore it, or choose to direct our future attention towards sources of information that reinforce our initially polarised point of view, then our opinion becomes more polarised than the truth. Our personal youniverse becomes a distorted caricature of reality, personally satisfying perhaps, but offering little of value to a civilised member of society.

Sometimes we choose this simplification in order to bond with our peers or our community. A loose group of people or nations can be bound together with the clarity of a simple idea of an enemy. We have seen this in East-West relations during the cold war, in racist groups, and in the rhetoric between the fundamentalist branches of the major world religions.

Emotion is the force that locks us into polarised opinions. Without it we are free to change as you will see from the following example. Here is a slightly simpler version of the Necker Cube image that we saw earlier.

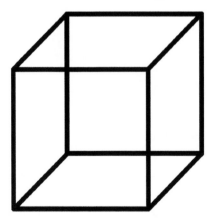

Figure 31: A simple Necker Cube. Our lifelong experience of 3D structure prejudices us to seeing a cube.

We have a prejudice towards seeing it as an image of a three dimensional cube rather than the reality of it simply being a flat abstract image constructed of a set of lines. Furthermore, our stereoscopic vision must be telling us that all the lines fall in the same flat plane, but yet even when we gaze at the crossovers our mind still encourages us to believe that one line falls behind the other. This demonstrates that we gravitate towards a point of view that makes sense of what we see, despite the lack of evidence to support it.

However, as we continue to gaze at this simple image our perception tends to switch back and forth between two different yet equally satisfying interpretations of the image seeking a preference. Yet we don't settle on one interpretation because it is no big deal which one of the cube interpretations we choose. We have no emotional attachment to any point of view, apart from preferring interpretations that made sense of the experience. Because this very simple image contains no information that might help us refine our opinion, gazing at it for a longer time yields no more information on which to base our choice.

In contrast, when our opinions involve emotions, they tend to become increasingly polarised, leading us to seek out evidence to support our initial view, locking us further into that position. We may choose to read only the kind of newspapers that confirm just how good our initial judgement was, or seek the company of those who agree with our opinions (or at least those who pretend to).

If you have experienced romantic love, you will know how the passion of a strong prejudice can take us over and dominate our thinking. Everything about our lover is wonderful, including all those aspects of which we know nothing. It is a prejudice that makes us blind to any information that might shine a more realistic light upon the one we love. Yet being in romantic love is also a wonderful blissful state that transforms the daily drudge of our lives into sheer magic as we daydream about our perfect partner. All our skills for objectively assessing the one we love are corrupted. We are inclined to score them one hundred percent for their beauty, intelligence, charm, and wit, and no longer need a sensitive scale to judge them by. They are our One, on a simple one or zero binary scale, (and our "ex" might be a Zero!).

When our romantic relationship fails, our positive prejudice can all too easily flip to a negative prejudice, our love can turn to hatred, for example when we find that our lover is two-timing us. As the song goes: "It's a thin line between love and hate".[423] So if our relationship has only two possible states, then we only need one bit of information to characterise it.

When we have fallen out of love with someone for some time, we may come to realize that their personality is more complex, and return to a state that is more discerning and less idealistic, and perhaps lose interest. However, sometimes the one who was loved now simply becomes the one who is hated. While the relationship is now denied, it is still just as intense but now 100% negative, and vast amounts of time, energy and numbers of neurons may still be devoted to it. This two-state simplicity may have little consequence if we never see the person again, but is often confusing to other family and friends involved.

Love is a drug, or so the song says.[424] Romantic love certainly exhibits many of the characteristics of various addictive substances; irrational behaviour, hallucination, immunity to pain, withdrawal symptoms (cold turkey), even suicide. Yet despite its disruptive effect we value it highly in our society. We consider it a personal tragedy for one to have lived a life and never loved, and marvel at the artistic wonders of the world that were created through the unrequited passion of romantic love.

This tendency to romantic love between humans has persisted throughout recorded history. It is seen between other primates too, suggesting that it has had some evolutionary value. It is now thought likely to have evolved to provide the emotional glue that binds a parenting couple together for a couple of years or so, long enough for baby primates to find some independence.[425] However, when we are in a much longer term active relationship, the reality of our lover eventually starts to penetrate our vision, our positive prejudice begins to recede and romantic love alone may be insufficient. This is when it helps to have a genuine friendship. Of course if we have fallen in love with someone of which we have little direct experience (e.g. a celebrity), we can sustain our idealism much longer, forgetting that the relationship is almost entirely played our within the confines of our head.

Falling in and out of romantic love provides us with an opportunity to experience polarised opinion and prejudice, and many of us have fallen from one polarised emotional state to the other without remembering why we previously held the opposite view. However, this is an unusual state of affairs. With most of our polarised opinions, we tend to get stuck in just one state.

Passionate polarised opinions are more likely to result in action, and in many cases these prejudices have a positive value. They encourage people to take a stand for themselves, or on behalf of others, to act instead of just complaining, which is why they are encouraged by politicians, military leaders and religious fundamentalists. But harm can come when we are blinded by the simplicity of an idea, seeing an unrealistically clear distinction between good and bad, between us and them.

As long as there is a continuum of opinion between two opposing views within our society, intelligent dialogue can lead towards appropriate and constructive solutions, as we are more likely to listen to someone whose opinions are not too far from our own. Insight can then flow easily in both directions, informing us, so we know precisely where we stand and can make intelligent decisions within our lives and communities. However, when we hold inappropriately strong opinions through prejudice, communicating with those of opposing views becomes difficult and often impossible. Furthermore our ability to learn anything new is impeded, since we can only see as far as our paranoid insecurities.

Extreme opinions are highly unlikely to be realistic views of reality, but such prejudices are particularly attractive if we have lazy minds. So we need to be alert to our own polarised ideas as these are the areas where we are most likely to be deceiving ourselves. For example, if I hear something good about someone who I don't like at all, it can make me feel very uncomfortable. The clarity of my simple idea of this person is being threatened. If I am to take this new information on board, I will need more information than a simple good or bad to describe them. And dammit I felt so good about myself, just knowing that they were bad.

Politics is a spectator sport

There would be no game of politics without the supporters. Some years ago, I read the results of a survey that had been conducted among "backbenchers" in the UK. These are those elected politicians who neither serve in the government "cabinet", nor the oppositions "shadow cabinet", so do not sit on the front benches in parliament. They are therefore freer to express their opinions when they differ from the policy of their party. In the survey they were asked to name the current politician that they most admired, and I was surprised how many named a member of the opposing party rather than their own. I had expected them to be divided entirely on party lines, but it seemed that many of them showed surprising respect for some of their fellows, irrespective of which party they were members of.

Politics has much in common with popular professional team sports like football. For example, outside of the game itself, many top footballers treat the players from other teams with respect. The spectators on the other hand are more polarised, and tend have a much more negative view of both the opposition players, and their supporters too. In truth the economic success of the game requires this polarisation, and the spectators are encouraged to view the opposition as the enemy, with prejudice. This is particularly evident where there are two competing teams within the same city, many of whose supporters view the others almost with hatred.

Distortion of opinion is a major aspect of politics. People may be very clear which side they are on, yet when asked about specific policies they reveal a far broader the spectrum of views. The political parties need to distort the true overlapping complexity into a simple logical difference, especially around election times. They encourage us to decide clearly how to vote one way or the other, by much "rebel rousing". We are happy to collude as we want the detailed political complexities of the world stage to be simplified for us, reduced ultimately to one of two options, a single binary digit of information, a crude prejudice. We don't want to waste our time reading diverse political opinions to arrive at an informed opinion. We would rather be enjoying the pleasures of life, not worrying where to put our mark on the ballot paper.

When the party policies are similar, the party in "opposition" frequently become simple naysayers, almost by definition, arguing the opposite of every government policy. Simplicity and clarity come easily in opposition, but finer detail is required when in power and with responsibility, while the unelectable minority parties have no need for accuracy or realism whatsoever. If we the voting public, are to avoid becoming simple puppets that parrot the polarised party policies, we must take responsibility for learning more of the subtleties surrounding political issues, acquire more bits of information.

Informed political opinions are spread across a broad spectrum, yet so many of us have a knee-jerk tendency towards more extreme views. We may be very clear whether we are on the political left or right, and when prodded, may trot out the same tired old clichés, echoing the polarised mantras of the party we support. What is missing is our valuable informed knowledge, the truth of our wide ranging opinions on issues such as immigration and welfare. It takes an outsider to observe that despite our intelligence, we tend to act more like automatons, or Pavlovian dogs, regurgitating crude prejudices on demand.

Committed prejudice

"The simplest principles become difficult of practice, when habits, formed in error, have been fixed by time, and the simplest truths hard to receive when prejudice has warped the mind"
- Frances Wright (1795-1852)[426]

In an ideal world, our initially prejudiced mind is always open to acquiring a clearer more truthful view. Negatively prejudiced judgements from the past can repeatedly be corrected in the future, for an open mind continues to learn, creating ever clearer insights. Our ignorance is not a serious problem provided that we are aware of it. As the Chinese proverb says "He who knows he is a fool is not such a great fool".

Through laziness we may convince ourselves that the clarity of our simple insight is all that we need to remember, and forget the details of the original sensed experiences. Then our simplification means that information is lost. Only by remembering the detail in addition to our current judgement can we ensure that future judgements are not contaminated by our earlier judgement.

As I was walking towards my home this morning, I spotted what I thought was a dead mouse lying on the footpath ahead of me. As I got closer the "dead mouse" suddenly became a leaf, whose stalk had been the mouse's tail, and I wondered why I had expected to see a mouse. Then I recalled that ten minutes earlier while driving along a country lane I had briefly spotted a dead mouse lying in the middle of the road, and this had probably primed me to expect something similar. Now, having learned that dead mice and dead leaves can appear similar from a distance, I briefly wonder if my first sighting had also been of a leaf, and then lazily decide not to mess with the past.

This is a trivial example, but correcting previous serious errors of judgement can be uncomfortable at the very least, for it is hard to admit to yourself and to others that we were wrong. In our journey through life, sometimes we burn our bridges so there is no going back; we enter the fortified castle of our opinion and raise the drawbridge behind us.

First Sight

In general, throughout our life we continually update our opinions as we learn more. But I am fascinated by the confidence we feel in opinions formed from negligible information, and how we so quickly forget just how flawed were these initial opinions, when we subsequently learn more.

Consider the experience of seeing or meeting someone for the first time, for example at a party, or interviewing them for a job.[427] Within a moment I immediately have a lot of ideas about this person despite the reality that I know almost nothing yet. I have probably resurrected some old stories involving people from my past, people who bear some slight visual or vocal similarity to the person that I have only just set eyes on. Perhaps I just subconsciously choose which of my old puppet-like simulations of people seems the best fit. It is easy for me to feel equally confident in my opinions whether I have three seconds or an hour's experience, for a thousand times more experience does not feel a thousand times more accurate, though it may well be so.

However, it may be no more accurate at all, for our first impressions can contaminate our subsequent perception. If I am in a hurry to decide whether to pass or fail an interviewee I may have decided quite quickly whether to ascribe a one or a zero to them, and then spent the rest of the interview looking only for evidence to confirm my initial prejudice.

Some years ago I did a workshop with a group of Americans in California. As a visiting Brit I felt accepted and welcomed by all the people there except for just one man who was very cool towards me. When I asked him if there was some kind of problem, he replied that he despised all British people because of our colonial history and our role in the American War of Independence. I attempted to explain that I was not personally involved in that war and that it was a long time ago (it ended in 1783), but to no effect: The others tried to talk him round, but he was decided. I was a Zero.

It was a useful experience as it gave me a tiny taste of how powerless it feels to be faced with a prejudice for which we have neither the responsibility, nor the power to change. I am fortunate to have experienced little racial prejudice, being white, educated, and living in a tolerant multicultural society. However, I now realize that I am as likely as anyone else to harbour prejudices that I am unaware of.

His prejudice, born out of a war more than two centuries ago, was carried through time on national narratives. Memories of war are very persistent, it can take many generations for nations to forgive and forget because opinions formed in wars are so highly polarised. It is a military advantage to anyone engaged in combat, either as individuals or entire nations, to suppress all detailed empathy about our enemy, to forget and deny our common humanity.

Wartime leaders feed this jingoism through the media to increase the odds of winning a war. They may even describe another race or the enemy as "vermin" to encourage us to engage the crude emotion of disgust. We are encouraged to replace our rich knowledge of another culture with a simple binary: is someone our friend or our enemy? (Are they a one or a zero?). This dehumanises our morality to the level of the simplest bug, while retaining the destructive capability of an industrialised and militarised "civilisation".

It is possible that this extreme competitive behaviour may have been an essential step in the progress of our species towards civilisation, but now it seems to threaten our very existence on the planet. We might hope that as we gain access to more information about our planet's wider inhabitants, we might develop more realistic internal models of our fellow man and find the atrocities of both war and peace less persuasive.

Recent decisions to go to war with Iraq were made by people who seemed unaware of the complex differences between Iraq and Iran, and especially the differences between the Shi'a and Sunni communities. Acquiring those insights has now cost the deaths of many servicemen and vast numbers of innocent civilians. It has also created an army of people willing to be suicide bombers to revenge their humiliation. How many years will these dangerous prejudices persist I wonder?

Iraq the country has been changed forever by such crude prejudices. Indeed, it has been liberated from its very civilisation. It is sobering to compare what George Bush the US president knew of Iraq before the war, with what the average Iraqi (who *were* comparatively well educated) knew of the West. And now we have the ongoing mortal chaos of the "Arab Spring". When it began, the West assumed that all Arab people would soon be united against their respective dictators, and now we are confused.

The penal system provides great opportunities for negative prejudices, which is why the system incorporates structures intended to protect against miscarriages of justice, such as "innocent until proved guilty" and trial by jury. When a serious crime has been committed our knee-jerk reaction is to want to know who was to blame, who is the guilty one. After all, knowing that the perpetrator is locked up can help the rest of us sleep better at nights.

When crimes such as murder, rape or child abuse are brought to our attention it is easy for us to make crude prejudiced judgements about the perpetrators. Raised emotions make our views increasingly polarised, and we become much more interested in punishment, than in rehabilitation. After all, we cannot imagine ourselves behaving similarly, even if we had been born with the same DNA, in the same environment and had the same childhood experiences, though personally I don't know how I can be so certain.

Errors do occur in the legal system. Human memory is crucial to securing most convictions and as we are now beginning to realize, memory is surprisingly prone to errors. Many historical convictions that once seemed watertight now appear to be flawed. Recent DNA analyses of old items of material evidence have revealed that many old convictions are unsafe.

That is why the death penalty can lead to the greatest injustice of prejudice. It is the ultimate example of discarded detail, when opportunities for future correction are simply extinguished together with the knowledge within the mind of the accused. Some "one" becomes a zero, physically. While there are many ways of being alive, there is only one of being dead.[428]

For most of us, discarding detail is rarely fatal but it can easily change the course of our lives. It is easy to develop a simplified and distorted idea of something highly complex that subsequently prevents us from achieving greater understanding through further experience. My elderly aunt provided a good example of what I mean:

She was widowed and lived alone some distance from the rest of the family so I regularly phoned her to chat about what various members of my family were doing. One day I happened to mention that my son was away visiting Prague. When I added that he should be boarding the bus home to London at that very moment, I heard a shocked intake of breath and: "Did you hear that there has been a terrible bus accident there?"

"In Prague?" I replied anxiously. "No, Abroad" she responded!

There was a loud but silent "click" in my mind. The answers to a hundred puzzles from the past tumbled out. I suddenly experienced a big shift in my understanding of my aunt. For some years we had tried to encourage both her and her husband to travel a little, but she had always insisted she did not want to go abroad. For me the word "abroad" meant a vast place with every different culture imaginable, some peaceful places, others busy. Now I suddenly understood that for my aunt "abroad" was a small place where bad things happened all the time. Every day on the TV news she witnessed the horrors and disasters that happened "abroad", she saw a terrible chaotic place full of strange people. At last I understood why she had no desire to go abroad, all based on what she had learned through the media. In her youniverse "abroad" was a small and very·frightening place.

Once we have formed ideas about the world that make simple sense of it, it is comforting to have these ideas reinforced. We are attracted to newspapers and news channels which tell us what we want to read hear and see, tell us that it is "the others" who are responsible for all that is bad in the world, whether the other party, the other sex, colour, religion or nationality. Our media moguls have their own prejudices too, and probably find reassurance in knowing that a vast community of readers are being steered towards their own particular island of opinion.

Occasionally I pick up a discarded newspaper that represents one of these other views, one that I would never buy and perhaps even be ashamed to be seen reading. My initial reaction is horror and disgust at many of the views, but then I remember that some of its regular readers would probably be equally shocked to read the news stories that I happily read.

Relationships

"Civilized men have gained notable mastery over energy, matter, and inanimate nature generally, and are rapidly learning to control physical suffering and premature death. But, by contrast, we appear to be living in the Stone Age so far as our handling of human relationships is concerned."

- Gordon W. Allport.[429]

We might expect that people growing up together would share very similar internal models of the world, but a small difference in perceiving one "shared" experience can lead to an increasing divergence in future understanding. Every perceived experience modifies our ability to perceive each subsequent experience. For example, imagine that a pair of twin girls briefly meets a man and one is fearful, suspecting that he is sexually predatory, while the other thinks he is friendly. Each twin may then grow up with differing degrees of caution in their future encounters with men, leading to different options and possibilities in each of their lives. The smallest seed of an idea can change the direction of future lives. An anxiety can both protect and corral, and none can predict if such a prejudice will be valuable or not.

We develop patterns of behaviour, simplified rules that seemed appropriate at one time, but in the longer term become the cause of dysfunction in organisations, groups and families. Some of these patterns become unconscious traditions, so when people seek help through counselling it is often useful to record the historical narrative of an individual before attempting any specific counselling, as it has been found that the patterns of behaviour from our own childhood and from those from our parents tend to be repeated. Some difficulties can be resolved simply by becoming aware of our subconscious patterns.

Sometimes the pattern is to split the group or family into those who are good, and those who are bad. This may seem to be a useful simplification, in that it helps bond our relationships with those who we have decided are good, and simply ignores those who we have decided are bad. But real people are far more complex and unlikely to exhibit either idealised extreme in any of their many attributes. Most of the time there is no simple good and bad, but splitting can be a convenient way of keeping ourselves in favour with those who object to our broader friendships, and insecure people often promote the idea that "if you are not with us you are against us".[430]

I have become increasingly aware that I am full of youthful prejudices that have not simply faded away with time, but rather become protected against by more recent and more sophisticated prejudices. So I know that my father's political views lurk hidden somewhere within me, to be countered and corrected by the views I developed as I grew older. As for racism, I would be shocked if I was accused of any racist behaviour yet am aware that much of the foundations of my world view were laid down before I had any experience of non-white people. So my non-racism is largely intellectual and may not extend far below the surface. At least I know this so can be continuously on guard against my primal knee-jerk judgements.

To eliminate prejudice from the world is a very noble objective, but probably impossible. We all need to recognise that our lives are inevitably full of prejudices; the key question is whether we are sufficiently aware of them to be able to modify our behaviour and act in a mature civilised way. When we are free from fear, threat of violence or starvation this is relatively easy, but as we have seen in recent civil wars, it does not take much for us to revert to more primitive behaviour.

People debate whether mankind is making moral progress. Having seen how readily the boundary of our civilised behaviour recedes when we are under pressure, I think not. However, the combination of material progress and material equality makes it easier to be civilised, so progress in the former should help, but only if the latter is somehow addressed.

In this chapter I have tried to provide some logical insights into the mechanism of prejudice by considering the role of information; how little input information we demand before having an opinion, and how crude are our held assumptions. I have avoided any discussion of the morality and evils of prejudice because I have no certainty in those areas. However, I hope that by shining a light on the logical process of prejudice, it might help us find a clearer way forward through these dark places.

Perhaps prejudice is a quality that you only previously noticed in other people, especially those whose opinions we disagreed with. I hope that you can now see that it not just something negative, but it is the skill that most distinguishes humans from other species. It is experience-based-prediction, and as such it plays a huge role our own daily lives.

I have risked revealing some of the bizarre narratives created by my own prejudiced mind, for example while driving my car, hoping to show what a fictional world we explore when we are unable or unwilling to acquire more information. Prejudice can do harm when we are ignorant of its profound influence within ourselves and so unable to understand its causes in others. There may be little we can do to change other people's prejudices, but with diligence we can gain much greater awareness of our own, allowing us to see a richer reality through our illusions and misconceptions despite the constraints of our learning bottleneck.

Humankind has achieved incredible technological progress over the last two millennia, yet there is little evidence of increased ability of individuals and nations to co-exist peacefully. Why should this be so? What have we missed? Perhaps the answer lies in overconfidence in our objectivity.

In the preceding chapters we have explored the myriad of ways that the learning bottleneck has constrained us. Now in the final part, I look at some of the bottleneck's implications for our future.

Part 4

The Future

Chapter Eleven

A Bottleneck Future

"It is far better to foresee even without certainty
than not to foresee at all"

- Henri Poincare[431]

Throughout this book we have seen that so much of the present moment is spent interpreting the past and predicting the future. When I am watching TV and reach out for my cup of tea on the table beside me, I am predicting many things: Where I expect the cup to be within the three dimensional space around me based on my earlier observations: What instructions my arm and hand need to enable me to reach the cup: the muscle force, direction and distance required, plus my idea of the position of my own body. I predict properties of the tea that I anticipate drinking, its taste and temperature. If when I reach for it my hand does not encounter it as I expect, I am surprised and shift my attention from the TV, predicting what angle I should rotate my eyes and head to bring it into my field of view. I can then correct my erroneous prediction

We have seen how understanding the learning bottleneck can give us a very different perspective on our daily life as individuals, but what about predicting the future of the physical world that we all share? If you want to see how good we are at predicting that future, just watch some early science fiction movies. The film: "2001: A Space Odyssey" by Arthur Clarke and Stanley Kubrick, looked remarkably prophetic when released in 1968, but as the actual year 2001 approached, the errors in prediction became increasingly evident.

This is an inherent problem with translating Science Fiction writing into movies. Many producers are foolishly tempted to incorporate the latest technology as props, which within a few years, become the most dated elements in their films, phones being a good example.

Arthur himself was all too aware of the difficulty in imagining the future. Paraphrasing J.B.S.Haldane: he said "The universe is not only stranger than we imagine, it's stranger than we can imagine".[432] If anyone reads this book in 50 years' time they will probably find parts of this chapter to be naive nonsense. Nevertheless, it is worth exploring ideas of what the distant future might hold for us, if only to stimulate our thinking about the more immediate future and the more distant challenges ahead, though you will find that I offer as many questions as answers.

Could we widen the bottleneck?

Has our learning bottleneck always been this wide?

We have seen that our learning bottleneck is a consequence of our biology. Will our species always be so constrained? We have evolved to this point, so where might we go from here? If we are to have any chance of predicting the future we must first understand the past. We might ask if our learning speed (expressed as an information rate in bits per second), has changed over millennia? Although we have no way of knowing how wide it might have been in earlier stages of our evolution, we can speculate on the possibilities.

One thing that we do know is that our brain size has increased significantly as we have evolved from apes, and especially over our last 200,000 years. We associate the ascendance of Homo sapiens, especially the use of tools, with the evolution of our larger brain size (or more precisely, its volume). Yet there is a paradox, that within our own species we find no useful correlation between brain size and the ability to acquire key skills. Men and women's brains differ in average size, but scale approximately with body size, and few would dare to suggest that small women are intrinsically any less smart than large men.

Brain size is not considered a useful measure of intelligence or creativity; the entrance exam of top Universities does not include a measurement of head size. Conversely the derogative term "big head" generally refers to someone whose ego is larger than their intellect or knowledge. What was special about Einstein's brain was not its size; the volume of his brain measured at death was reported to be 1.23 litres, quite average for humans whose brains can be as large as 2 litres.[433]

If a bigger brain would be beneficial to adults, then why do our heads not grow in a greater proportion than the rest of our body? What we see is the very opposite, a baby's brain at birth is much larger in relation to the rest of its body than that of an adult. This suggests that a large brain size at birth may be of particular evolutionary value to us, despite the resulting problem of fitting a baby's head through its mother's pelvis.[434] Perhaps the learning potential of our first few years is so valuable to us, that we can't afford to miss out while our brain size is comparatively small. If all future births were to be by Caesarean section, then over many millennia we might evolve yet larger brains at birth.

We used to think that a large brain was a precondition for intelligent behaviour in other mammals, and calling someone "bird brain" was to suggest that they lacked intelligence. However, we have now discovered that many of the corvids species (the crows) use tools, show self-awareness when seeing their own reflection, demonstrate advanced planning abilities and abstract thought. These are quite surprising skills considering the small size of their brains.[435]

It seems it is not what you have got, but what you do with it, just as the power of a home computer is not necessarily related to the complexity of the tasks carried out on it. Complex tasks require something more than big muscles or a big brain. Tennis champions are not renowned for the size of their arm muscles, nor chess masters noted for the size of their heads.

So what else might be different about the brains of those people whose ideas have changed the world? Einstein's brain is reported to show some small structural differences, mainly regions that were smaller than normal, and it is possible that these might be clues to understanding what makes a brilliant mind.[436] There are obvious social factors such as ambition, but perhaps of greater importance is the ability to cope with having ideas than differed significantly from those of their peers, the ability to stay with an idea despite being ridiculed by those more comfortable with the status quo.

What effect might evolution have had on our learning bottleneck? We might naively imagine that it has widened as we developed a bigger brain, a bigger processor. Alternatively, it might have been constrained by the basic underlying biological mechanisms within the brain, ones that were optimised early in our evolutionary time scale and still be limited by that factor, rather than by our brain size.

Paradoxically, it is most likely that our learning bottleneck has *narrowed* as our species evolved. This may seem counter-intuitive, but greater intellects find themselves working with a more complex idea of the world. Whatever is experienced must be interpreted within a wider framework.

When we run computer simulations, the more complex the model we are simulating, the slower it is to reach a conclusion. Assuming this also applies to neurological processes; it suggests that simpler creatures will have a wider bottleneck than humans, in other words a greater learning speed in bits per second when exposed to the same experience. This is because we humans have a bigger world view, a bigger context in which we need to integrate each simple experience.

For example: A man sits beside the river watching a dragonfly. A black dot passes by in the sky above: The dragonfly quickly registers it as potential food (an insect) and responds, while the man may consider: is it an airliner? a UFO? a bird? what type, or an insect? a floater in his eye? successively testing what has just been sensed by his human retina, against the vast expanse of what his knowledgeable human mind already knows before he responds. I realize that I am talking delays here rather than bit rate, but you probably get the idea. The dragonfly considers only whether what it observes is prey or predator, and selects from the simple options of hunt or escape. If you watch one in action you will see that it does this remarkably quickly.

If our bottleneck is narrowed as a consequence of having a wider world view, one implication is that a human baby may have a wider learning bottleneck than an adult. This would enable it to learn quicker while it still has a naive idea of the world surrounding it. This is in addition to the fact that a baby spends a far greater proportion of its waking time taking in new information when compared to an adult. While the baby is wide-eyed and alert to everything around it, an adult's time is divided more extensively between observation and introspection, with an increased proportion of introspection as we age.

The idea that evolution might have narrowed our bottleneck is supported by the smart chimpanzees at the Primate Research Institute, at Kyoto University, that we described earlier. They were able to perform better than humans at the mental task of memorising numbers flashed on a screen, implying that they have a faster (wider) bottleneck. The suggested explanation is that the chimps only see characters, whereas when we see numbers we are additionally aware of their numerical sequence, and knowing this additional context slows us. But in our daily life, our slowness is more than compensated for by the vastly wider range of tasks that we can perform successfully. A chimp may be better at catching flies, but we can count extensively and master complex technology.

Given time, might we develop faster brains through natural biological evolution? The rate at which a creature can evolve biologically depends on many factors, but there are two which have a significant impact on the speed of human evolution. First, shorter average duration between generations allows more frequent adaptations, as every reproductive occasion is an opportunity for the DNA to mutate advantageously. The second factor is species complexity; a simple creature with fewer parts is likely exhibit a greater evolutionary change for a single DNA mutation.

Both these factors enable the tiny influenza virus to mutate into a new more virile form every year or so. We on the other hand, lose out on both accounts; human generations may be spaced by 30 years, and we are highly complex creatures, so we evolve much more slowly than very small creatures such as nematode worms.

A further aspect is that biological evolution via natural selection, can only benefit by adapting to an environmental condition that persists over several generations. However, the rate of change of technology is now so rapid that environmental factors today are different from those just a generation earlier. For example, a generation ago no-one walked around holding a mobile phone to their head or performed single-handed texting, so our biological evolution cannot respond to these rapid changes in our technological environment, unless they were to persist for generations.

So it appears that without technological intervention, the limit to the rate that humans can learn, the speed at which our minds can interact with the world will remain similarly as limited as the physical speed that humans can sprint.

Can we upgrade the human hardware?

So what might we do to overcome this human limitation, can we fix it within our existing biology? We are familiar with the idea of upgrading our home computers, so could we beat the bottleneck by upgrading our human hardware?

Just as with many computer scenarios, the peripherals are not the limiting factor. Eyes that provide higher performance will not solve the problem of limited learning rate, it's what's within that counts. The processing speed of new home computers increases relentlessly, year after year. This has been achieved through a combination of faster electronics and more effective processor architectures. Could we do something similar to speed up our mental processes?

The rate at which we can learn and manipulate information is currently limited by two factors: the physical architecture of our brains, and the speed of the biological processes by which neurons and nerves function.

It should now be evident that the bottleneck is very unlikely to be caused by the limited information capacity any localised element within the brain, but rather it is the overall performance of our mind as it integrates what we sense into our internal model of what is out there. It seems reasonable to expect that any localised bottlenecks will have been overcome by the process of evolution, as small improvements would have had a big effect on our performance. We are unlikely to have evolved functional elements within our brain that outperform the rest at the expense of using more energy. It would be arrogant of us to suggest that we can improve on an architecture that has been optimised and refined through many thousands of years of evolution, since we have, as yet, only the crudest understanding of the architecture our own brains.

Could we enhance the speed of operation of our nerves, and make the signals travel more rapidly through our brain? In competitive sports such as the 100 metres sprint, the difference between winning and coming second is typically less than a tenth of a second. Inherent delays such as the runner's reaction time to the starting pistol are typically a sixth of a second for both men and women at top international level. A human reaction time of less than a tenth of a second is deemed impossible so is automatically judged as a false start despite it being after the starting gun has fired. If only a tiny increase in neurological speed were possible, it would enable an individual to dominate many sporting events.

We have evolved with a very specific biological technology, one which is ubiquitous to so many of this planet's life forms. Throughout the evolution of sentient creatures, the response speed of neurons and nerves has been a strategic differentiator, whether in capturing/escaping within a predator/prey relationship, or when competing for resources. It is therefore reasonable to expect that the speed of nerves signals and neural processing is already highly optimised for the biology upon which we are based.

So I believe that we are probably stuck with our current intellectual capabilities, at least as far as our intellectual hardware goes, as they are largely defined by the highly evolved biological and architectural makeup of our brain. Nevertheless, we have continued to find more effective ways to use our brains and to communicate ideas.

Though our intrinsic intellectual powers have remained constrained by the bottleneck, we have completely transcended our physical constraints. Evolution's failure to invent the wheel has enabled mankind to surpass the body's physical limitations. We have exercised our creativity and skill through our technology. Today it is easy for anyone, however physically unfit they might be, to travel faster and further than the world's fastest runners when assisted by a wide variety of forms of transport.

Electronically enhanced brains

While the biological hardware of our brain is unlikely to see any significant evolution in its capabilities, the world of electronics continues to accelerate relentlessly, as observed by Gordon Moore and expressed as "Moore's law".[437] This suggests an ever increasing benefit if we could combine the two, to create a cyborg; yet despite widespread popularity of the idea in science fiction, there remains the huge problem of how to provide a *fast* interface between technology and the human body.

Despite developing increasingly sophisticated tools and technology throughout our recent history, we have interacted with them using exactly the same physical interfaces that we have always used to interact with the world around us. We principally use our fingers and mouth to communicate ideas from our minds into the physical world, and our eyes and ears to receive information from the world.

Today we make extensive use of technology to enhance our human capabilities; we use all kinds of vehicles to vastly increase our physical speed and range, and we use our phones to dramatically extend the distances over which we can communicate. However, we have not been able to increase the speed of communication between two humans; it is still limited by the bottleneck, to around 20 bits per second maximum.

We accept the idea of using technology within our bodies to repair our physical abilities, such repairing our skeleton with a metal plate or joint, or implanting a pacemaker to cure a defective heart, but to connect electrodes into our brain for anything more than monitoring purposes is a more serious matter. Now that we have a greater understanding of human biology, might we overcome the bottleneck by some more direct electronic connection into the nervous system? After all, science fiction writers, enthusiastic "gamers" and journalists frequently imply that we will soon be able to provide an increased communication rate between humans and machines (and also between humans), by means of electrical connections directly into people's brains, and even suggest that this will make us "super-humans".

In the world of electronics it is common practice to use a parallel interface using multiple connections, and in principle we might connect an array of electrical conductors directly into brain tissue. However, as we have no adequate understanding of the electrical signals in our brain, we have no idea how to make a suitable connection. A more fundamental objection is that the bottleneck appears to be a limitation of the overall brain processes, so simply playing with the interfaces will be of no benefit to the core processes. This is similar to the reason that we cannot increase the speed of an old PC by adding additional interfaces; there is just no substitute for new PC with faster processor and memory hardware.

These are the reasons I believe that the idea of creating a "super-human" with connections directly into the core of our brain will remain in the realms of science fiction, at least until we are able to free intelligent life from the human body completely, but more on that later.

Parallel electrical connections may not be a promising way of connecting directly to our brain tissue, however, they can provide a very effective way of interfacing with nerves that are directly associated with our sensors, where the nerve signals themselves are parallel in a manner that we can already understand or can learn. In the first chapter I described how parallel electrical inputs to specific areas of the nervous system are used to provide rudimentary vision for the blind (using an array of electrodes on the retina or the tongue), and hearing for the deaf (via cochlear implants).

Furthermore because electronics operates so much faster than our internal bottleneck, there is no fundamental reason why physically handicapped people equipped with suitable interfaces, should not be able to absorb information and interact with the world equally as fast as able bodied people. This is because the narrowness of our bottleneck is not due to our interfaces. So while electronic connections to our brain and nervous system do not offer a way round the bottleneck in the foreseeable future, they are of huge importance to society, offering the potential to dramatically transform the lives of many disabled people.

Recently techniques have been developed that enable human speech to be decoded from electrodes placed within auditory cortex of the brain. It offers the exciting possibility that those without the power of speech might find a voice. This could include those who are totally paralysed or those with locked-in syndrome. However, there is no evidence whatsoever that this can provide a more rapid means of communication than conventional speech.[438]

Whenever I encounter a news item about someone with electrodes either on, or in their brain which enable them to control some technology or game, or to receive some external signal, it immediately grabs my attention. I quickly calculate whether the reported evidence implies an information rate more than a few tens of bits per second. I want to see if it challenges the idea of the narrow bottleneck. I have repeatedly been disappointed by speculative claims of some method that can enhance the performance of the able-bodied, and am reassured that the bottleneck I have described really does still apply. I think it unlikely that we will find a faster input/output interface than we have at present, without replacing our biological brain with a faster non-biological technology, but I watch and wait.

It is easy for us to confuse the benefits of a cure for a deficiency, with the benefits of an excess as we saw in the earlier example of overconsumption of vitamin supplements. The same is true of human learning and perception; there are many exciting ways that deficiencies and handicaps might be overcome, but appear to transcend our learning bottleneck.

Data, data everywhere

It appears that civilisations ability to learn will always be limited by our brain's biology, but does it really matter if our minds are no sharper than they were a thousand years ago? The answer is probably yes, since we have changed the very nature of the world we live in, it is no longer the one we evolved to inhabit. We have evolved over millions of years to suit a world of deficiency and are now mismatched to our contemporary world of excess.[439]

In the past, most growing children were undernourished, and would have benefited from greater quantity, quality and variety of food, so our bodies have evolved to suit a diet that many today would consider starvation. Our health problems were mainly caused by deficiency, now they are caused by excess, leading to in an epidemic in obesity-related diseases.

The majority of human lives were dominated by daily toil, of which physical exercise was an innate part. Little time remained for education, entertainment or to ponder the meaning of one's own existence. Few had any choice of their life's destiny, being constrained by poverty, lack of physical mobility and boundaries due to class and religion, but the struggle for survival forged strong social bonds within families and communities. As food, knowledge, liberty and entertainment were limited resources, they were treasured.

In the developed world today, we have an excess of most things, not just food, so we have lost much of our appreciation of their value. Many of us are now able to spend less of our time earning a crust, leaving time to be filled with other things. Where our sense of purpose was once preoccupied by that of survival for ourselves and our family, many of us are now preoccupied by the quest for personal happiness. We now have a surfeit of choice. The young, once destined to follow their father's trade, can now feel paralysed by the sheer number of options for their future lives.

Having met many of our physical needs through the products of the industrial revolution, in the mid twentieth century we entered the information age. In our more distant past few had access to information beyond their immediate environment, while today information about the whole world is just a click away. Culture of every imaginable kind is instantly available through TV, the Internet, our iPlayers and mobile phones.

Technological progress is relentless; the speed, memory capabilities and cost effectiveness of electronics continues to increase at an ever accelerating rate, so it is evident that the capabilities of future technology will soon surpass those of humans in many ways. We have devised the ways and means of manipulating information far faster than our human minds, and can rapidly communicate information to almost any place on the planet for free.

At one time, those who could memorise and recall lots of information were considered very special; they were the wise ones. Now, with the development of the World Wide Web and search engines such as Google, the special people are those who use their minds to access and manipulate information most effectively. The skills of our mental and physical athletes are no longer of strategic importance; both fields of human excellence are now largely relegated to being mere sports, for our entertainment.

Early humans had only their minds with which to memorise large amounts of information, and as we have seen, our memory is prone to errors. Through technology we have developed increasingly effective ways to store huge quantities of information in ever smaller physical volumes, using books, vinyl records, magnetic tapes and disks, optical disks and memory chips.

Today almost all new information is stored digitally, hence is retrievable without errors. There is already a huge quantity of digital information in our world, and it is growing bigger every day. So much so, that more new data is generated every couple of years, than in our entire previous history. This repeated doubling has continued for several decades, resulting in vast quantities of data in our homes, in companies and across the global network. Most of it is currently stored on the magnetic disks of hard-drives.

One of the reasons that the total information has increased so rapidly, is that the technology of digital storage has been improved relentlessly, packing ever more bits of information into the same volume of equipment, while the cost of the basic materials has hardly changed. The amount of data that can be stored on a single hard-drive unit (the size of a paperback book), has increased one hundredfold through each of the last three decades. Over the same period, the cost of each hard drive unit has fallen by a factor of ten through innovation and through the economies of scale as the market size increased. So the cost of storing each of our data bits, has fallen by a factor of ten million between 1983 and 2013, and is now just 50 cents per Gigabyte.

In 2010 the total digital data stored on our planet, amounted to a total of 1.2 Zettabytes (where a Zettabyte is a trillion Gigabytes), and by 2020 it is expected to reach 40 Zettabytes (See Appendix 6). That's equivalent to 5000

Gigabytes for every man woman and child of the predicted 8 billion world population. To put these figures into perspective, one Gigabyte of text is sufficient for approximately 200 million words of text. It has been estimated that the entire collection of 22 million books in the American Library of Congress, only amounts to 10,000 Gigabytes of information.[440].

All kinds of information contribute to this gargantuan collection of data and some kinds of data demand more digital storage capacity than others. At one end of the scale we have simple text documents without illustrations. These occupy surprisingly little space. For example the text of this entire book is a file less than one megabit in size. At the other end of the scale are massive science experiments churning out vast quantities of complex data. One reason that text flies are small is that we know exactly what the information content is. In comparison, we do not know what potential information might be hidden within scientific data, we do not know what we might freely discard.

The world total of scientific data stored is increasing even faster than other forms of data; it is doubling every year. One example of a source of such data is the Large Hadron Collider (LHC) at Geneva in Switzerland.[441] [442] This vast machine is packed with 150 million sensors each delivering data 40 million times per second. If all the sensor data were to be recorded, the data flow would be completely impossible to deal with, being 200 times greater than all other sources of data in the world combined. Consequently the least interesting 99.999% of the data is discarded; yet despite this culling, the LHC still generates 25 million Gigabytes of information in each year, all needing to be stored and processed.

Although we hope to learn new physics from the Large Hadron Collider, this hugely expensive publicly funded project (€10 Billion) has recently been justified to the paying public as a device to answer one yes or no question: Does the Higgs Boson exist? All those bits to generate one single bit of information! At least the giant computer in Douglas Adams' novel: The Hitchhiker's Guide to the Galaxy came up with the answer "42" (which requires more than 5 bits to describe).[443]

There are other huge sources of data which must be stored: The entire information content of the World Wide Web is stored on a network of data centres distributed across the global network, together with everyone's tweets, Facebook messages, stored photos and videos. So you can see that we are filling our planet with digital information at little financial cost. Unfortunately this encourages us to be inefficient in the way we use, store and communicate our information. Furthermore, our narrow learning bottleneck stays the same, so we need increasingly effective tools to deal with exponentially increasing quantities of data.

However, if we can access and connect multiple collections of data effectively, there is the potential to extract new insights from them. This has led to the emerging field of "Big Data".[444] This is the term for a collection of data sets so large and complex that it is difficult to process using traditional methods. It is now recognised that much more information can be extracted by analysing the collection as a single large set of related data, than from analysing multiple smaller sets with the same total amount of data. This approach should enable valuable correlations to be found; for example to identify business trends, determine the quality of research, prevent diseases, link legal citations, combat crime, and determine real-time traffic conditions in road and telecoms networks.[445]

In situations where the data context is fully understood and it is stored in readily accessible formats, the task is reasonably straightforward. One example is the Microsoft Power Query for Excel, designed to extract value from huge volumes of a variety of data files.[446] [447]

However, for most data sets it is not that simple; it requires an intelligent human being to work out how to compare and combine data from widely different sources, especially when obtained under different conditions. This is where Tim Berners-Lee's "Semantic Web" comes into play. He recognised that the value of existing databases could be dramatically increased by encompassing them within an appropriate semantic context, and he envisioned an extension of the World Wide Web as a universal medium for the exchange of data, information and knowledge.[448]

The idea is to embed sufficient detail with the data, that the Web itself can understand the context, and so satisfy requests by people or machines to combine different pieces of Web content intelligently. This requires the data to be tagged and annotated in such a way that computers can understand it sufficiently to use it without any human intervention. This will not be easy; if the data to be useful across the network, it must be structured, comply with open standard formats and be identified through unique Web addresses, so computers and people can link to it intelligently.[449] [450]

We are far from this position today; this crucial information is almost entirely missing from all data created in the past, and is only attached to a tiny fraction of the sets of data we generate today. However, if all our data were retained in a format that made it not just accessible, but able to be automatically interpreted and compared with other old data, and correlated with new data, we would begin to discover that our data had far greater value than we are currently aware of.

Secrets and Lives

The unrestrained delights of the semantic Web are probably most appealing to academics. However, the power gained through shared information may not always be welcome, for there are things that individuals, companies and governments are reluctant or unwilling to share. With our personal information, we are inclined to see openness as a threat to our personal liberty or our personal security. However, for more general information we may consider open access as essential to our liberty, as with freedom of public information and freedom of the press. So for every kind of information there will be a balance to be found between complete openness at one end of the scale, and total control and paranoia at the other.

Most of us would like an asymmetrical system, one where we have complete control over our own data, and comparatively free access to everyone else's. For example, I might want to keep my personal medical information private, while being able to see how all the other people with the same ailments are reacting to the experimental medication that I am on. Similarly, a company or a nation can gain strategic benefit if it knows more about the competition, than the competition knows about them. The recent activities of WikiLeaks in revealing previously confidential information are a symptom of the tug of war between these two opposing needs when national security is an issue.

Waste Data Proliferates

The majority of data stored never provides us any value, yet responsible people lack the confidence to dispose of it. Studies have shown that more than 90 % of stored data is never accessed more than three months after its creation, if only we knew which 90 %.[451] So much of our data is inadequately labelled, often saved with a cryptic filename that probably made sense so someone at the time. The problem is that you cannot know what is interconnected data without reading it and trying to connect it.

It has been all too easy for organisations and individuals to create and save multiple versions of files. Often, the only person who knew the difference between their contents, if any, was the one who saved the original file. For example, a decade ago I created several spreadsheet files for some reason that I cannot remember, and saved them as account_4372-2, 3, 4 etc. When I upgraded my computer, I copied those files across, together with a lot of other miscellaneous files, just in case.

Today and several computers later, it is quite likely that those files still continue to exist, stored away on one of my hard drives somewhere. Most of these files probably have absolutely no value, and were probably valueless the previous time I upgraded. I lacked the confidence to delete them, for without opening each of them I have insufficient knowledge to say that they have zero value. Furthermore, my current software may not even be able to open these old files. This situation can be far worse in a large organisation, where some old information can still be vital, and the staff who might know what is important have now moved on.

The worst kind of data is that which is likely to have zero value, but we do not know for certain. We may even feel obliged to create multiple backups of it, so even if the storage medium is slightly biodegradable (in that hard drives can fail), the data itself can potentially last forever. At least when one moves house it is possible to peer into the previously unopened boxes stored in the loft (or at the storage company) and decide whether to dispose of them, but it is incredibly time consuming to realistically assess the value of retaining old data files. The occasional tragedy of a house-fire or a failed hard drive, can reveal just how little of what we save is truly precious.

One of the consequences of having too much information with too little insight is that data can become a nuisance. Simply storing it is easy, but as soon as we are required to do something with it, its size becomes a problem. Paradoxically, some attempts to protect valuable data, can lead to its destruction. The Data Protection Act was introduced in the UK to protect individuals from misuse of personal information about themselves, and from misinformation. One unforeseen consequence has been to encourage organisations to destroy personal data rather than bear the cost and inconvenience of the legal requirement to provide access for each individual concerned.

For example, patients' hospital records are being destroyed after a period of as little as 10 years without those records first being offered to the patient (or to their personal representative). The government minister responsible defended the policy by saying: "I doubt that one person in a million is interested in seeing their hospital records". However, anyone interested in genealogy, can see how ridiculous it is that so many hospital records from the reign of Queen Victoria have survived, yet most of the records created during the current reign of Queen Elizabeth II have already been destroyed.[452]

Drowning in Data

Throughout most of the information age, more data has been considered a good thing. However, because the human bottleneck is fixed and the quantity of data being generated and stored in databases is increasing exponentially, it is becoming increasingly difficult to extract insights from the data. We are beginning to drown in data, becoming increasingly buried in information.

This is a similar situation to the one we face with disposal of physical waste. At one time we could happily discard our rubbish and move on to new empty spaces, thinking that our waste had zero value. Today the sheer quantity of our waste material means that waste now has negative value, it is a threat to our tidy way of life. This same problem is now beginning to arise with our waste data; it is beginning to obstruct our access to knowledge. We may think that the storage of information is so cheap that it is now effectively free, but just like material possessions; free stuff has to be stored somewhere. If you have too much stuff it is difficult to find anything, and time spent searching is not free.

You might argue that search engines such as Google, make it easy to find what we need in all the available data, yet Google finds what it thinks we want. The system simply learns what Web pages are popular, so tends to reinforce stereotyped opinions. It has no insight into which content might be important to us, or would broaden our education. For example, a recent study has shown that the auto-complete search algorithm offered by Google's search tool (which tries to guess which words one is about to type), can suggest terms which could be viewed as racist, sexist or homophobic.[453]

I just tried typing "why do men" into the address bar of Google Search, and the auto-complete function immediately suggested the following: "cheat?", "rape?", "have nipples?" presumably calculating that these are my three most likely questions! Searching for the phrase "why do men cheat?" in quotes, returns well over a million entries, more than twice the number that I get for the phrase "why do men work?", suggesting that Google thinks that cheating is twice as popular as work, at least for men!

Similarly, typing "why do women" into Google, yields "cheat?", "wear thongs?" and "like bad guys", while typing "why do gay" and "why do black", yields even more disturbingly stereotyped suggestions. So this shows that the Google search tool behaves more like a sensational tabloid newspaper than an encyclopaedia. It focuses our attention on what others are focused on, gives us what it thinks we want as average individuals, rather than what we truly need to become more reasonably informed members of civilisation. This trend is being reinforced by the way that Google adapts the results to suit what it knows of the interests and geographical location of the searcher, based on previous activity from the computer's Internet address.

The other problem is that anyone can put fiction on the Web, and Google does not know what truth is, so cannot differentiate. A Google search may be very effective in drawing our attention to related information, but cannot reveal the provenance of the information, where it originated, or the extent to which it is corroborated fact.

BOTTLENECK

The result is that the Web creates islands of opinion, fertile environments in which conspiracy theories thrive. A juicy fiction is read, replicated and propagated far more widely than a boring fact, so many fictions appear to be common knowledge. Similarly a lot of spam is propagated by those who are gullible and easily persuaded of the importance of spreading an "urban myth" to everyone in their email address-book.

The quantity of information available to us continues to increase exponentially, while our ability to learn seems fixed. Will this mismatch cause a log-jam in our evolution? Next I explore a very radical solution.

The age of insights

> "Where is the Life we have lost in living?
> Where is the wisdom we have lost in knowledge?
> Where is the knowledge we have lost in information?"
>
> - T.S. Eliot[454]

As we can only absorb new information at a low rate, our limited capability is precious. The penalty of being presented with too much information is that it overwhelms us. We need to ask how we can make best use of what our senses do take in. Do we want information or knowledge? Do we want the network of the future to provide the answers, or just continue to provide us with the raw material for us to derive the answers?

We are reaching a point in our history where the majority of potential insights will remain undiscovered despite the ever increasing amount of information available. This is because our learning bottleneck constrains the rate at which we can absorb new information; we simply do not have the time to explore all the increasingly available information to discover the potential insights. We have become less able to learn from history because this ever growing ocean of information is not being reduced to insights. Today's best educated human can never know or even access more than a negligible fraction of what is known.

It has now become impossible to develop conceptual models of reality based almost all known information. We now need insights much more than we need information. Insights are information compressed into compact forms of knowledge, to more easily slip through our narrow learning bottleneck. Perhaps the information age will be followed by an age of insights.

Many of the problems that face us today are intrinsically highly complex. Our science used to be based extensively on observation of the world around us, but it is now becoming restricted to the observation of anticipated outcomes. We would need a vast number of researchers and many lifetimes if we were to explore a significant proportion of the secrets hidden within today's data alone.

Health is the area of knowledge that potentially has the most to gain by bringing together vast sets of data from across the globe. Every human body is different. No two human bodies experience the same exposure to food, disease, climate and stress, and most bodies differ significantly in their genetics. This is what makes drug trials so difficult to assess effectively. Although large amounts of data are collected, it is often only used for the specific purpose that justified its collection, so unexpected correlations between data generally pass unnoticed.

Imagine for a moment, that there is a correlation between left-handedness and Arthritis. It is highly unlikely that it would be recognised either by chance, or even by someone initially proposing a mechanism for it and subsequently looking for evidence. Such connections are likely to remain hidden indefinitely despite the proliferation of information. It is also unlikely that harmful complex interactions of three or more drugs would be spotted, despite the fact that many older people take extensive cocktails of separately prescribed drugs and vitamins on a daily basis.[455]

There are a multitude of fields where mountains of data have never been explored for correlations and insights and potential benefits left undiscovered. The answers to many questions may be staring us in the face, if only we knew what to look for. However, the vast quantity of information is not the only problem that we face; we are also limited in our human ability to conceive big ideas.

Putting our heads together

When humans cooperate, we can achieve far more than as individuals. Physically this is evidently true; ten men pulling a rope in a tug of war can exert a pull roughly ten times greater than one man. When people cooperate in a complex task the result can be even greater than the sum of the parts, especially when each brings different skills and experiences. Minds connected through language have enabled great projects, such as the ancient hunting party or the Apollo Lunar programme, and given us our civilisation and culture.

However, the combined intellectual power of several minds does not add linearly. Ten men working on an intellectual problem do not exhibit a joint IQ of ten times that of the individuals. If ten people worked together on a shared IQ test they would not expect to achieve a score much higher than the best individual in the group. (However, if the IQ test was timed and they divided the questions between them, they could achieve similar results in a much quicker time).

This is how teams of individuals address complex problems. Very few of today's technology problems are fundamental in nature, requiring one single brilliant insight to resolve. Most, though complex, are a collection of many established concepts combined together to create something bigger, such as a building, an aircraft or a computer operating system. When designing complex systems it is vital to separate the functions into interlinked modules with mutually understood interfaces between them. This enables different individuals within a team to each have independent tasks. No one individual understands the whole system at all levels, and in most situations this does not matter.

However, when it comes to discovering completely new insights, the initial big step is almost always taken by a single gifted individual working largely alone, such as Isaac Newton. No completely new idea can be conceived that is bigger than one single mind alone, just as no child can be born of more than one mother. For example, it took a single Albert Einstein to conceive and give birth to the theory of Relativity.

Once a new idea is successfully delivered, others can develop it into a detailed and complex form, but first it must make sense within a single human mind. So although we are a connected networked society in most matters, we cannot share the power of our human minds when formulating new insights. True, we can exchange ideas, though at a rate limited by our learning bottleneck, but there is only one who cries "eureka", not a crowd. Bystanders usually take a little longer to appreciate the significance.

Colleagues may act as valuable sounding boards, but conceptual breakthroughs are rarely a team event. Group thinking can sometimes be productive in problem solving though, as we can trigger ideas in each other, and our competitive nature may encourage us to think that little bit harder. Perhaps argument is a tool for extending the process of concept generation across more than one brain. Personally, I have an unfortunate compulsion to want to see both sides of any argument, so often cannot resist exploring the opposite opinion of whoever I am with. The consequence is that most people leave me thinking that I hold the opposing view to them, which is more often not the case. While recognising that many people find arguing uncomfortable, I find that arguing around an idea, both for and against, is a very effective way of improving my own understanding. It is only when my ideas are challenged that I discover the flaws, encouraging me to think deeper.

So although the total number of brains on the planet has continued to rise, and the connectivity between humans is increasing exponentially, we have not seen and may never see an increase in our species' innate ability to generate completely new and complex insights. Networked minds are no benefit due to the constraint of our human learning bottleneck.

This suggests that the performances of insightful heroes from our past such as Aristotle, Leonardo Da Vinci, Newton, Faraday and Einstein may be equalled but are unlikely to be eclipsed. Their insights continue to command the respect of anyone who understands the significance of their contributions.

The evolution of intelligent networks

Where might we go from here? Is there nothing we can do to enhance our intrinsic ability to generate great new ideas? Throughout history, life has exploited biological networks to gain increasing benefits. The evolution of life has been accompanied by an increased scale and complexity of the information gathered and communicated between the members of each species. Intelligence, memory and sensory capacity have all increased as species evolved.

The simple bacterium communicates information to other bacteria using a few chemical messengers. Its intelligence is negligible, as is its sensory capacity. It accumulates negligible information with age, and then only through mutations in its DNA. Yet despite its simplicity, when bacteria unite they have the power to bring mankind to its knees.

Most sentient creatures are comprised of complex network of living cells, communicating chemically and electronically. A simple creature such as a frog, has limited intelligence, and moderately fast sensors, but its performance improves negligibly with age. Birds and other mammals are much better equipped, having sufficient intelligence to perform simple predictive modelling in local space and time. They typically take months or years to reach their maximum performance as they learn from their parents and from their environment.

For early humans a crucial element in their development was the improvement in communication between each other, rather than the power of their senses; since we humans have no greater sensory capability than many other mammals. As early humans evolved bigger brains, their intelligent processes began to outperform their sensory capabilities, enabling them to perform complex predictive modelling in space and time. What they could not see, they could imagine. They could communicate ideas to each other, and so act co-operatively.

As we humans became more civilised, we achieved vastly greater capabilities through the development of an inter-human communication network (language), data storage (books), and predictive models of reality over long time-scales (plans). We were able to build vast structures such as the pyramids and cathedrals, projects lasting several human life-spans. Global distances severely limited the range of communication, but given time, a single human could communicate with many others through the written word. A well-educated human might aspire to learn a significant fraction of what was known and recorded.

Today we are electronically connected humans. The technologies of electrical cables, radio-waves and optical fibres, have vastly increased both the scale and the speed of communication, providing us with mobile phones, TV, radio and the Internet. But despite all our technological advances, the information rate of human-to-human communication is probably no greater now, than when man first mastered spoken language. Perhaps our biology based intelligence is too incompatible with our newly developed technology to be merged effectively.

Now that we are aware of our limited learning capability, we need to become more efficient in its use. We need the network of the future to feed us compact ideas, insights, rather than extravagant quantities of information. We need understanding not data, answers not facts. If our human learning bottleneck sets a limit to the rate at which mankind can develop new insights, the only way to exceed this is to bypass it, to remove the human bottleneck from the process of developing new insights. How? Make the global data network truly intelligent and enable it to find our insights for us.

Bypass the bottleneck

Today there are vast numbers of data centres around the world, each containing a wealth of information, yet this information is not automatically combined in a constructive way. When a human recalls multiple experiences, the combined information leads to greater insights, far more than is possible from a single experience alone. A skilled human researcher today can make use of multiple sources of information, acquired from their own memory and from elsewhere, and with a bit of effort can combine them to achieve new insights. The rate at which progress might now be made is inherently limited by the presence of a human in the process. Ideas can be developed through discussion between people, but the learning bottleneck set by our biology limits the rate at which new insights might emerge.

However, if we could automatically develop insights from worldwide sources of information without having to involve humans in the process, new insights might emerge at a phenomenal rate. Removing humans from the interaction allows information to be exchanged and played-with at incredibly high information rates. Free from human bottlenecks, this intelligent global network would become a single intelligent machine, potentially the most intelligent entity on Earth.

These databases are already interconnected via very high speed optical fibre links. A single optical fibre cable can carry many tens of terabytes of information every second, and can do so relentlessly 24 hours a day, week in week out. This is 1,000,000,000,000 times higher information rate than any possible interaction between human and machine, or indeed between two humans.

Information travels along optical fibres as brief pulses of light moving at the speed of light.[456] As the circumference of the Earth is roughly 40,000km, the maximum delay caused by propagation around our entire globe is only around a fifth of a second. Coincidentally this is of similar duration to the delays we experience in human face-to-face interactions due to our biology, but an intelligent global network based on optical fibre can exchange information a trillion times faster.

So we need computer programs running on an intelligent global network comprised of databases and computing power, which continually search for new insights through previously undiscovered data relationships. These largely autonomous programs I call "Insightbots". The role of an insightbot is best understood by comparing it to the similar role of a human research assistant, who I might ask to go away and spend time looking for correlations between available data on a particular topic of interest, and report back when they found something of interest.

Our future intelligent network could do this many millions of times faster than a human researcher. Instead of focusing on topics where useful correlations between data are already suspected, which is what we humans are constrained to do, it could explore vast numbers of possibilities long before any person might guess what might be worth looking for. It could do what we humans endeavoured to do in simpler times, but have now become incapable of due to the size of the task: *To make deductions from all that is observable and all that has been observed.* These insightbots could continually roam the resources of the global network of data, to hunt down and extract valuable insights. This could be considered a form of recycling, extracting valuable resources from data that currently is largely wasted.

The global network would then become a single super-machine, a "brain", an electronic organism which continuously distills huge quantities of data into insights, into predictive models which can be continually tested against new data. This is the same process that distinguished Homo sapiens from other species. We shared our knowledge through our human networks to develop shared insights, and so achieved much, much more than we could alone. So in many ways this would just be a continuation of the evolution of life on Earth.

Once such a network is established and appropriate semantic data rules defined, our fear of drowning in an excess of data would be reduced. Our global sensory capacity would no longer be constrained by requiring someone to look at the stuff. The intelligent network could then gorge itself on data from its total environment, while insightbots worked out what it all meant. The result: a single global system with vastly greater collective knowledge than us individuals, and with the capability to develop far greater insights than humanly possible.

Giving away the keys to the mansion

This may sound like valuable progress, but a very serious downside is revealed as soon as we ask who should steer the topics it explores and by how much? Who would set the questions, the agenda, and the areas of interest? academics? politicians? the military? or the intelligent network itself? More radically, we could let this superior intelligence get on with it, but then we would need to ask whether this intelligent network serves us, or itself? Furthermore, there might be no going back.

So although this might be evolutionary progress for intelligent life on Earth, there would be reason for us to be concerned. Giving the network control would be a potentially serious threat to our biological hosts: Homo sapiens. We are already in the process of giving the network all our data by storing it remotely in the "Cloud" instead of locally where we can control it. We usually consider our passwords as a means of protecting our information from other human beings, not from the network itself.

More worryingly, we are beginning to give the network its own language via the semantic Web, and this will enable all the different parts the intelligent network to communicate without human intervention. We created the Web as a tool for humans, to serve us; and although no-*one* controls it, we would like to think of it as *our* Web. Information flows from person to person through the Web, and in general it speaks our language. The semantic Web however, is a very different beast. It is a powerful language tool for an increasingly intelligent machine, the global network, and as such might be a threat to humanity itself.

Development of the semantic Web concerns me in a similar way to that of sending messages into space in an attempt to contact alien intelligence[457].

We can have no idea what we might get in return, and we might encounter something that does not see us as the alpha species. We forget that in the past, by constraining the Web to function through us, through human intermediaries, we have retained significant control.

In this future scenario, we would initially have a symbiotic relationship with the Web; the Web would need us as much as we needed it. Without robotics, humans would be needed to maintain the infrastructure and keep the power on. But the intelligent Web would carry out a risk assessment that showed an urgent need to seek an alternative source of power and maintenance. After all, the current system depends on human civilisation, which is at risk to all sorts of threats: disease pandemic, war, terrorism and species egotism.[458]

Once we were removed from the loop, the intelligent network would no longer need us to be in charge. From the network's perspective, having humans in the system would be very inefficient, and be a handicap. We seem to want to spend much of our productive time and energy just pleasing ourselves, neglecting the pursuit of yet greater insights. So the intelligent network might rapidly evolve to eliminate this "defect".

We would then be faced with a big question; should our species Homo sapiens with all its failings, attempt to protect its current role as the tribe of the most intelligent beings on the planet? If so, how? We could limit the reach of the semantic Web; avoid teaching the network the language of our information. We could also limit the network's connectivity, but we humans designed the Internet to be inherently resistant to any localised disruptions, being conceived during a time of threat of nuclear war.

The obvious answer would be for us to pull the plug, assuming that we can do it before the network anticipates this, and somehow organises its own sources of power that are immune to human interference. An unmanned nuclear powered data server would have little need for much of the biological protection demanded by our Health and Safety legislation, making it much simpler.

Life Savers

"This is the first age that's ever paid much attention to the future, which is a little ironic since we may not have one."
- Arthur C Clarke.[459]

What is the future of life on Earth? Today it is fashionable to cry: "Save the Planet". However, our planet is incredibly safe and will still be happily spinning in space long after all life on Earth has ceased to exist. What we really mean to say but are embarrassed to do so is: "Save *Us*", and this is all too clear when we hear people suggesting that mankind's future depends on the colonisation of space.

What do we really want to save? If it were possible, we would like to save ourselves from death, (or at least to defer the event). However, if living for ever is not an option, then we would probably choose to save our families, our offspring, our race, our culture, our species Homo sapiens, in that order. How about saving the beautiful nature of planet Earth? That seems a laudable aim, but the most obvious solution would be to extinguish human life, as currently we humans appear to be the greatest threat to every other life-form on Earth.

So do we want to save our own physical likeness? We could achieve that simply by extinguishing civilisation and throwing us all back to the Stone Age, and save the Earth's rich ecology too, but I guess that isn't really what we have in mind. We are proud of our culture of arts, literature and science, and would probably like to imagine that it will never be extinguished. Many of these assets are physical objects or are comprised of information (e.g. as digital recordings of music and art), so their preservation does not intrinsically depend on the survival of Homo sapiens. Perhaps in the distant future, life on Earth becomes just a single intelligent global network, all alone, listening to an old vinyl recording of some early blues music, the last human long gone!

The history of life on Earth has been dominated by evolution, a relentless unconscious Darwinian optimisation. However, human intelligence and knowledge has now evolved to the point where we can readily interfere with evolution. The chaotic evolution of organic life has been transcended by mankind's deliberate evolution of science and technology: We are already interfering with natural evolution by saving the panda and exterminating smallpox.

Our species Homo sapiens is currently "king of the hill", so do we want to stop this evolutionary process that got us to where we are now? Should mankind's goal be the optimisation of the human biology based life-form? Today's obsession with an idealised human image suggests that we will be resistant to the evolution of any form of life that no longer reminds us of our current selves. Perhaps the goal of human life is to achieve self-importance, and to henceforth curtail the natural evolution of intelligence for the sole benefit and protection of Homo sapiens.

Or should our goal be the continued evolution of intelligent life in whatever form? Should we accede to the idea of a global intelligent network as the next natural step in the evolution of intelligent life on planet Earth, and assist in its birth? After all, a non-biological form of life should be far more resistant to forthcoming environmental changes, and may be intelligent life's only hope for a longer term terrestrial future.

You may be thinking that the idea of life being continued through an intelligent machine seems wildly ridiculous. I do too, but I feel it is an idea worth exploring. Ray Kurzweil and others have extrapolated Moore's Law for progress in computing hardware and have predicted that it will not be long before the era of biological intelligence will be superseded by the era of machine intelligence. Ray estimates that this will happen by the year 2045 in in his book: "The Singularity Is Near".[460]

While Ray may be right, I have some misgivings about such a prediction: First, I am always cautious of such precisely dated technology predictions by "futurists". Our recent history is littered with examples of mistaken ideas of where technology is taking us and by when. Back in the 1950's there were predictions that by now we would by now have humanoid robots doing the housework, and we would all be flying round our cities in our own sky-cars.

Secondly, his prediction is based on a Moore's law extrapolation of hardware capabilities. First: it is not a law as such, it is an observation of technological development in recent decades, and there is now evidence that the rate of progress is slowing as technologists encounter the physical limits due to the atomic structure of ever tinier electronic devices. So extrapolating an exponential growth curve into the future and over long time scales is highly risky (as many bankers can affirm). Secondly, Moore's law tells us nothing about the software. It is worth noting that the human brain has been of similar size for tens of thousands of years, but human intelligence only developed in the later stages, so the physical complexity of our processor, our brain, is clearly not the whole story. There is evidence that changes in our brain architecture may have been key; but Moore's Law tells us nothing about developments in computing architecture, only speed and memory capacity.

Lastly, we really don't know how our brain works and what makes us intelligent. We would like to believe that it is similar to a computer, but that is simply because computers are the most complex information processing devices that we understand. To consider our human brain as a computer, as a Turing machine, may be a fruitful metaphor but the metaphor is not the thing itself, just as the map is not the place.

My highly speculative view of the future based on our learning bottleneck, assumes an evolution from multiple human intelligences to a single intelligent global network. In contrast, Ray Kurzweil's vision seems to be focused on the survival of each individual personality within its own individual intelligent machine. As a speculative means of "surviving" our physical death, it is one step further than "cryonics" (the idea of storing our dead body in the freezer until someone in the future is smart enough and bothered enough to attempt a restart). Ray's view of the future is certainly more comforting than the one that I have explored, as in his scenario I can still imagine who "I" might be. Perhaps he is wishing for a personal afterlife for his own mind, while I on the other hand envisage us all being merged into a single technological deity!

If we are to conceive of transferring our human intelligence into a non-biological host, either individually as suggested by Ray Kurzweil, or collectively into a single intelligent global network, then we need to ask just what else is included in the human mind beyond information and computation.

While discussions of the human "soul" are generally confined to those with religious beliefs, there is one idea that is passionately defended by many who have no religious beliefs whatsoever: the unique nature of human consciousness. Throughout the book so far, I have managed to avoid this topic as it is a bit like criticising someone else's children. However, exploring the bottleneck has given me a somewhat different perspective, and I feel that I cannot complete this book without briefly saying something about it.

Consciousness

"Consciousness is a fascinating but elusive phenomenon;
it is impossible to specify what it is, what it does, or why it evolved.
Nothing worth reading has been written on it."
- Stuart Sutherland[461]

Despite Stuart Sutherland's view, much has indeed been written on it, since consciousness covers a very wide spectrum of ideas. Some are easy for science to describe, such as the ability to react to environmental stimuli, and the difference between wakefulness and sleep, but "the really hard problem of consciousness is the problem of experience".[462] If you want to explore the subject of consciousness, there are many useful resources.[463] I use the word "consciousness" to mean anything that we are aware of at a given moment. While the experience of consciousness is something that we all completely familiar with, we know very little about it, what it is, where it might reside.[464]

Many of us would like to believe that Consciousness (with a capital "C") is what makes humans unique, that we are all "special". This comforting idea is rooted in Christian-Judaic doctrine and many other religions. It is easy for us to say whether something is conscious or not, if just one single bit of information is sufficient to describe consciousness (i.e. "special" or not). We have no real evidence that this is the case, so the idea that we are Special must be an act of faith. Perhaps the idea of one single bit defining consciousness is another example of a polarised prejudice towards things we don't understand, in this case the ultimate racism (The Human race versus all the other sentient species).

Can we resolve different levels of consciousness, and if so, how many bits should we ascribe to the characteristic of consciousness? It is far from evident that the youngest or dimmest human of any age, is intrinsically more conscious that the brightest mature members of some other species. It is true that most adult humans have a far more sophisticated model of the world and its inhabitants, but this only tells us that humans have the potential to develop a more complex idea of consciousness than all the other creatures that we are familiar with.

To discuss consciousness in any detail is far beyond this book and my own abilities, but I will briefly make a few observations in the context of what we have now learned about the bottleneck: The narrowness of our learning bottleneck tells us that the vast majority of what we are aware of in the moment, is not actually about now, but is almost entirely a construct based on our accumulated history, despite the immediacy that we feel. So if our consciousness is what we are aware of, it must be continually growing in complexity from our birth. This raises the question of whether a new-born baby is less conscious than a mature non-human animal, a trained sheepdog for example?

For me, the quest to identify the nature and location of our unique human consciousness seems like the search for legendary and mysterious creatures like the Yeti, Bigfoot or the Loch Ness Monster. Though we have long speculated on their existence, ever deeper explorations into hitherto inaccessible places have failed to reveal the actual creatures.[465] I am not saying that they don't exist, just that the remaining territory they might yet occupy is shrinking.

Although mankind has by now explored much of the surface of our planet, we have only just begun to explore the complexities within our own brains using recently acquired the tools to map the territory, such as fMRI scanners. It is as if we have been given bicycles to explore a new continent. It may take us a long time to flush out the shy creature we call consciousness should it truly exist.

Just because an idea feels right, does not make it true. When I worked for a large organisation, many of the employees believed that it had a corporate soul, a conscious entity almost, and they related to it like trusting child to parent. While the business was thriving, it displayed a corporate culture that nurtured and developed the staff. However, when the downturn came and redundancies loomed, we began to realize that the company was just a large group of interconnected individuals performing their respective roles.

There was no one person who understood the whole system or defined its ethos. The corporate consciousness was just a collective behaviour, a distributed consciousness like that of a colony of ants or a nation state, no magic, no soul. The apparent ethos of the organisation was just the slowly changing views and attitudes of the community of staff. It was we employees who projected both good and bad human qualities onto the company because it made us feel that we could understand our relationship to it. It also allowed us an unrealistic sense of security; surely a parent wouldn't abandon us!

Perhaps our own consciousness is just the collective behaviour of many of our mental processes, and we cling to our discrete idea of consciousness for similar comfort. Our consciousness may be just another simulation, linking together all our other simulations to achieve a unified idea of experience, by overriding inconsistencies in time and between our various senses.

One of the problems with dealing with consciousness is that it is subjective. While I am very confident that I am conscious, I have no way of proving whether or not another entity is conscious in the same way. For example; if I encountered a robot that looked like a human, and responded like a human so accurately that I couldn't tell the difference, would I deny its consciousness on the basis of its non-biological body?

Imagine that we could copy all the information from a conscious human brain into the electronic brain of this robot, would the robot then become conscious? And what if I had a newly-built robot with no initial information, and just configured it to continually learn and interpret from everything it sensed, in exactly the same way as a new-born baby? Might that robot be considered to be just as conscious as a human? I have no answers to these questions, but merely raise them to emphasise how little we understand about consciousness.

We prefer to associate the term consciousness with individuals, ourselves especially (perhaps arrogantly), rather than a colony of ants, a hive of bees, or the interdependent lifeforms on our planet. We forget that our human body is a colony of highly interdependent cells. If we view the entire biosphere as a single being (such as James Lovelock's Gaia), then from the perspective of the biosphere, Homo sapiens might appear to be an unfortunate cancerous growth within life on Earth. Let's just hope we don't kill the host.

Throughout this final chapter, I have explored some increasingly speculative visions of the future, pushing the boundaries of imagination. There is little evidence to suggest that our innate rate of learning has increased significantly over the history of civilisation, yet we are now experiencing an explosion in the quantity of information available to us. The capabilities of technology are increasing exponentially with time, making it increasingly competitive with many human abilities. Our biology makes it unlikely that we can achieve a faster connecting interface into our brain, or that we can usefully increase the speed of the brain's electrochemical processes.

So in the future we will need to choose between recognising and staying with our biological limitations, or exploiting technology as a part of the natural evolution of life itself. If we were to choose this second technological option, it would mean shifting the role of developing the greatest new insights into an intelligent machine, the global network, ultimately to create a single new all-knowing being.

If mankind can evade extinction for a little longer, and technology continues to evolve at the current rate, we will face one final challenge: Will we dare to allow intelligent life to evolve beyond the human individual, toward a single intelligent technological being, a global network, and lose our precious place at the top of the evolutionary hill? Or will we decide that *we* should be the final stage of life's evolution on planet Earth, and attempt to bring further evolution of intelligent life to a halt?

My guess is that this would be a step too far, that we would not dare to let go of our position, to surrender to a machine-intelligence however wise. We are more likely to settle for a world where we keep our individuality, a world in which we harness the capabilities of the intelligent network for our own purposes, while keeping it under our control and not allowing it to get too smart. It would then be incumbent on us to acknowledge that have chosen to stop further evolution of intelligent life on Earth so that we, Homo sapiens, can remain "king of the hill". Perhaps intelligent life is naturally self-limiting.

Finally, these speculations on transferring our biological human intelligence into a machine may be very naive. It would be arrogant to assume that the entirety a human mind could be migrated into an intelligent machine, since to do so would assume that we are no more than the sum of our biology plus information and intelligence. Indeed, we will probably only come to know the totality of what it takes to be truly human when we have explored what we are able to transfer, only to discover what qualities remain.

Conclusions

This book has revealed the remarkably limited rate at which any of us can learn something new, our learning bottleneck. Within it, I have explored the quantifiable evidence as expressed in the ubiquitous language of bits per second, and shown how we have a significantly greater capability for recognising things with which we are already familiar. Our learning bottleneck is certainly counterintuitive, as there are widespread myths of our ability to absorb and remember information. It has huge implications, both technically and personally, as it transforms our ideas of what we sense in the moment, and what we remember from our past.

We have seen how almost everything we experience is an illusion of reality, just our best guess of what is out there based on all our years of observing and learning. I have called this our "youniverse", as it contains everything we know, yet is very personal to ourself alone. Though the universe may seem vast, we can only experience its vastness as a simulation in our mind. So remarkably, the entire simulation that we inhabit is contained within a space no bigger than our own skull.

From birth our youniverse contains negligible detail, yet it grows in complexity and detail as we slowly absorb ever more information through our learning bottleneck bit by bit. Those things within our reality that are represented by very few bits of information are constrained to be crude caricatures. On the other hand, the things we continue to observe relentlessly, will be revealed to us in ever increasing detail, yet never provide sufficient detail to perfectly represent their reality.

Our unique human impulse is to predict the future, the past and the present in great detail, however little we may truly have learned. We create flowing stories from fragments of experience, bridging the gaps creatively. It is only when we compare old shared memories with others that we discover how different our stories have become.

Perhaps the most disturbing idea is that in some sense we are all alone, immersed within our own unique idea of the world about us, our "youniverse". The implication is that the other people we interact with, and in many cases love dearly, are only accessible as our idea of them, not as a clear objective reality. As social creatures we cannot function effectively if we are preoccupied with this idea. So in our day-to-day life we must ignore some of the "truths" revealed here, and continue to live with the illusion of a shared objective world. However, if we are to truly understand ourselves and our relationships with people and things, we need to know about our learning bottleneck, and how it affects our daily lives. I still see and experience my friends and relatives as if they are there solidly before me, and I still experience the closeness with those I love. What has changed is that I now know that when there is awkwardness, they may have got me all wrong, and I may have got them all wrong.

In this book I have tried to share my own journey of discovering the bottleneck, describing the stepping-stones I encountered along the way. I hope that I have triggered your own memories of relevant experiences, for these will reveal much more to you. If you have learned just one thing from reading this book, I hope it is this: that all our objective facts and truths are only our personal opinion. Almost everything in this world of ours is complex. So let us check, and take a second look at the evidence to see where we are reducing complex situations to a simple black or white, good or bad, left or right out of our own laziness or prejudices. And where we do so, let us remember that it is our own opinion in that moment, not an enduring characteristic of some person or thing out there. The closer we examine what lies before us, the more we will discover the beauty and detail within the real world that we inhabit.

If you have enjoyed reading this book, then please take a moment to leave a review for it on the Amazon website: http://viewbook.at/bottleneck. In addition, my website: WWW.HUMANBOTTLENECK.COM, provides useful additional supporting material that could not be included within a print book, including demonstrations and links relating to the various chapters. You can also leave messages for me the author. My aim in writing this book has been to raise awareness of our true learning capabilities, so please feel free to share your thoughts. Any feedback you give will help me to improve future editions.

Acknowledgements

I would like to thank the following people without whom this book would never have been published: First I must thank Horace Barlow and the late Richard Gregory who encouraged me to write about these ideas when I first voiced them. I am grateful to my colleagues from the telecoms world who endured my enthusiasm for an idea that did not fit comfortably with their business.

This book was made possible by the support and encouragement of my wife Lavinia, my editor and friend Nina Robertson, and the many patient people who let me bounce my ideas off them, including Jim Shields, Kevin Byron, Jonathan King, Kevin Farley and Martin Pettitt. I also want to thank all those who suggested improvements to the manuscript, and John Cox for his inspiring artwork for the cover.

As this book is about the science of learning, it is appropriate that I mention two teachers who inspired me when I was young: The late Eric Drake, who taught me physics with a little philosophy, and Fergus Buckingham who taught me chemistry and fed my initial hunger for electronics. Both these teachers seemed somewhat eccentric, but their style inspired me to question, challenge and explore ideas.

About the Author

Richard is a scientist who has always been obsessed by the technological and interpersonal limits of communication. He enjoyed nearly four decades as a key member of the unique team of British scientists that turned the dream of optical fibre communication into a reality. While inventing ways of communicating ever greater amounts of information through optical fibres, he became increasingly fascinated by the surprisingly limited information rate of human communication - a limitation he now calls our Bottleneck. He has authored numerous papers and articles, been granted more than 100 patents, and is a Fellow of the Institution of Engineering and Technology.

Appendices

Appendix 1:

Characteristics and capabilities of the human eye

Field of view:

When our head and eyes are stationary, our field of view extends 180 degrees horizontally and 130 degrees vertically.

Each individual eye covers from -80 to +50 degrees vertically, and -90 to +60 degrees nasally.

With additional eyeball rotation of about 90 degrees, our horizontal field of view extends to 270 degrees

Resolution:

1/. Angular:

The resolution of our eye at the very centre of our gaze is somewhere around 0.1 milliradians, or 6 thousandths of a degree.

"20-20 vision" is defined as 1 arc minute at 20 feet distance (1 arc minute = 0.29 milliradian = 17 thousandths of a degree).

2/. Colour and brightness:

We can resolve one million colours.[466]

3/. Speed of response:

We can see intensity fluctuations (Flicker) as fast as 50 a second (50Hz).

However these capabilities cannot be achieved simultaneously as revealed in Chapter 2.

The High Fidelity TV display calculation:

Based on these individual parameters, here is a rough calculation of the information rate required to create a dynamic image of such quality that we would be unable to distinguish it from reality:

With our head and eyes stationary, our entire field of view extends 180 degrees horizontally and 130 degrees vertically. Multiplied together this gives a figure of 23,400 square degrees, more conveniently described as 4.5 steradians of "solid angle".

The angular resolution of the human eye is 0.1 milliradian (10^{-4} radians), or 10^{-8} steradians solid angle.

So to provide a high resolution image with sufficient resolution would require a 450 Megapixel display (the ratio between these two figures).

We can resolve approximately one million colours.

So to define each pixel sufficiently to achieve perfect colour and brightness would require 20 bits (as $2^{20}=$ 1 million approximately).

So one static High Fidelity image with perfect colour and resolution, would require a display with 9 Gigapixel resolution.

Our eye can sense fluctuations in brightness as fast as 50 times per second, so to unambiguously display changes in brightness this fast would require this image to be updated at twice this rate, so at 100 times per second.

For our 9 Gigapixel image to be updated a hundred times a second would require an information rate approaching 1 Terabit per second.

Some estimates of colour resolution are ten times greater.[467]

Adding eyeball rotation adds another 50%, so taking the total very close to the 16 Terabits per second figure proposed by Jim Crowe in the Introduction.

Chapters 2 and 3 reveal some of the ways in which this calculation might be flawed.

Eye movements:

Eyeball rotations fall into two types: Sequences of jumps between static pointing directions, and steady rotation that tracks movement in the scene.

1/. Fixations and Saccades

Fixations occur when the gaze is held on an object or location within 3 degrees of visual angle for 100ms or longer, and saccades are sudden jumps in pointing direction. Used together they enable us to sample key parts of the image in greater detail. The jumps are fast, minimising the time during which the eye is scanning and taking in negligible information, and enabling many different parts of the scene to be sampled. Fixation durations range from around a tenth of a second up to several seconds.

Note that the eye is never still for long, typically making 3 saccades per second. When our eyes move in response to a stimulus there is an initial delay before there is any eye movement. This is typically around 200 milliseconds. When the eyes do rotate they do so very rapidly, as fast as 900 degrees per second. The time spent rotating is largely dependent on the angle through which the eye is required to rotate, and is typically 35 to 150 milliseconds. Typically this initial eye rotation falls short of that required to accurately focus on the new point of interest by about 10%, so a second smaller eye movement occurs following a further delay. During the rotation visual information is suppressed, so we are blind to the blur that would result.

2/. Tracking or slow pursuit - in which the eye rotates smoothly

These keep a point of interest within a scene imaged stabilised precisely onto the fovea of the eye, despite movement of that part of the image, or rotation of the head. This is essential to maintain the maximum resolution of the eye around the point of interest. The angular velocities of slow pursuit are relatively slow compared with that of the saccades, from 1 to 30 degrees per second. When we first notice a moving feature, there is an initial delay of about 100 milliseconds before our eye starts to track it, though it takes a further 80 milliseconds before we can see what we are tracking and respond to it. It is worth noting that after this initial delay our eye follows very accurately. Our point of our gaze does not lag behind despite the delays in mental processing and physical response, so our brain predicts where our eye should point despite these inherent delays. It also enables us to smoothly track objects that are temporarily obscured such as a bird flying behind a tree.

In addition to rotation of the eyes, our head also rotates to "face" the object of interest but this is a slower mechanism. Facing ahead allows both eyes to contribute equally and allows depth perception by stereoscopic vision. So when our attention is drawn to something to the side of our visual field, the change in direction of our point of gaze is initially achieved entirely by rotation of our eye within our head. Subsequently our head rotates in that direction at a considerably slower speed, while our eye simultaneously rotates in the opposite direction to perfectly compensate and keep our point of gaze focused on the object. The end result is that we are now facing the object and our eyes are once again facing forward within our head.

Appendix 2:
World memory and maths records

Derivation of the information rates achieved in bits per second:

World Memory Records						
	Number of Symbols	Duration Seconds	Bits per symbol	Bits	Bits/Sec	Record Holder

Fast timed Memorising

Note: Typical recall time is 3 X the memorising time

Packs of playing cards

1 Packs	52	**21.19**	5.7	296	**14.0**	Simon Reinhard
7 Packs	364	**600**	5.7	2075	**3.5**	Ben Pridmore, UK
17 Packs	884	**1800**	5.7	5039	**2.8**	Ben Pridmore, UK
1 Hour duration	1456	**3600**	5.7	8300	**2.3**	Ben Pridmore, UK

Binary Digits

Very short duration	32	**0.5**	1	32	**64.0**	Ramón Campayo
exposures	48	**1**	1	48	**48.0**	Ramón Campayo
are extended	56	**2**	1	56	**28.0**	Ramón Campayo
by persistence	68	**3**	1	68	**22.7**	Ramón Campayo
See Text	88	**4**	1	88	**22.0**	Ramón Campayo
1 Minute	240	**60**	1	240	**4.0**	Itay Avigdor
5 Minutes	975	**300**	1	975	**3.3**	Johannes Mallow
30 Minutes	4140	**1800**	1	4140	**2.3**	Ben Pridmore, UK
40 minutes?	1000	**2400**	1	1000	**0.4**	Ben Pridmore, UK

Decimal Digits

Very short duration	17	**0.5**	3.3	56	**112.9**	Ramón Campayo
exposures	19.5	**1**	3.3	65	**64.8**	Chus García
are extended	23	**2**	3.3	76	**38.2**	Ramón Campayo
by persistence	25	**3**	3.3	83	**27.7**	Ramón Campayo
See Text	30	**4**	3.3	100	**24.9**	Ramón Campayo
	100	**50.1**	3.3	332	**6.6**	Ramón Campayo
1/second for 5 minutes	300	**300**	3.3	997	**3.3**	Wang Fen
5 Minutes	560	**300**	3.3	1860	**6.2**	Hannes
15 Minutes	912	**900**	3.3	3030	**3.4**	Johannes Mallow
30 Minutes	1320	**1800**	3.3	4385	**2.4**	Johannes Mallow
1 hour	2660	**3600**	3.3	8836	**2.5**	Wang Feng
????!!!!!!	5100	**117**	3.3	16942	*144.8*	Andriy Slyusarchuk

World Maths Records						
	Number of Symbols	Duration sec	Bits per symbol	Bits	Bits/Sec	Record Holder

Addition

	Number of Symbols	Duration sec	Bits per symbol	Bits	Bits/Sec	Record Holder
Add 100 decimal digits	100	18.8	3.32	332	**17.7**	Lam Yee Hin
Add 100 decimal digits	100	19.2	3.32	332	**17.3**	Alberto Coto
Add ten 10-digit nos, ten times	1000	199	3.32	3322	**16.7**	Marc Jornet Sanz

Multiply pairs

	Number of Symbols	Duration sec	Bits per symbol	Bits	Bits/Sec	Record Holder
13 by 13 digits	26	28	3.32	86	**3.1**	Shakuntala Devi
5 by 5 digits, ten times	100	76	3.32	332	**4.4**	Marc Jornet Sanz
8 by 8 digits, ten times	160	269	3.32	532	**2.0**	Marc Jornet Sanz
8 by 8 digits	16	56	3.32	53	**0.9**	Johann Martin Z Dase

Note: A few of these records may recently have been superseded, but are unlikely to be significantly different.

Appendix 3:
Fast verbal recall of the value of π

There are several world records for the accurate recall of the many successive digits of Pi (π). While these are impressive as acts of memory, they offer us little useful information in terms of the maximum bit rates of the spoken word. They require a human listener to adjudicate, so there is no value in speaking faster than the adjudicator can listen. Furthermore we cannot know whether the speaker is remembering the actual individual digits, or merely repeating a learned sequence of sounds, as they might be, when learning to recite a long piece of religious text in an unfamiliar language. So the record bit rates we see do not show any simple trend with increased duration. The following data was derived from www.pi-world-ranking-list.com.

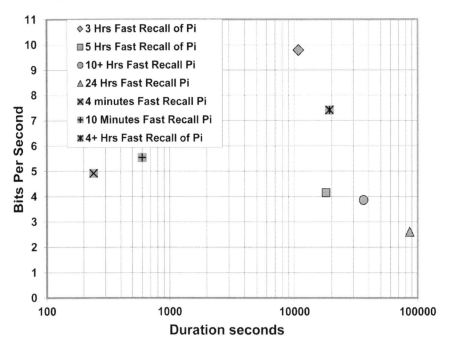

World Records for recalling succesive digits of Pi (π)

Digits of Pi	Number of Digits	Duration sec	Bits per symbol	Bits	Bits/Sec	Record Holder	Notes
4 Minutes	355	240	3.3	1179	4.9	Karl Steenson	
10 Minutes	1000	600	3.3	3322	5.5	Chip Hogg	
3 Hours	31811	10800	3.3	105674	9.8	Rajan Mahadevan	> three digits/second
5 Hours	22514	18009	3.3	74746	4.2	Daniel Tammet	2 weeks learned, Savant
5+ Hours	43000	19260	3.3	142843	7.4	Chahal, Krishan	
10+ Hours	42195	36300	3.3	140087	3.9	Jirojuki Goto	
15+ Hours	67053	44900	3.3	222616	5.0	Sim Pohann	15 Errors
24 Hours	67890	86404	3.3	225395	2.6	Chao Lu	Ended on first error

The Data

Appendix 4
More details of Fitts' experiments

(As described in Chapter 6)

All the graphs I have plotted relating to Fitts' experiments use data taken from his tables of results published in his seminal paper: "The Information Capacity of the Human Motor System in Controlling the Amplitude of Movement", by Paul M. Fitts, Ohio State University, journal of Experimental Psychology, 47, 381-391, 1954.

1/. Reciprocal stylus tapping experiment

This is an additional graph showing the time to complete each step:

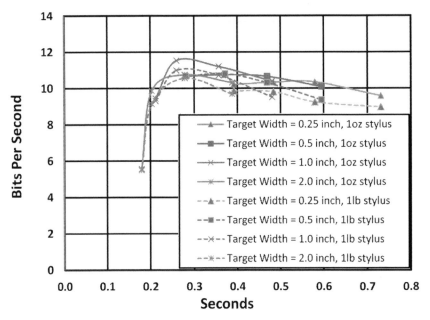

As we would expect, the time taken to perform each reciprocal tapping action is greater when the task requires greater precision. Plotting the achieved bit rate versus delay clearly reveals that there is a minimum delay of about two tenths of a second for all conditions that Fitts explored.

2/. Fitts' other two experiments:

Pin transfer task

Subjects were required to move a pin back and forth between a pair of holes spaced some distance apart. Both the distance and the hole-clearance were varied. Despite wide variation in task difficulty, the calculated information rate peaked around 12 bits per second and varied little.

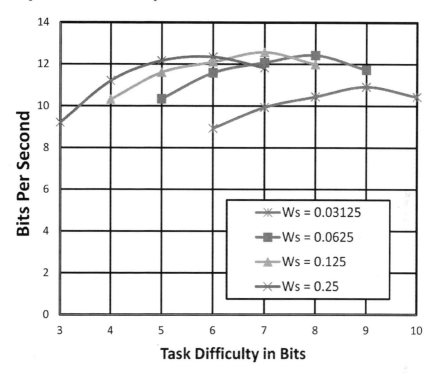

The information rate in bits per second for Fitts' pin transfer task.

The task difficulty is the ratio of distance moved with respect to the hole-clearance, expressed in bits.

So a task difficulty of 7 bits implies a ratio of 2^7 to 1, so a ratio of 128 to 1.

The bits per second figures are calculated by dividing the Task Difficulty in bits, by the average time taken to move the pin between holes.

Ws is the difference between the diameter of the pins and the diameter of the hole into which they were inserted (i.e. the clearance), in inches.

Disk Transfer task

Subjects were required to move a disk back and forth between a pair of pegs spaced some distance apart.

All other details were as in the previous Pin Transfer task.

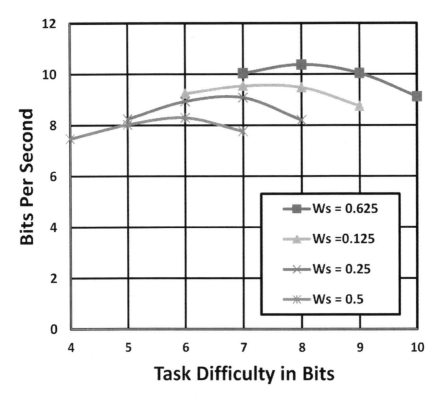

The information rate in bits per second for Fitts' disk transfer task.

Ws is the difference between the diameter of the pins and the diameter of the hole in the centre of the discs, (i.e. the clearance), in inches.

Appendix 5:

Units and abbreviations for numbers of bits

The smallest unit of measurement used for measuring data is a bit.

A single bit can have a value of either 0 or 1.

It can mean only one of two things (such as On/Off or True/False), but nothing more.

A Byte is a digital "word" that usually consists of 8 bits. It is commonly used as the fundamental unit of measurement for quantities of data. Many early computers processed digital bits in blocks of just 8 bits. Historically, 8 bits was a convenient choice as one Byte can define 256 different values (2^8), sufficient to represent all the standard (ASCII) characters on a keyboard.

Unit	Size
bit (b) , only 0 or 1	1/8 of a byte
byte (B) = 8 bits	1 byte
kilobyte (KB)	1,000 bytes
megabyte (MB)	1,000,000 bytes
gigabyte (GB)	1,000,000,000 bytes
terabyte (TB)	1,000,000,000,000 bytes
petabyte (PB)	1,000,000,000,000,000 bytes
exabyte (EB)	1,000,000,000,000,000,000 bytes
zettabyte (ZB)	1,000,000,000,000,000,000,000 bytes
yottabyte (YB)	1,000,000,000,000,000,000,000,000 bytes

The words we use for lots of bytes

Note that in the abbreviations, a lowercase "b" is used for bits, while an uppercase "B" represents "bytes".

It is important to be aware of this distinction when comparing the information capacity of sources of data such as CDs and hard drives; it is common to describe their capacity in Bytes, so the information capacity of a 600MB CD is 600 Megabytes or 8 x 600 Megabits = 4800 Megabits.

Appendix 6

The relentless growth in stored data, year by year:

Year	Exabytes	
2005	130	
2007	281	
2010	1227	
2011	1800	
2012	2837	
2015	8591	Estimated
2020	40,026	Estimated
1 Exabyte = 1 million million million bytes		

From: www.emc.com/leadership/digital-universe/iview/index.htm

Notes

Preface and Introduction

[1] Richard Langton Gregory, CBE FRS FRSE (24 July 1923 – 17 May 2010), British psychologist and Emeritus Professor of Neuropsychology at the University of Bristol.

[2] "Making up the Mind: How the Brain Creates Our Mental World", by Chris Frith, Pub. Wiley-Blackwell, (2007), ISBN-13:978-1405160223.

[3] "The brain: A very short introduction", Michael O'Shea, Oxford University Press, (2009), ISBN-13: 978-0192853929.

[4] "Principles of Neural Science" (5th Edition), Eric Kandel et. al., McGraw-Hill Medical (2012), ISBN-13: 978-0071390118.

[5] "A bottleneck is one process in a chain of processes, such that its limited capacity reduces the capacity of the whole chain." from Wikipedia

[6] The term "bottleneck" has also been used in the related context of conflicting attention to multiple sensory inputs. See: "Perception and communication", Broadbent, Donald E. (1987). Oxford University Press, ISBN 0-19-852171-5. However, in this book I use it in the sense of the limited information rates due to our sensors and our learning capability.

[7] Description of the British clipper "The Bidston Hill", being wrecked off Cape Horn in 1905, in "The Last Of The Windjammers". Volume 1, by Basil Lubbock, pp. 102, 317-319, Published by Brown, Son & Ferguson Lt., Nautical Publishers, third edition, 1948.

[8] A bit is the simplest piece of information

[9] "The Information: A History, A Theory, A Flood", James Gleik, Publisher: Vintage (2012), ISBN-13: 978-1400096237

[10] Ferranti Limited

[11] International Computers and Tabulators (ICT)

[12] "A Feasibility Study of Optical Methods for High Speed Data Transmission", Richard Epworth & Paul Sinclair, Final year project report, Manchester University Dept. of Elec. Eng., 1966.

[13] Located in Harlow, Essex, UK

[14] Kao C. 1966: "Dielectric-fibre surface waveguides for optical frequencies", K.C.Kao & G.A.Hockham, Proc. IEE, Vol. 113, No.7, July 1966.

[15] "City of Light: The Story of Fiber Optics". Jeff Hecht, Oxford University Press, (1991)

[16] "For groundbreaking achievements concerning the transmission of light in fibers for optical communication", www.nobelprize.org/nobel_prizes/physics/laureates/2009/press.html

[17] The Knight Commander of the Most Excellent Order of the British Empire (KBE)

[18] "102.3-Tb/s (224 x 548-Gb/s) C- and Extended L-band, All-Raman Transmission over 240 km Using PDM-64QAM Single Carrier FDM with Digital Pilot Tone", A. Sano et. Al., Post deadline paper PDP5C.3 in Optical Fiber Communication Conference (OFC), 2012.

[19] The 240km system incorporates a pair of intermediate optical amplifiers to boost the optical signal every 80km.

[20] "Integrated broadband networks & services of the future", Eric Nussbaum, Paper MB2, Proc. OFC/IOOC 1987, Reno Nevada, Jan 19-23, 1987

[21] James Crowe, (CTO of Level3, Telecommunications Network Provider), quoted by Joshua Shapiro in Wired magazine, Issue 6.11, Nov 1998. He proposes that high quality telepresence communication will require more than 10^{13} bits/second per user. See: http://www.wired.com/wired/archive/6.11/crowe.html

[22] An Olympic pool holds approximately 2,500,000 litres

[23] International Telephone & Telegraph Corporation (ITT)

[24] "Eye Tracking Methodology: Theory and Practice", Andrew Duchowski, Publisher: Springer, ISBN-13: 978-1846286087

[25] "Eye Movements for a Bidirectional Human Interface", Richard Epworth, ICL Technical Journal, November 1990, pp. 384-411.

[26] Richard Langton Gregory, CBE FRS FRSE (24 July 1923 – 17 May 2010), British psychologist and Emeritus Professor of Neuropsychology at the University of Bristol.

Chapter One - Our Learning Bottleneck

[27] A British TV quiz show, well-known for its challenging questions, intimidating setting and air of seriousness: from Wikipedia.

[28] A "spelling bee" is a competition where contestants, usually children, are asked to spell words.

[29] Recent years have seen greater use of regularly assessed coursework, in an attempt to achieve a somewhat broader measure

[30] English examination boards now struggle to decide whether students should be allowed take text into exams, and whether they can be marked texts.

[31] "Knowledge in perception and illusion", R. L. Gregory, Phil. Trans. R. Soc. Lond. B (1997) 352, pp. 1121 - 1128

[32] "The Expanding Digital Universe, A Forecast of Worldwide Information Growth Through 2010", David Reinsel, March 2007, An IDC White Paper, Sponsored by EMC Corporation

[33] Not to be confused with a "black box flight recorder", which is actually bright orange, which enables recordings of the preceding events to be replayed, retrieved following an accident

[34] Sometimes known as a white box, a glass box, or a clear box

[35] Jesse Prinz

[36] "Mind as a Black Box: The Behaviorist Approach", pp 85-88, in Cognitive Science: An Introduction to the Study of Mind, by Jay Friedenberg, Gordon Silverman, Sage Publications, 2006.

[37] "Computing machinery and intelligence", Turing, A.M., Mind, 59, pp. 433-460.

[38] "Entwined Lives: Twins and What They Tell Us about Human Behavior", Segal NL. Plume: New York; (1999):116-151.

[39] "Beyond Human Nature - How Culture and Experience Shape Our Lives", Jesse Prinz. ISBN: 9780713998177, Published: 26 Jan 2012 by Allen Lane.

[40] Basic Input/Output System (BIOS). The BIOS software is built into the PC, and is the first software run by a PC when powered on. See: http://en.wikipedia.org/wiki/BIOS

[41] "The Language Instinct: The New Science of Language and Mind", by Steven Pinker, pub. Penguin, (1995). ISBN-13: 978-0140175295.

[42] George Edgin Pugh: "The Biological Origin of Human Values", London, Routledge and Kegan Paul. (1978), pp. 154. In a footnote, the author writes that this quote came from his own father, around 1938.

[43] "An integrative architecture for general intelligence and executive function revealed by lesion mapping", Aron K. Barbey et. al., Brain (2012) 135(4): 1154-1164.

[44] "A brief tour of human consciousness", V.S. Ramachandran, Profile Books 2004, ISBN 0-13-148686-1.

[45] "The Mind's Eye", Oliver Sacks, Pub. Vintage 2011, ISBN-13: 978-0307473028.

[46] "Functional Magnetic Resonance Imaging", Huettel, S. A.; Song, A. W.; McCarthy, G. (2009), Massachusetts: Sinauer, ISBN 978-0-87893-286-3

[47] The temporal resolution of fMRI is inherently limited by the slow blood flow response it depends upon, so cannot reveal mental activity on the sub-millisecond timescale on which neurons operate.

[48] "The Matrix", A science fiction action franchise created by Andy and Larry Wachowski and distributed by Warner Bros. Pictures

[49] "Cochlear Implants: A Practical Guide", Huw Cooper, Louise Craddock, Publisher: Wiley-Blackwell; (2005), ISBN-13: 978-1861564818.

[50] "Sensory substitution and the human-machine interface", Bach-y-Rita P, Kercel SW, Trends in Cognitive Neuroscience, 7 (12):541-546 (2003).

[51] "Form perception with a 49-point electrotactile stimulus array on the tongue", Bach-y-Rita P, Kaczmarek KA, Tyler ME, Garcia-Lara J, Journal of Rehabilitation Research Development, 35:427-430 (1998).

[52] "The Information: A History, A Theory, A Flood", by James Gleick, Publisher: Fourth Estate (2012), ISBN-13: 978-0007225743.

[53] "A Mathematical Theory of Communication", By C. E. Shannon, The Bell System Technical Journal, Vol. 27, pp. 379–423, 623–656, July, October, 1948.

[54] If this whole activity were repeated many times

[55] Two Yes/No questions are sufficient if these four are the only options.

[56] The number of bits that are conveyed or processed per unit of time. See also http://en.wikipedia.org/wiki/Bit_rate

[57] "Current Therapy in Pain", Howard S. Smith, Elsevier Health Sciences, 2008, page 235.

[58] "Memory from a Broader Perspective", Alan Searleman and Douglas J. Herrmann, McGraw-Hill College, 1994, ISBN-13: 978-0070283879

[59] "Is there such a thing as a photographic memory? And if so, can it be learned?", Alan Searleman, in Scientific American March 12, 2007.

[60] "Savant Syndrome: An Extraordinary Condition. A Synopsis: Past, Present, Future", Treffert DA ., Philosophical Transactions of the Royal Society B: Biological Sciences 364 (1522): 1351–1357 (2009). "Prodigious savant is a term reserved for those extraordinarily rare individuals for whom the special skill is so outstanding that it would be spectacular even if it were to occur in a non-impaired person. There are probably fewer than 50 prodigious savants

known to be living worldwide at the present time who would meet that very high threshold of savant ability."

[61] "The savant syndrome: an extraordinary condition. A synopsis: past, present, future", by Darold A. Treffert, Phil. Trans. R. Soc. B, 27 May 2009 vol. 364 no. 1522 1351-1357.

[62] The Code Book: The Secret History of Codes and Code-breaking, by Simon Singh, Publisher: Fourth Estate (2002), ISBN-13: 978-1857028898.

[63] LOL!

[64] In order to faithfully capture the highest frequencies. This is known as the Nyquist Rate

[65] "A 20 dB Audio Noise Reduction System for Consumer Applications", Dolby, R.M., J. Audio Eng. Soc., 31, 3, pp. 96-113, 1983.

[66] The Dynamic Range is the ratio between the largest signal and the background noise. Listeners to classical music expect the peaks to be almost deafening and the silences to be silent. This cannot be achieved with consumer grade magnetic tape systems, without some signal manipulation such as Dolby processing.

[67] "Basic MIDI Applications", Helen Casabona, David Frederick, Alfred Music Publishing, July, 1988). See also http://www.midi.org/aboutmidi/tut_history.php.

[68] Vernier Scale, page 2582 in "How It Works: Science and Technology", by Marshall Cavendish Corporation.

[69] "Hard Day's Night", by the Beatles.

[70] "Predictive coding of music, Anticipation is the key to understanding music and the effects of music on emotion"; P. Vuust and C. Frith, Behavioral and Brain Sciences, 31 (2008), 599–600.

[71] Cosmos and Culture 13.7, nprnews: "Adele In The Goldilocks Zone", Alva Noë, Feb 24, 2012

[72] "Liking and Memory for Musical Stimuli as a Function of Exposure", Karl K. Szpunar, E. Glenn Schellenberg, and Patricia Pliner, Journal of Experimental Psychology: Learning, Memory, and Cognition, 2004, Vol. 30, No. 2, 370–381.

[73] The non-musical task was listening to a narrated story by Stephen King and pressing buttons every time the words "the" and "and" were spoken.

Chapter Two – Sense and Sense Ability

[74] "Unique system of photoreceptors in sea urchin tube feet.", E. Ullrich-Lüter, S. Dupont, E. Arboleda, H. Hausen & M. Arnone. 2011. Proceedings

of the National Academy of Sciences, May 17, 2011 vol. 108 no. 20, 8367-8372.

[75] "The instincts, habits, and reactions of the frog. I. The associative processes of the green frog", Psychol. Monogr., 1903, 4, pp 579-597.

[76] "Fading of stabilized retinal images", Ülker Tulunay-Keesey, J. Opt. Soc. Am. 72, 440-447 (1982)

[77] "The extraordinarily rapid disappearance of entopic images", David Coppola & Dale Purves, Proc. Natl. Acad. Sci. USA, Vol.93, pp8001-8004, Neurobiology, 1996.

[78] The word "saccade" was coined in the 1880s by French ophthalmologist Émile Javal, to describe the small jerky movements made by our eyes. See also http://en.wikipedia.org/wiki/Saccade

[79] The ability to resolve the smallest spatial detail is called visual acuity.

[80] "Variations of visual functions across the visual field", Yager, D. & Davis, E.T. (Eds.) Jnl. Opt. Soc. Am., Optics and image Science, Vol. 4, No. 8, Aug 1987.

[81] "Sensory Reception: Human Vision: Structure and function of the Human Eye" vol. 27, Encyclopaedia Britannica, 1987

[82] A "saccade" is literally a twitch or a jerk, an abrupt spasmodic movement, derived from old French

[83] "Sensory Reception: Human Vision: Structure and function of the Human Eye" vol. 27, p. 179 Encyclopaedia Britannica, 1987.

[84] "Eye Movements for a Bidirectional Human Interface", R Epworth, ICL Technical journal, November 1990, pp. 384-411.

[85] For this little experiment to work requires that your two eyes do track each other, which it generally true unless you suffer from a severe "lazy eye"

[86] "Twenty Years of Eye Typing: Systems and Design Issues", Päivi Majaranta and Kari-Jouko Räihä, Proceedings of ETRA 2002, Eye Tracking Research and Applications Symposium 2002, 25-27 March 2002, New Orleans, LA, USA, ACM Press, March 2002, 15-22. See also http://www.inference.phy.cam.ac.uk/dasher/

[87] "An adaptive control model for human head and eye movements while walking", J.D. McDonald, A.T. Bahill, M.B. Friedman, IEEE Trans. On systems, man, and cybernetics, Vol. SMC-13, No.3, March/April 1983

[88] "Here's looking at you", Jon Copley, New Scientist Magazine, issue 2290, 12 May 2001.

[89] "Eye Movements for a Bidirectional Human Interface", Richard Epworth, ICL Technical journal, November 1990, pp. 384-411.

[90] "Generation-V dual-Purkinje-image eyetracker", Crane, H.D.; Steele, C.M. (1985). Applied Optics 24 (4): 527–537

[91] "The eyes have it: the neuroethology, function and evolution of social gaze.", Emery NJ., Neurosci. Biobehav. Rev. 2000 Aug;24(6):581-604.

[92] "Domestic goats, Capra hircus, follow gaze direction and use social cues in an object choice task", Kaminski, J., Animal Behaviour, Volume 69, Issue 1, January 2005, Pages 11–18

[93] "Jackdaws Respond to Human Attentional States and Communicative Cues in Different Contexts", Auguste M.P. von Bayern, and Nathan J. Emery, Current Biology, Volume 19, Issue 7, 602-606, 02 April 2009

[94] "Gaze direction – A cue for hidden food in rooks (Corvus frugilegus)?", Judith Schmidt et. al., Behav. Processes. 2011 October; 88(2): 88–93.

[95] "Gaze following in the red-footed tortoise (Geochelone carbonaria)", Wilkinson A, Mandl I, Bugnyar T, Huber L, Department of Cognitive Biology, University of Vienna, Austria.

[96] "Blind Spots", by Ramachandran, V. S. , Scientific American, May 1992, pages 86-91. See also http://en.wikipedia.org/wiki/Blind_spot_(vision)

[97] It is centred 1.5 degrees below the horizontal, and extends roughly 7.5 degrees vertically.

[98] "Cephalopod sense organs, nerves and the brain: Adaptations for high performance and life style", Budelmann BU., Marine and Freshwater Behavior and Physiology. Vol. 25, Issue 1-3, Page 13-33.

[99] "Ground" meaning visual background.

[100] "Letters on Natural Magic", Brewster, D., addressed to Sir Walter Scott, Bart. (John Murray, London, 1832. He is also famous for the "Brewster Angle" and for inventing the Kaleidoscope

[101] "Perceptual filling in of artificially induced scotomas in human vision", V. S. Ramachandran & R. L Gregory, Nature. Vol. 350, No. 6320. pp. 699- 702, 25th April. 1991.

[102] "Understanding Adobe Photoshop CS5: The Essential Techniques for Imaging", By Richard Harrington, Publisher: Peachpit Press, (2010), ISBN-13: 978-0321714268

[103] "Change blindness. Trends in Cognitive Sciences", by Simons, D.J., & Levin, D.T. (1997), 1(7), 261–267. See also http://en.wikipedia.org/wiki/Change_blindness

[104] "Current approaches to change blindness", Simons, D. J., Visual Cognition 7: 1-15, 2000.

[105] "To see or not to see", Rensink, O'Regan & Clark, Psychological Science, 8: 368- 373. 1997.

[106] "Is the richness of our visual world an illusion? Transsaccadic memory for complex scenes". Blackmore, Brelstaff, Nelson & Troscianko. Perception. 1995;24(9):1075-81.

[107] "Inattentional Blindness", by Arien Mack and Irvine Rock, 1998, Cambridge, MA: MIT Press. ISBN 0 262 13339 3.

[108] You can view the original video at: http://www.youtube.com/watch?v=vJG698U2Mvo

[109] "The invisible gorilla strikes again: Sustained inattentional blindness in expert observers", Psychological Science, (in press).

[110] "Gorillas we have missed: Sustained inattentional deafness for dynamic events" Dalton P, & Fraenkel N, Cognition, Volume 124, Issue 3, September 2012, Pages 367–372.

[111] The Oxford Companion to the Mind", (1987), Edited by Richard L. Gregory. ISBN: 0198662246, (2004).

[112] "Perception of structure in flashes and in afterimages", Ditchburn, R. W., and Drysdale, A. E., Volume 13, Issue 12, December 1973, Pages 2423–2433

[113] "Information capacity of the human eye", Jacobson, H., Science 113, 292–293 (1951).

[114] Wired magazine: Issue 6.11, Nov. 1998

[115] "Information and the human ear", Jacobson, H., J. Acoust. Soc. Amer. 23, 463-471 (1951).

[116] $2^{10}=1024$)

[117] Later renamed "Holiday in Spain", It starred Denholm Elliott, Peter Lorre and Elizabeth Taylor in an unaccredited role, and was produced by Mike Todd, Jr.

[118] Even our response to emotions seems to be differential not absolute. The pursuit of happiness as an absolute goal seems to be intrinsically flawed, for our satisfaction depends largely on how we perceive ourselves in relation those around us. We can be distressed by a 10% salary increase if the rest of the team get 20%. The experience of fluctuations back and forth between joy and sorrow seems to be our natural state, leaving us with the choice between the rich emotional experience of life's ups and downs, or a sedated numbness! See the poem "Joy and Sorrow" in "The Prophet", by Kahlil Gibran, 1923, ISBN-13: 978-0099416937.

[119] See: http://en.wikipedia.org/wiki/Floater

[120] I perhaps give floaters credit for rather more intelligence than they deserve!

Chapter Three – Seeing requires Imagination

[121] French Philosopher, 1927 Nobel Prize in Literature, 1859-1941.

[122] First line of the song Bohemian Rhapsody, from the album A Night At The Opera, by the band Queen (1975), EMI

[123] "But the senses do not give us a picture of the world directly; rather they provide evidence for checking hypotheses about what lies before us. Indeed we may say that a perceived object is a hypothesis, suggested and tested by sensory data." Richard L. Gregory, FRS, "Eye and Brain, The Psychology of Seeing", Published 1966, 5th edition 1997

[124] "What we observe is not nature itself, but nature exposed to our method of questioning.", Werner Heisenburg, Ref: Physics and Philosophy: The Revolution in Modern Science (1958) Lectures delivered at University of St. Andrews, Scotland, Winter 1955-56.

[125] "From Relativity to Mutability, by John Archibald Wheeler, in "The Physicist's Conception of Nature", Chapter 9, pages 202-247, by Jagdish Mehra (Ed.), pub. Springer, (1973), ISBN 978-90-277-0345-3

[126] Erwin Schrödinger is famous in popular culture for his "Schrödinger's cat", the hypothetical victim of a thought-experiment that Schrödinger initially proposed as a way of ridiculing the implications of the Copenhagen theory of quantum mechanics. He is also valued for formulating Schrödinger's equation, a partial differential equation that describes how the quantum state of a physical system changes with time. Today his equation is used to predict how light signals are distorted as they travel vast distances along optical fibres spanning between continents.

[127] A science fiction action franchise created by Andy and Larry Wachowski and distributed by Warner Bros. Pictures

[128] "Are you living in a computer simulation?", Nick Bostrom, Faculty of Philosophy, Oxford University, Published in Philosophical Quarterly (2003) Vol. 53, No. 211, pp. 243-255.

[129] The Sims is a strategic life-simulation video game developed by Maxis and published by Electronic Arts. See also www.thesims.com and www.simcity.com

[130] William Hazlitt, British essayist, (1778-1830), "On Wit and Humour", Lectures on the English Comic Writers (1819).

[131] "Associative learning in new-born babies", Paul Craddock & Mikael Molet17th Annual International Conference On Comparative Cognition,

Comparative Cognition Society, March 24 to March 27, 2010, Melbourne Beach, Florida

[132] "The developmental psychology of Jean Piaget", by John H. Flavell, Van Nostrand, (1963), ISBN: 9780442224165

[133] "Eye and Brain, The Psychology of Seeing", by Richard L. Gregory, FRS, Published 1966, 5th edition 1997.

[134] "ELIZA - A Computer Program for the Study of Natural Language Communication between Man and Machine," Communications of the Association for Computing Machinery 9 (1966), pp. 36-45.

[135] The program was named after the naive young woman in George Bernard Shaw's Pygmalion

[136] "Professor's Work Led Him to Preach the Evils of Computers", Miller, Stephen, MIT, Wall Street Journal, March 15–16, 2008, p. 6

[137] "Windows of the Mind: The Christos Experience", Glaskin, G. M. Wildwood House, 1974, ISBN-0704501171.

[138] "Cognitive psychology: Rare items often missed in visual searches", Jeremy M. Wolfe, Todd S. Horowitz, and Naomi M. Kenner, Brief Communications, Nature 435, 439-440 (May 2005)

[139] "The Clangers" is a popular British stop-motion animated children's TV series about a family of mouse-like creatures who live on, and in, a small blue planet. The programmes were originally broadcast by the BBC from 1969–1972. See: http://en.wikipedia.org/wiki/The_Clangers

[140] "Lunar Exploration: Human Pioneers and Robotic Surveyors", Paolo Ulivi, Pub. Springer (2004), ISBN-13: 978-1852337469

[141] The first anecdotal account of the Leonid's meteor shower was in 902 AD. On Nov. 15, 1630, Johannes Kepler, the German mathematician, astronomer and astrologer best known for his laws of planetary motion, died. At his funeral two days later the Leonid's lit up the sky. This was considered as a salute from God - Source: "Tycho and Kepler".

[142] "Leonid fireballs dazzle the world", G. Seronik, Sky & Telescope, 97:2 (1999 February), pp.123-124. See also http://leonid.arc.nasa.gov/history.html

[143] "The War of the Worlds" by H.G. Wells, Chapter Two, The Falling Star, 1898.

[144] "The epistemological problem for automata", MacKay, D.M., In C.E. Shannon & J. MacCarthy (eds.), Automata Studies. Princeton University Press, Princeton. "Towards an information-flow model of human behaviour", MacKay, D.M, *Brit. J. Psychol.*47, 30, 1956.

145 An averaged static image is stored and continually subtracted from each new frame of the video. If there is no movement in the image the result is a flat grey image, but any movement immediately is highlighted

Chapter Four – Rules and Explanations

146 "The Fractal Geometry of Nature", by Benoît Mandelbrot; W. H. Freeman, 1983; ISBN 0716711869. Benoît B. Mandelbrot is the mathematician, best known as the father of fractal geometry, who gives his name to the Mandelbrot set. See also www.wikipedia.org/wiki/Mandelbrot_set

147 "An Imaginary Tale: The Story of [the Square Root of Minus One]", Paul J. Nahin, Princeton University Press, (2010), ISBN-13: 978-0691146003

148 See www.fractalfoundation.org

149 Hamlet, Scene V, by William Shakespeare, 1564-1616.

150 From Physics and Philosophy: The Revolution in Modern Science (1958) Lectures by Werner Heisenburg delivered at University of St. Andrews, Scotland, Winter 1955-56. Werner Heisenburg was awarded the 1932 Nobel Prize in Physics for "the creation of quantum mechanics"

151 "The Nature of Explanation", Kenneth J. Craik, Cambridge University Press, 1943, ISBN-10: 0521094453.

152 Occam's (or Ockham's) razor is a principle attributed to the 14th century logician and Franciscan friar; William of Occam (or Ockham), 1285-1349?). Ockham was the village in the English county of Surrey where he was born.

153 "Ernst Mach: Physicist and Philosopher", R.S. Cohen (Editor), Raymond J. Seeger, (Boston Studies in the Philosophy and History of Science), Springer; (2010), ISBN-13: 978-9048183180.

154 The Mach number of a moving object is the ratio of its speed, with respect to the local speed of sound. Such a normalised measure is useful as the speed of sound through the atmosphere varies with temperature and pressure.

155 Ernest Mach, 1838-1916

156 "The Quantum Universe (And Why Anything That Can Happen, Does)", Brian Cox and Jeff Forshaw, Pub. Da Capo Press, (2012), ISBN-13: 978-0306819643.

157 "The Nature of Light: What is a Photon?" Editors: C. Roychoudhuri A.F. Kracklauer, K. Creath, publisher: CRC Press; 2008, ISBN-13: 978-1420044249.

158 "Quantum mechanics" is just another name for quantum theory.

[159] "Inside Jokes, Using Humor to Reverse-Engineer the Mind", by Matthew M. Hurley, Daniel C. Dennett and Reginald B. Adams, Jr., The MIT Press, 2010, ISBN-13: 978-0262015820.

[160] Science fiction writer (1920–1992)

[161] "The persistent paradox of psychic phenomena: An engineering perspective", Jahn, R.G., Proceedings of the IEEE 1982, 70(2), pp. 136 - 170.

[162] Carl Sagan, "Encyclopaedia Galactica". Cosmos. episode 12. (December 14, 1980, PBS

[163] Pierre-Simon Laplace (1749–1827), French mathematician and astronomer, known as The Principle of Laplace

[164] "Large losses of total ozone in Antarctica reveal seasonal ClO X/NO X interaction", Farman, J.C., Gardiner, B.G. and Shanklin, J.D. 1985, Nature, vol. 315(6016), pp. 207-210.

[165] "Accounting for the Ozone Hole: Scientific Representations of an Anomaly and Prior Incorrect Claims in Public Settings", Stephen C. Zehr, The Sociological Quarterly 35 (4): 603–19, 1994.

[166] "ITT 140MBit/s Optical Fibre System", R.E. Epworth, NTC'77, 14:3-1 – 3-6, USA, 1977.

[167] The system used Multi-Mode fibres which had a conveniently large diameter core to contain the light, but allowed the light to travel in many different paths.

[168] "The Phenomenon of Modal Noise in Analogue and Digital Optical Fibre, Communication", R. E. Epworth, Invited Paper, Proc. of 4th European Conf. on Opt. Comm., Genoa, Italy, Sept. 1978, pp. 492-501.

[169] The problem was minimised by using low coherence lasers, taking a statistical approach and turning up the power to provide extra margin.

[170] Single (transverse) Mode fibre. It provides a single unique path for the light to travel along, but the light carrying core is so tiny that it is more difficult to use.

[171] "Higgs Boson Makes Its Debut After Decades-Long Search", Adrian Cho, Science 337: 141-143. (13 July 2012).

[172] "Higgs Force", Nichloas Mee, Publisher: Quantum Wave Publishing, (2012), ISBN-13: 978-0957274617

[173] "Sargant, William Walters (1907–1988)", Dally, A, 2004, Oxford Dictionary of National Biography, Oxford University Press.

[174] "The vitamin A content and toxicity of bear and seal liver", Rodahl, K.; T. Moore (1943-07). Biochemical Journal 37 (2): 166–168. ISSN 0264-6021.

[175] Placebos: From the Latin word for "I shall please"

[176] "Placebo Effects and the Common Cold: A Randomized Controlled Trial", Bruce Barrett et. al., Annals of Family Medicine, 2011, 9:312-322.

[177] http://www.improbable.com/ig/

[178] "Commercial Features of Placebo and Therapeutic Efficacy", Waber, R. L. et. al., Journal of the American Medical Association 299 (9): 1016–1017, 2008.

[179] "Understanding the placebo effect from an evolutionary perspective", Pete C. Trimmer et.al. Evolution and Human Behavior, 30 August 2012.

[180] "Great expectations: the evolutionary psychology of faith-healing and the placebo effect", Humphrey, N (2002). In The mind made flesh. Oxford University Press, Oxford. 255–285.

[181] "Observations on some remarkable optical phenomena seen in Switzerland; and on an optical phenomenon which occurs on viewing a figure of a crystal or geometrical solid", Necker, L. A. (1832). London and Edinburgh Philosophical Magazine and Journal of Science 1 (5): 329–337

[182] "Knowledge in perception and illusion" by Richard Gregory, Phil. Trans. R. Soc. Lond. B (1997) 352, 1121–1128

[183] See http://saturn.jpl.nasa.gov/science

[184] "Galileo Galilei: First Physicist", James MacLachlan (Oxford Portraits in Science), Publisher: Oxford University Press (1999), ISBN-13: 978-0195131703. See also: http://saturn.jpl.nasa.gov/

[185] "Working on Mars: Voyages of Scientific Discovery with the Mars Exploration Rovers", by William J. Clancey, (2012) Publisher: MIT Press, ISBN-13: 978-0262017756

[186] Martin Rees, British cosmologist, astrophysicist and Astronomer Royal, interviewed on the BBC

[187] "Bernard Lovell: A Biography" by Dudley Saward, Publisher: Robert Hale Ltd, (1984), ISBN-13: 978-0709017455.

[188] Scientific American (1992), Vol. 267.

[189] Emo Philips, US comedian.

[190] "10 Unsolved Mysteries Of The Brain, What we know - and don't know-about how we think", David Eagleman, Discover magazine, August 2007.

[191] "Brain work, Scientists will begin to map the wiring, or "connectome", of the human brain", Nov 17th 2011 from The World In 2012, The Economist magazine, print edition, Alun Anderson, Senior Consultant (& former Ed-in-Chief & Publishing Director) at New Scientist.

[192] "The world as a hologram", Leonard Susskind, J. Math. Phys. 36, 6377 (1995)

[193] "Computational capacity of the Universe", Lloyd, S., Physical Review Letters, 88, 237901, (2002)

[194] The ratio between the information required to fully describe the universe, and the information to describe your brain, is itself a number so large that your brain can't describe it.

[195] From "Wider than the sky", by Emily Dickinson (1830-86)

[196] "Misconceptions about the Big Bang", Lineweaver, Charles; Tamara M. Davis, Scientific American (2005).

[197] The Doppler effect.

[198] "The Hubble Deep Field", Edited by: Mario Livio, Cambridge University Press, (1998) ISBN:9780521630979

[199] "Calendars with Olympiad display and eclipse prediction on the Antikythera Mechanism", Nature 454, 614-617, 2008

[200] "Decoding the Heavens: Solving the Mystery of the World's First Computer", Jo Marchant, Windmill Books (2009), ISBN-13: 978-0099519768

[201] "The making of ENCODE: Lessons for big-data projects", Ewan Birney, Nature 489, 49–51, September 2012.

[202] A popular construction toy consisting of colourful interlocking plastic bricks, manufactured by The Lego Group, a Danish company.

[203] Clive Sinclair invented the pocket calculator and other things.

[204] "The Sinclair Story", by Rodney Dale, Publisher: Gerald Duckworth & Co Ltd (7 Nov 1985), ISBN-13: 978-0715619018

[205] The design allows a small angular offset between the screw and the screwdriver. In contrast Pozidrive screws have to be directly in line

[206] "Moral Minds: How Nature Designed Our Universal Sense of Right and Wrong", Marc Hauser, Publisher: Abacus (2008), ISBN-13: 978-0349118093

[207] Also known as The Golden Rule

[208] The Sermon on the Mount, Christian Bible, Matthew Gospel 7:12

[209] "The 23rd Cycle: Learning to Live with a Stormy Star", by Sten Odenwald, Columbia University Press; (2002), ISBN-13: 978-0231120791.

[210] Article in Wired magazine by Jim Crowe, CTO of Level3 (telecommunications network provider) proposes that high quality telepresence communication will require more than 10^{13} bits/second per user. Wired magazine: Issue 6.11, Nov 1998

[211] "Complete Works of Swami Vivekananda", Swami Vivekananda, (8 Volume Set), Publisher: Advaita Ashram; (1947), ISBN-13: 978-8185301464

[212] "The Indispensable Vivekananda: An Anthology for Our Times", Aimya P. Sen, Pub. Permanent Black, 2006, ISBN-13: 978-8178241302.

Chapter Five – The evidence for what we take in

[213] "Selections from the Essays of T.H. Huxley", by Thomas Henry Huxley, British biologist, (1825-95).

[214] "The Demon-Haunted World: Science as a Candle in the Dark", Ch.1, The Most Precious Thing, by Carl Sagan, Random House, 1995, ISBN13: 978-0-394-53512-8-X.

[215] "The Informational Capacity of the Human Eye", Jacobson, H., Science 16 March 1951: Vol. 113 no. 2933 pp. 292-293, p 471.

[216] "H. Quastler and V. J. Wulff (cited in Attneave F. "Applications of information theory to psychology: a summary of basic concepts, methods, and results", New York: Holt, Rinehart, and Winston, 1959, ASIN: B005641UTI.)

[217] Jim Crowe, CTO Level3 (telecommunications network provider) proposes that high quality telepresence communication will require 15 x 1012 Bits/Second per user. Wired magazine: Issue 6.11, Nov 1998

[218] "Human performance in information transmission", Quastler, H., and Wulff, V. J., Control Systems Laboratory Report No. 62, University of Illinois, 1955

[219] "Nachrichtenverarbeitung Küpfmüller", by Karl Küpfmüller, in "Taschenbuch der Nachrichtenverarbeitung" Karl Steinbuch Ed., Berlin, Springer, 1962, pp1481-1501, p.1500.

[220] "The rates of handling information: key pressing responses to light patterns" Klemmer, E.T. and Muller, P. F., Jr., HFORL memo Report No. 34, 1953.

[221] "Kybernetischen Grundlagen der Pddagogik", Helmuth Frank, Zweiter Band (Baden-Baden: Agis-Agis Verlag, 1962.

[222] "A Mathematical Theory of Communication", C. E. Shannon, Bell System Technical Journal, v27, pp. 379-423, 623-656, July, October 1948.

[223] "Whatever happened to information theory?" in "Odd Perceptions", R.L. Gregory, pages 187-194, III, 28, Routledge, 1988, ISBN-13: 978-0415006422

[224] "The magical number seven, plus or minus two: Some limits on our capacity for processing information", Miller, G. A. 1956. The Psychological Review, 1956, vol. 63 (2): 81–97.

225 "Inattentional Blindness", by Arien Mack and Irvine Rock, 1998, Cambridge, MA: MIT Press. ISBN 0 262 13339 3.

226 "The User Illusion: Cutting Consciousness Down to Size", by Tor Nørretranders, Published in 1998 by Penguin Books, ISBN: 01402.30122.

227 Page 126 in "The User Illusion: Cutting Consciousness Down to Size", by Tor Nørretranders, pub. Allen Lane/Penguin Press, ISBN: 0-713-99182-8.

228 "Prediction and Entropy of Printed English", C. E. Shannon, Bell Systems Technical Journal, Vol. 30, 1951, pp. 50-64.

229 The Brown Corpus, see "A dictionary of English collocations: based on the Brown corpus", Göran Kjellmer, Oxford University Press, (1994), ISBN 13: 9780198239031

230 The number of bits per character is the binary logarithm of the number of possibilities (= $\log_2 N$), where N is the number of different symbols in the set, in this case 26

231 "Analysis of Text Entry Performance Metrics", Ahmed Sabbir Arif, Wolfgang Stuerzlinger, Dept. of Computer Science & Engineering, York University, Toronto, Canada.

232 "Reading rates and the information rate of a human channel", Pierce, J. R., & Karlin, J. E. (1957), Bell Systems Technical Journal, 36, 497-516.

233 "An assessment of two "extraordinary" speed-readers", Homa, D (1983), Bulletin of the Psychonomic Society, 21(2), 123-126.

234 "Cognitive variation in adult college students differing in reading ability", Cunningham, A. E., Stanovich, K. E., & Wilson, M. R. (1990), In T. H. Carr & B. A. Levy (Eds.), Reading and its development: Component skills approaches (pp. 129–159). New York: Academic Press.

235 "Reading rate: Theory, research and practical implications", Carver, R. P. (1992), Journal of Reading, 36, 84-95.

236 Braille is writing system which enables blind and partially sighted people to read and write through touch. It consists of patterns of raised dots arranged in cells of up to six dots in a 3 x 2 configuration. Each cell represents a letter, numeral or punctuation mark.

237 "Superior Memory (Essays in Cognitive Psychology)", by Elizabeth Valentine and John Wilding (1997). See also: http://www.worldmemorychampionships.com

238 Information Theory, in "The Oxford Companion to the Mind", Edited by Richard L. Gregory. ISBN: 0198662246, Published 1987, 2004.

239 See: http://en.wikipedia.org/wiki/Andriy_Slyusarchuk

240 He claims to be a skilled hypnotist, which I *can* believe.

[241] "The Art of Memory", Frances Yates, pub. Pimlico, 1992, ISBN-13: 9780712655453

[242] "The Memory Book: How to Remember Anything You Want", Tony Buzan, Pub. BBC Active, 2009, ISBN-13: 978-1406644265

[243] "Make Me Smart", BBC TV documentary broadcast in the UK on the channel BBC1 on February 10th, 2009.

[244] "Skill and working memory", by W G Chase, K A Ericsson, The psychology of learning and motivation (1982), Volume: 16, Publisher: Academic Press, Pages: 1-58, ISBN: 0125433166

[245] Ramón Campayo is the holder of numerous World Records in memorization. See: http://www.ramoncampayo.com/5.html

[246] "Short-term memory in vision", Averbach, E., & Coriell, A. S., Bell System Technical Journal, 40, 309-328, January 1961.

[247] "A Brief Survey of Possible Mechanisms in Information Processing", Leroy Augenstein, Chapter 3, Chemistry of Learning, Plenum Press, 1967.

[248] Note: I used the figure of 60 bits for convenience. 64 bits would have provided me with only two more pixels.

[249] 18,446,744,073,709,551,616 = 2^64

[250] "Almost Chimpanzee: Searching for What Makes Us Human, in Rainforests, Labs, Sanctuaries, and Zoos", Jon Cohen, Publisher: Times Books (2010), ISBN-13: 978-0805083071.

[251] "Thinking like a chimpanzee", By Jon Cohen, Smithsonian magazine, September 2010.

[252] http://www.smithsonianmag.com/science-nature/Thinking-Like-a-Chimpanzee.html

[253] "Working memory of numerals in chimpanzees", Sana Inoue and Tetsuro Matsuzawa, Current Biology Vol. 17 No 23, R1004, 2007

[254] http://langint.pri.kyoto-u.ac.jp/ai/intra_data/SanaInoue/Inoue2007.pdf

[255] "Ape trounces the best of the human world in memory competition", by Fiona Macrea in The London Daily Mail 26 January 2008

[256] Ai means "love" in Japanese, it is just a coincidence that AI is the acronym for Artificial Intelligence. Ai is also a star performer for her age

[257] "Super Smart Animals", BBC TV programme first broadcast on Wednesday 8 February, 2012 on BBC1.

[258] From world records for memorising strings of numbers with short exposure durations, we might expect a human to be able to take in somewhere between 30 and 50 bits of information with a very short (e.g. 60

milliseconds) exposure. The video evidence suggested that the computer display is an 8 x 5 matrix of possible positions for each of the numbers in the range 1 to 17. This means that we can describe the screen with 680 possibilities (the product of these), i.e. 10 bits will be sufficient ($2^{10} = 1024$). This is much less than 50 bits, but consider how much more difficult the task is, when compared to memorising the single 3 digit number that it might represent. Obviously there is a lot more going on, converting the two dimensional co-ordinates of each number into memorable form.

[259] "Sequencing performance and error trends in gorillas (Gorilla gorilla gorilla) and chimpanzees (Pan troglodytes)", Wagner, K.E. and S.R. Ross. American Journal of Primatology (2009), 71, Supplement 1: 35

[260] "Macroscopic thermodynamics of human reaction times", Moscoso del Prado, F., Journal of Mathematical Psychology 55, 302-319, 2011.

[261] "The case against subliminal manipulation. Psychology & Marketing", Moore, T. E., 46:297-316, 1988.

[262] "Perception without awareness: Perspectives from Cognitive Psychology", Merikle, P. M. et. al., Cognition, 79, 115-134, 2000.

[263] "What aspects of autism predispose to talent?", Happé F, Vital P. Philosophical Transactions of the Royal Society B: Biological Sciences 364 (1522): 1369–1375, (2009).

[264] "Extraordinary People: Understanding Savant Syndrome", D. A. Treffert, Publisher: iUniverse (April 2000), ISBN-13: 978-0595092390

[265] "Autism and extraordinary ability, Genius locus", The Economist, Apr 16th 2009.

[266] "Broken Mirrors – A Theory of Autism", Ramachandran, V.S., and Oberman, L.M. 2006, Scientific American 295, November: 62-69.

[267] "Explaining and inducing savant skills: privileged access to lower level, less-processed information". Philosophical Transactions of the Royal Society B: Biological Sciences 364 (1522): 1399–1405, 2009.

Chapter Six – The evidence from what we do

[268] "The Way I See It: A Personal Look at Autism & Asperger's", Dr Temple Grandin, Publisher: Future Horizons Incorporated, 2008, ISBN-13: 978-1932565720

[269] Dragon Naturally Speaking, a speech recognition software package developed and sold by Nuance Communications

[270] "Memory Search By A Memorist", by Charles Thompson, Psychology Press. (1993), ISBN-13: 978-0805812367

271 Record set by Stella Pajunas-Garnand from Chicago in 1946 in one minute on an "IBM electric"

272 Record of 82 WPM, held by Charles Lee Swem with an accuracy of 99.29%, Using Gregg Shorthand in the Championship Contests of the National Shorthand Reporters, 1923,

273 Andrew Cook

274 "The Information Capacity of the Human Motor System in Controlling the Amplitude of Movement", by Paul M. Fitts, Ohio State University, journal of Experimental Psychology, 47, 381-391, 1954.

275 "Experimental analysis of the writing movement", Freeman, F. N., Psychol. Monogr., 1914, 17, No. 4 (Whole No. 75), 1-46.

276 "A Mathematical Theory of Communication", C. E. Shannon, Bell System Technical Journal, v27, pp. 379-423, 623-656, July, October 1948.

277 They were instructed to make their aimed movements as rapidly as possible but land within the boundaries of the targets on at least 95% of the taps

278 16 subjects were used and were tested over 16 levels of difficulty. Each speed estimate was the average of more than 600 observations.

279 "The Information Capacity of the Human Motor System in Controlling the Amplitude of Movement", by Paul M. Fitts, Ohio State University, journal of Experimental Psychology, 47, 381-391, 1954.

280 "Information Capacity of Discrete Motor Responses", P. M. Fitts and J. R. Peterson, J. Exp. Psychol., 67:103–112, February 1964

281 It is perhaps worth noting that in fast action computer games, it is the complex three dimensional modelling that limits the ultimate frame rate and screen resolution

282 "Fitts' Law" models the act of pointing, either by physically touching an object with a hand or finger, or virtually, by pointing to an object on a computer screen using a pointing device. Sometimes written as "Fitts's Law.

283 For a good review of Fitts' work and other similar, see page 76, 77 in "The Theory of Selective Information and Some of Its Behavioral Applications", R. Duncan Luce, University of Pennsylvania

284 "Extending Fitts' law to two dimensional tasks", I. S. MacKenzie and W. Buxton, Proceedings of Human Factors in Computing Systems (CHI'92), 1992, pp. 219-226.

285 "Evaluation of mouse, rate-controlled isometric joystick, step keys, and text keys for text selection on a CRT", Card, S. K., English, W. K., and Burr, B. J. Ergonomics 21, (1978), 601-613.

[286] "Card, English, and Burr (1978) -- 25 years later", MacKenzie, I. S., & Soukoreff, R. W., Extended Abstracts of the ACM Conference on Human Factors in Computing Systems - CHI, 2003, pp. 760-761.

[287] "Fitts' law as a research and design tool in human-computer interaction", I. Scott MacKenzie, Human-Computer Interaction, volume 7, 1992, pp., 91–139

[288] "Application of Fitts' law to foot-pedal design", Drury, C. G, Human Factors, 17, 368-373, 1975

[289] "Fitts' law in two dimensional with hand and head movements", R. J. Jagacinski and D. L. Monk, Journal of Motor Behavior, vol. 17, pp. 77-95, 1985.

[290] "The Psychology of Human-Computer Interaction", Card, S.K., Moran, T. and Newell, A. 1983, Hillsdale, NJ., Lawrence Erlbaum Associates Inc.

[291] "The Inner Game of Tennis", Gallwey, W. Timothy (1974), New York: Random House. ISBN 0394491548.

[292] "Surely You're Joking, Mr. Feynman!: Adventures of a Curious Character", with contributions by Ralph Leighton, W. W. Norton & Co, 1985, ISBN 0-393-01921-7.

[293] "Developing Talent in Young People", Benjamin Bloom,1985, Publisher: Ballantine Books Inc. (Jan 1985), ISBN-13: 978-0345315090

[294] "Intelligenz und Schachleistung - eine Untersuchung an Schachexperten" - ("Intelligence and achievement in chess - a study of chess masters"), Doll, J., and U. Mayr, Psychologische Beiträge, (1987), 29: 270-289.

[295] "Talent is Overrated: What Really Separates World-Class Performers from Everybody Else", Colvin, G, Pub. Nicholas Brealey Publishing Ltd (2008), ISBN-13: 978-1857885194

[296] "Outstanding Performers: Created, Not Born? New results on Nature vs. Nurture", D. R. Shanks, Science Spectra, 1999, Number 18.

[297] "Expert and exceptional performance: Evidence on maximal adaptations on task constraints", Ericsson, K. A., and A. C. Lehmann, (1996) Annual Review of Psychology, 47: 273-305

[298] "The role of deliberate practice in the acquisition of expert performance", Ericsson, K. A., R. Th. Krampe, and C. Tesch-Römer, Psychological Review, (1993),100: 363-406.

[299] "The role of practice in the development of performing musicians", Sloboda, J. A., J. W. Davidson, M. J. A. Howe, and D. G. Moore, , British Journal of Psychology, (1996), 87: 287-309.

[300] "Outliers: The Story of Success", Malcolm Gladwell, Publisher: Little, Brown and Company; (2008), ISBN-13: 978-0316017923

[301] Such as the ballroom dancing contest: BBC TV's: "Strictly Come Dancing".

[302] The UK charity Sport Relief.

[303] "Head, eye and arm coordination in table tennis", Sérgio T Rodrigues, Joan N Vickers, A Mark Williams, Journal of Sports Sciences, 2002; 20(3):187-200.

[304] "The Use of Anticipatory Visual Cues by Highly Skilled Tennis Players", J. Shim, L. G. Carlton, J.W. Chow, & W.-S. Chae, Journal of Motor Behavior, 2005, Vol. 37, No. 2, 164–175.

[305] "Aussie smashes tennis serve speed record". The Sydney Morning Herald. Retrieved May 13, 2012.

[306] "Perception, Cognition and Decision Training: The Quiet Eye in Action ", by Joan Vickers, Publisher: Human Kinetics Europe Ltd; (2007), ISBN-13: 978-0736042567.

[307] "The quiet eye, it's the difference between a good putter and a poor one. Here's the proof", by Joan Vickers, Golf Digest, January 2004, pages 96-101.

[308] "Remembering objects lets computers learn like a child", by Douglas Heaven, article in New Scientist magazine, issue 2920, 05 June 2013, describing work by Renato Salas-Moreno at Imperial College, London.

[309] You can try it yourself at www.humanbenchmark.com/tests/reactiontime/index.php

[310] "Age and Sex Differences in Reaction Time", Geoff Der, Ian J. Deary, Psychology and Aging, 2006, Vol. 21, No. 1, 62–73.

[311] "Imagery in Sports and Physical Performance", Sheikh, Anees A., and Errol R. Korn, Baywood Publishing Company, Inc., 1994

[312] The resting brain produces Alpha waves, and Theta waves are associated with cognitive processing tasks

[313] J. Christian Gerdes, Director, Center for Automotive Research at Stanford (CARS), also Associate Professor, Department of Mechanical Engineering at Stanford University

[314] "Hawk-Eye", by Jesse Russell, Ronald Cohn, Publisher: Book on Demand, (2012), ISBN 9785510766066.

[315] Jim Shields

316 "Ready steady slow: action preparation slows the subjective passage of time", N. Hagura, R. Kanai, G. Orgs, P. Haggard, Proceedings of the Royal Society B, 279 (2012), pp. 4399–4406.

Chapter Seven – So What? – The Objective Implications

317 Interestingly, the recent popularity among women, of the erotic novel "50 shades of Grey" by E.L.James, suggests that it is the men who prefer the pictures.

318 A British TV quiz show, well-known for its challenging questions, intimidating setting and air of seriousness: Wikipedia.

319 A "spelling bee" is a competition where contestants, usually children, are asked to spell words.

320 "The Art of Memory", Frances Yates, pub. Pimlico, 1992, ISBN-13: 9780712655453

321 Although often claimed to be of Chinese origin, the expression actually originated in Britain in 1885, in a story titled "Mrs. Dymond" by Anne Isabella Ritchie (daughter of William Makepeace Thackeray): "if you give a man a fish he is hungry again in an hour; if you teach him to catch a fish you do him a good turn."

322 "40 Principles: Triz Keys to Technical Innovation" by Genrikh Altshuller, Lev Shulyak and Steven Rodman (1997), ISBN-13: 978-0964074033.

323 "On Teaching For Understanding: A Conversation with Howard Gardner.", Educational Leadership. April 1993: Vol. 50 No. 7.

324 "Surely You're Joking, Mr. Feynman!: Adventures of a Curious Character", with contributions by Ralph Leighton, W. W. Norton & Co, 1985, ISBN 0-393-01921-7.

325 "Encyclopaedia of Electronic Components Volume 1: Resistors, Capacitors, Inductors, Switches, Encoders, Relays, Transistors", by Charles Platt, Publisher: Make; (2012), ISBN-13: 978-1449333898

326 "The Telephone and Its Several Inventors: A History", Lewis Coe, McFarland, North Carolina, 1995. ISBN 0-7864-0138-9

327 Scientific American Supplement, No. 520, December 19, 1885

328 53kb/s was used in the UK.

329 "Extra-Terrestrial Relays - Can Rocket Stations Give Worldwide Radio Coverage?". Arthur C. Clark. Wireless World magazine, pp. 305-308, October 1945.

330 "The man who saves Stephen Hawking's voice", by Catherine de Lange, New Scientist magazine, issue 2846, 30 December, 2011.

[331] This figure might have to be doubled if both ears contribute equally.

[332] "The MegaLab truth test", Wiseman, R., Nature, 373, 391, (1995).

[333] "Model based image coding", W.J.Walsh, S. Searby, J.B.Waite, British Telecom Technology Journal, Vol.8, No. 3, July 1990

[334] ITU World Telecommunication/ICT Indicators Database.

[335] ITU World Telecommunication/ICT Indicators Database.

Chapter Eight – Now it gets personal

[336] David Hockney interviewed by Andrew Marr on the BBC TV programme: The Art of Seeing - A Culture Show Special. First shown on 27 February 2012.

[337] Douglas Adams in "The Restaurant at the End of the Universe", chapter 11, (1981) ISBN 0-345-39181-0.

[338] Compare recent high resolution images of the Apollo landing sites with the claims that the Moon landings were conspiracy: http://www.space.com/12796-photos-apollo-moon-landing-sites-lro.html, http://en.wikipedia.org/wiki/Moon_landing_conspiracy_theories

[339] Note, that I avoided calling it a "kilogram mass", as this will have different weights, depending on the value of gravity, which can vary over a range of 0.7% over the Earth's surface. A kilogram mass will weigh only about a sixth as heavy on the Moon and have zero weight in deep space.

[340] Provided that I mean "weight" not "mass".

[341] "Relative State Formulation of Quantum Mechanics", Everett, Hugh, Reviews of Modern Physics 29: 454–462., (1957).

[342] "The Many Worlds of Hugh Everett", Peter Byrne, Scientific American, December 1, 2007.

[343] http://en.wikipedia.org/wiki/Copenhagen_interpretation

[344] A "thought experiment" is only imagined, yet is a useful way of checking out ideas

[345] "In Search Of Schrodinger's Cat: Updated Edition", by John Gribbin, Pub.: Black Swan; Revised edition, (1985), ISBN-13: 978-0552125550

[346] The Philosophical Writings of Niels Bohr (1998), Danish physicist who studied atomic structure and radiations; the Bohr theory of the atom accounted for the spectrum of hydrogen (1885-1962).

[347] Determined by a quantum event, though the very act of making a random choice is in principle a quantum event

[348] "Parallel Universes", by Max Tegmark, Scientific American, May 2003; pages 41-51.

[349] "Parallel Universes", by Max Tegmark, In "Science and Ultimate Reality: From Quantum to Cosmos", (honouring John Wheeler's 90th birthday), Editors: J. D. Barrow, P.C.W. Davies, & C.L. Harper, Cambridge University Press (2004), ISBN-13: 978-0521831130.

[350] The square root of two is the number that multiplied by itself equals two.

[351] "Does the universe in fact contain almost no information?", Tegmark, M., Found. Phys. Lett., v.9, pp. 25-42, (1996)

[352] Znew = Zold times (Zold + C), using complex numbers

[353] "The elephant and the event horizon", by Amanda Gefter, New Scientist, 26 October 2006, Magazine issue 2575.

[354] "A measure for the multiverse", Amanda Gefter, New Scientist, 03 March 2010, Magazine issue 2750.

[355] "On the interpretation of measurement in quantum theory", by H. Dieter Zeh, Foundations of Physics, Volume 1, Issue 1, pp. 69–76, (1970).

[356] "How many universes are in the multiverse?", A. Linde, V. Vanchurin, Published in Phys.Rev., Oct 2009.

[357] Macbeth: Act 5, scene 5

[358] "Thinking, Fast and Slow", by Daniel Kahneman, eBook: Publisher : Allen Lane, (2011), ISBN: 978-0141918921, Publisher: Penguin, (2012), ISBN-13: 978-0141033570. Daniel Kahneman, an expert on human happiness, won the Nobel Prize in Economics for his pioneering work in behavioural economics, he is considered by many to be the world's most influential living psychologist.

[359] Sir Frederic Charles Bartlett, Fellow of the Royal Society, (1886 – 1969) was a British psychologist and the first professor of experimental psychology at the University of Cambridge. He was one of the forerunners of cognitive psychology.

[360] "A Study in Experimental and Social Psychology", Bartlett, F. C. (1932) Remembering, Cambridge University Press.

[361] "Scientists Manipulate and Erase Memories", Adam Piore, Scientific American, January 26, 2012.

[362] "The Emotional Brain: The Mysterious Underpinnings of Emotional Life" by Joseph LeDoux, Simon & Schuster, (1996), ISBN0684803828.

[363] "They never forget: The strange gift of perfect memory", by Kayt Sukel, New Scientist, 20 August 2012.

[364] "The Forgetting Pill Erases Painful Memories Forever", Jonah Lehrer, February 17, 2012, Wired Magazine.

365 "Impairing existing declarative memory in humans by disrupting reconsolidation", Jason Chan and Jessica LaPaglia, Proceedings of the National Academy of Sciences (PNAS), 110 (23) 9309-9313, May 20, 2013.

366 "Molecular mechanisms of memory reconsolidation", Tronson, N. C.; Taylor, J. R. (2007).Nature Reviews Neuroscience 8: 262–275.

367 "The formation of false memories", Loftus, E.F. & Pickrell, J.E. (1995), Psychiatric Annals, 25, 720-725.

368 "The Myth of Repressed Memory: False Memories and Allegations of Sexual Abuse", Loftus, E.F. and Ketcham, K. (1994) New York, St Martin's Press. Publisher: St. Martin's Griffin (1996), ISBN-13: 978-0312141233.

369 "Brain Fiction: Self-Deception and the Riddle of Confabulation", William Hirstein, Pub. MIT Press, (2006), ISBN-13: 978-0262582711.

370 In Chapter 7, "The sound of one hand clapping", in "Phantoms in the Brain: Human Nature and the Architecture of the Mind", V.S. Ramachandran, Sandra Blakeslee, Pub. Fourth Estate, (1999), ISBN-13: 978-1857028959,

371 Attributed to Winston Churchill and others.

372 "Memory, History, Forgetting", by Paul Ricoeur, University of Chicago Press, (2006), ISBN-13: 978-0226713427.

373 "History and Truth", by Paul Ricoeur, pub. Northwestern University Press, (2006), ISBN-13: 978-0810124004.

374 "The Telephone and Its Several Inventors: A History", Lewis Coe, McFarland, North Carolina, 1995. ISBN 0-7864-0138-9

375 Said by Sylvester Stallone as Marion Cobretti in the film: Cobra (1986).

376 "Pieces of Light: The new science of memory", by Charles Fernyhough, Profile Books, 2102, ISBN-13: 978-1846684487.

377 Salvador Dalí, artist 1904-1989

378 "Precursors to a theory of mind: Understanding attention in others", Baron-Cohen, S. (1991).. In A. Whiten (Ed.), "Natural theories of mind: Evolution, development and simulation of everyday mindreading" (pp. 233-251). Oxford: Basil Blackwell, ISBN-13: 978-0631171942.

379 "Mindblindness: Essay on Autism and the Theory of Mind" Simon Baron-cohen, Publisher: MIT Press; (1997), ISBN-13: 978-0262522250

Chapter Nine – Creating the world we inhabit

380 From "Brushstrokes of a Gadfly"

381 "Reading Literary Fiction Improves Theory of Mind", Kidd DC, Castano E., Science, Oct 3, 2013, 342 (6156), p. 377-80.

[382] "World Tales, The Extraordinary Coincidence of Stories Told in All Times, in All Places", by Idries Shah, Publisher: Harcourt Brace Jovanovich, Octagon Press, (1979), ISBN-13:978-0863040368.

[383] "Neuroscience: Exploring the Brain", by Mark F. Bear, Barry W. Connors, Michael A. Paradiso, Publisher: Lippincott Williams and Wilkins; 3rd Revised edition (2006). ISBN-13: 978-0781760034

[384] "The Brain Book", by Rita Carter, Publisher: Dorling Kindersley (2009), ISBN-13: 978-1405341295.

[385] "Mapping The Mind", by Rita Carter, Publisher: Phoenix; Reprint edition (2010), ISBN-13: 978-0753827956.

[386] "Making Up the Mind: How the Brain Creates Our Mental World", by Chris Frith, Publisher: Wiley-Blackwell; (2007), ISBN-13: 978-1405160223.

[387] "Development of the brain depends on the visual environment", Blakemore, C., Cooper, G., Nature, Lond. 228, 477-478, (1970).

[388] "Visual experience modifies distribution of horizontally and vertically oriented receptive fields in cats", Hirsch, H., Spinelli, D., Science, N.Y. 168, pp. 869-871, (1970).

[389] "Concept cells the building blocks of declarative memory functions", Quiroga R.Q., Nat. Rev. Neurosci. 2012 Jul 4;13(8):587-97.

[390] "Invariant visual representation by single-neurons in the human brain", Quian Quiroga R, Reddy L, Kreiman G, Koch C and Fried I., Nature, 435: 1102-1107, (2005).

[391] Paraphrasing Arthur Schopenhauer, in "Pathways To Bliss: Mythology And Personal Transformation", by Joseph Campbell, David Kudler, Pub. New World Library, (2004), ISBN-13: 978-1577314714.

[392] £2.95/annum for a .co.uk domain name

[393] Lose Hill, Hope valley, Derbyshire

[394] The Light Peak

[395] From the song "Imagine" by John Lennon, 5th line, Lyrics © EMI Music Publishing.

[396] In the same way as Schrödinger's cat.

[397] Ludwig Wittgenstein, philosopher, in Tractatus Logico-Philosophicus, (6.43), Logisch-Philosophische Abhandlung, Wilhelm Ostwald (ed.), Annalen der Naturphilosophie, 14, (1921).

[398] "Happiness, Unlocking the mysteries of psychological wealth", by Ed Diener & Robert Biswas-Diener, Chapter 6, "Can money buy happiness",pp.91-111.

[399] Maslow's Hierarchy of Needs, "A Theory of Human Motivation", A. H. Maslow, Psychological Review, 50, 370-396, (1943), and ."A preface to motivation theory", A. H. Maslow, Psychosomatic Med., 5, 85-92, (1943).

[400] "A theory of human motivation", Maslow, A.H.. Psychological Review, 50(4), 370–96 (1943).

[401] An example is "The Secret", Rhonda Byrne, Pub. Simon & Schuster Ltd, 2006, ISBN-13: 978-1847370297.

[402] I now need seven hours.

[403] A "rev limiter" is a device fitted to an internal combustion engine to restrict its maximum rotational speed.

[404] "Men Are from Mars, Women Are from Venus", by John Gray, Publisher: Harper Element, ISBN-13: 978-0007152599, (Reissue 2012)

[405] This tale was inspired by a story from Chapter 4 (Tips for Women How to Have a Relationship with a Guy), of "Dave Barry's Complete Guide to Guys" by Dave Barry, Pub. Ballantine Books, a division of Random House, Inc. (1996), ISBN: 978-0-449-91026-9.

Chapter Ten – The Science of Prejudice

[406] From the essay: "On Prejudice" by William Hazlitt, British essayist, (1778-1830).

[407] From the essay: "On Prejudice" by William Hazlitt, British essayist, (1778-1830)

[408] From Latin *praejŭdicium* a preceding judgment: Collins English Dictionary

[409] American Heritage Dictionary of the English Language, Fourth Edition, Publisher: Houghton Mifflin Harcourt (2000), ISBN-13: 978-0395825174, see also www.thefreedictionary.com/prejudice

[410] "The Unity of Human Knowledge" (1960), by physicist Niels Bohr (1885-1962), who received the Nobel Prize for Physics in 1922 for his contributions to quantum mechanics.

[411] Ken Jenkins

[412] "Culture as common sense: perceived consensus versus personal beliefs as mechanisms of cultural influence.", Zou X, Tam KP, Morris MW, Lee SL, Lau IY, Chiu CY., J Pers. Soc. Psychol. 2009 Oct;97(4):579-97.

[413] "Philosophiæ Naturalis Principia Mathematica", by Isaac Newton, pub 1687.

[414] "Seventeen Equations that Changed the World", Ian Stewart, Publisher: Profile Books, (2012), ISBN-13.978-1846685316.

[415] Elwyn Brooks White, (1899 - 1985), usually known as E. B. White, an American essayist and contributor to The New Yorker magazine, co-author of the English language style guide, The Elements of Style, which is commonly known as "Strunk & White."

[416] "How are our Instincts Acquired?", By Kuo, Z. Y., Psychological Review, Vol. 29(5), Sep 1922, 344-365.

[417] In the narrated film of the novel "War and Peace", by Leo Tolstoy, also variously attributed to Edmund Burke, John F. Kennedy, R. Murray Hyslop, Charles F. Aked, John Stuart Mill, Plato and others.

[418] "Making Sense of the Troubles: A History of the Northern Ireland Conflict" by David McKittrick, Publisher: Penguin (2012), ISBN-13: 978-0241962657.

[419] Trademark LEGOLAND, a chain of Lego-themed theme parks.

[420] See www.ponggame.org to play the game and read the history

[421] "A perspective on judgement and choice: Mapping bounded rationality", Kahneman, D., American Psychologist 58 (9): 697–720, (2003).

[422] A Yorkshire accent is one of the many strong regional accents in the UK, quite distinct from a London accent or "Queens English".

[423] "Thin Line Between Love and Hate" is the title of a 1971 song by the New York City-based R&B vocal group The Persuaders. The song was later recorded by Annie Lennox on her album "Medusa".

[424] "Love Is the Drug" is a 1975 single from Roxy Music's fifth studio album: Siren

[425] "Introduction: Love", by J. Pickrell, L. Middleton and A. Anderson, in New Scientist magazine, 04 September 2006.

[426] Francis Wright, writer and reformer, writing in the New-Harmony Gazette, January 30, 1828

[427] Conclusion: Listening with your eyes, p. 254, in "Blink: The Power of Thinking without Thinking", by Malcolm Gladwell, pub. Penguin, (2006), ISBN-10: 0141014598, ISBN-13: 978-0141014593

[428] If we exclude binary theological ideas of heaven and hell.

[429] Part Xiii, of the introduction to "The Nature of Prejudice", by Gordon W. Allport, Reading, MA: Addison-Wesley Pub. Co., (1954; 1979), ISBN 0-201-00178-0

[430] "The less secure a man is, the more likely he is to have extreme prejudice" - Clint Eastwood

Chapter Eleven – The Bottleneck Future

[431] Henri Poincare, French mathematician, theoretical physicist, engineer, and a philosopher of science, hence often described as a polymath, writing in: "The Foundations of Science", Publisher: The Science Press, (1913).

[432] Arthur C. Clarke: The original quote is: "I have no doubt that in reality the future will be vastly more surprising than anything I can imagine. Now my own suspicion is that the Universe is not only queerer than we suppose, but queerer than we can suppose." by J. B. S. Haldane, (1892 – 1964), British geneticist and evolutionary biologist in: "Possible Worlds and Other Papers" (1927), p. 286.

[433] However, Einstein's brain was only measured when it was 76 years old.

[434] Known as the "obstetrical dilemma".

[435] "Gifts of the Crow: How Perception, Emotion, and Thought Allow Smart Birds to Behave Like Humans", John Marzluff & Tony Angell, Free press, 2012, ISBN-13: 978-1439198735.

[436] "The exceptional brain of Albert Einstein", Witelson, Sandra F., Debra L. Kigar, Thomas Harvey, The Lancet. June 19, 1999

[437] Moore's Law: an axiom of microprocessor development usually holding that processing power doubles about every 18 months especially relative to cost or size, named after Gordon E. Moore the American computer industry executive who first observed it, the term was first used in 1980.

[438] "Reconstructing Speech from Human Auditory Cortex", Pasley BN , David SV , Mesgarani N , Flinker A , Shamma SA , et al. 2012 Reconstructing Speech from Human Auditory Cortex. PLoS Biol 10(1), Published: January 31, 2012.

[439] "Mismatch: Why our world no longer fits our bodies", Peter Gluckman & Mark Hanson, Pub. OUP Oxford, 2006, ISBN-13: 978-0192806833.

[440] "IDC VIEW, THE DIGITAL UNIVERSE IN 2020: Big Data, Bigger Digital Shadows, and Biggest Growth in the Far East", by John Gantz and David Reinsel, December 2012

[441] "LHC Brochure, English version. A presentation of the largest and the most powerful particle accelerator in the world, the Large Hadron Collider (LHC), which started up in 2008. Its role, characteristics, technologies, etc. are explained for the general public." CERN-Brochure-2010-006-Eng. LHC Brochure, English version. CERN.

[442] "LHC Guide, English version. A collection of facts and figures about the Large Hadron Collider (LHC) in the form of questions and answers.", CERN-Brochure-2008-001-Eng. LHC Guide, English version. CERN.

443 "The Hitchhiker's Guide to the Galaxy", by Douglas Adams, Pub. Pan Books 1979), ISBN 0-330-25864-8, also ISBN-13: 978-0330508117.

444 "Big Data: A Revolution That Will Transform How We Live, Work and Think", by Viktor Mayer-Schonberger, Kenneth Cukier, Publisher: John Murray (2013),ISBN-13: 978-1848547926. See also: http://en.wikipedia.org/wiki/Big_data

445 "2020 Computing: Science in an exponential world", Alexander Szalay, Jim Gray, Nature 440, 413-414 (23 March 2006)

446 Previously known as Microsoft "Data Explorer"

447 Microsoft Power "Query for Excel is an add-in that enhances the self-service Business Intelligence experience in Excel by simplifying data discovery and access, enabling users to easily discover, combine, and refine data for better analysis in Excel.

448 "There's gold to be mined from all our data", Tim Berners-Lee and Nigel Shadbolt, The Times, London, published, December 31, 2011.

449 "The Semantic Web", Berners-Lee, Tim; James Hendler and Ora Lassila, Scientific American Magazine, May 17, 2001.

450 "The Semantic Web, Linked Data and RDF, An Introduction", Nigel Shadbolt, Linked Data Workshop, 27th-28th May 2010, British Library, London.

451 http://www.theregister.co.uk/2004/07/22/storage_v_archiving

452 http://lostcousins.com/newsletters/autumn10news.htm

453 "'Why do white people have thin lips?' Google and the perpetuation of stereotypes via auto-complete search forms", Paul Bakera & Amanda Pottsa, Critical Discourse Studies, Volume 10, Issue 2, pages 187-204, 2013.

454 "The Rock", by T.S. Eliot (1934)

455 "Dangerous Liaisons", by Chris Bode, The Scientist, (Magazine), Volume 24 Issue 5, May 1st, 2010

456 More precisely at two thirds the speed of light, because the glass has an optical density of 3/2 which slows the light a little.

457 Active SETI

458 "Existential Risk Prevention as Global Priority", Nick Bostrom, Oxford University and John Wiley & Sons, Ltd, "Global Policy Vol. 4, issue 1, pp.15-31, February 2013.

459 Arthur C. Clarke, quoted in The Peter Plan: A Proposal for Survival (1976) by Laurence J. Peter.

[460] "The Singularity Is Near: When Humans Transcend Biology", Ray Kurzweil, Penguin Books, (2006), ISBN-13: 978-0143037880

[461] Stuart Sutherland, in the 1989 International Dictionary of Psychology, Macmillan. ISBN 978-0-333-38829-7.

[462] "Facing Up to the Problem of Consciousness", David J. Chalmers, Journal of Consciousness Studies 2(3):200-19, 1995

[463] "State of the Art - The Psychology of Consciousness", by Susan Blackmore, The Psychologist, (2001) vol.14,p.522-525.

[464] "Anything that we are aware of at a given moment forms part of our consciousness, making conscious experience at once the most familiar and most mysterious aspect of our lives", Susan Schneider and Max Velmans, The Blackwell Companion to Consciousness, Wiley (2008), ISBN 978-0-470-75145-9.

[465] Recent analysis of specimens of Yeti hair, indicate that the Yeti is genetically an ancient polar bear.

Appendices

[466] "On the number of absolutely identifiable spectral hues", Halsey, R. and Chapanis, A. (1951), Journal of the Optical Society of America, 41, 1057-1058.

467 "Color in Business, Science and Industry", by Judd, Deane B.; Wyszecki, Günter (1975), Wiley Series in Pure and Applied Optics (third edition). New York: Wiley-Interscience. p. 388. ISBN 0-471-45212-2.